CW00543059

BREAD OF SHAME

AN ANCIENT TERM EXPRESSING THE GUILT OF UNEARNED GOOD FORTUNE

by
W.K. "Jake" Wehrell

Published by
AfterWit Books
afterwitbooks@gmail.com

This is a conceivable work of non-fiction. Names, characters, places, and incidents are the product of the author's imagination or his recollections. Any resemblance to actual persons, living or dead, events, or locales is possible.

All rights reserved
Copyright © 2022 by W.K. "Jake" Wehrell

No part of this book may be used or reproduced in any manner whatsoever without written permission from the author, except in the case of brief quotations embodied in articles or reviews.
ISBN: 978-0-9987632-8-6 (print)
ISBN: 978-0-9987632-9-3 (ebook)

ABOUT THE AUTHOR

W. K. Jake Wehrell's head-shaking array of adult activities result in him appearing in three TV documentaries, his photo in weekly news magazines, being portrayed by Robert Downey in a 1990 movie, and having residences everywhere from a bougainvillea-draped cottage on the French Riviera to a bamboo cage in Laos.

OTHER BOOKS BY THE AUTHOR

I Guess I Just Wasn't Thinking
Part One: Instead of Skipping Stones

I Guess I Just Wasn't Thinking
Part Two: The French Riviera, Leo, June, and Big Trouble

I Guess I Just Wasn't Thinking
Part Three:The CIA Secret Airline and Eureka! She Exists!

I Guess I Just Wasn't Thinking
Part Four: At the End of the Rainbow

GOODREADS RATING ★★★★★

John R. Review of *Part Three—I Guess I Just Wasn't Thinking*

Brilliant! A tour de force! You will never read a story such as this elsewhere. I have read several books dealing with the wars in Southeast Asia, including those about the Secret War in Laos, and none of them come anywhere close to this book as a first-person account of life and work in this war zone. The book stands alone as a testament to one man's struggle with himself and with the incredible dangers of jungle and mountain piloting. One may well conclude that the war effort in Southeast Asia was ill-fated, a huge embarrassment for the United States, and a disaster for the native peoples of these countries. Ample evidence of this has emerged since those days, and you will see this author was onto this terrible truth from the beginning.

This four-part book comes at you on more than one level. This third part is a stunning first-person account of the dangerous job of flying for that now famous CIA aviation operation. The author details his flights to land or drop cargo and people onto the scariest jungle or mountain tops while aware or what might be hidden by every cloud and fogbank, or from weapons aimed at him from every tree line. But equally impressive is the cringe-worthy dive into the mind and soul of this singular male who struggles constantly against his own doubts and fears, including one particular personal dread. Most males would not allow such access to their innermost secrets, but here you have that rare case where we are not allowed to avert our gaze from a terrible truth. This emotional rollercoaster evokes a mixture of admiration, disgust, and sympathy.

The missions described in this book deal mostly with Roger's piloting of small aircraft specifically designed to get in and out of short, rough strips hacked out of remote areas by natives using wooden shovels, on or behind the front lines. The reader is at a granular level with the worst places and moments of the war because these aircraft did the real dirty work for the CIA, especially in Laos where they used the native Hmong people as soldiers and irregulars. These pilots—such as the author, were the tip of the CIA's spear in fighting the Pathet Lao and the North Vietnamese regulars in Laos. However, it pains me to say that we eventually abandoned those brave and wonderful Hmong people in the same way we have betrayed the indigenous allies in other fights.

Part Four—the rest of the story is a mélange of good and hard times in a blizzard of third world countries and finally Mid-America. The tale concludes with a most, MOST surprising event, which I will leave to a "Goodreader" to discover. (I must say one would greatly benefit as I did, by starting with Part One of the series.)

TABLE OF CONTENTS

Chapters and Vignettes	Page

A Prologue VI
Chapter One: Recollections Growing Up 1
Chapter Two: A Summer I'll Never Forget.............................12
Chapter Three: If I Want a Man's Job, This Should Do It 24
Chapter Four: High School in a Nutshell................................33
Chapter Five: The Best Kept Secret Ever 43
Chapter Six: A Significant Fork in the Road 50
Chapter Seven: My Fateful Visit with Connie.........................55
Chapter Eight: Earning My Gold Wings 62
Chapter Nine: On My Own, and Something Nobody Expected............73
Chapter Ten: Seven Years Later...79
Chapter Eleven: My First Launch 87
Chapter Twelve: When the Moon Hits Your Eye Like a Big Pizza Pie.....94
Chapter Thirteen: A Night Launch and Big Trouble................106
Chapter Fourteen: The French Riviera..................................113
Chapter Fifteen: Why Are We Here in the Med?...................137
Chapter Sixteen: The Island of Rhodes................................142
Chapter Seventeen: A Not-So-Good At-Sea Period................153
Chapter Eighteen: Istanbul and Belkis.................................160
Chapter Nineteen: A World Famous Arms Dealer 171
Chapter Twenty: The Leonardo Da Vinci 182
Chapter Twenty-One: A Winter Recovery and a Real Scare 186
Chapter Twenty-Two: Valencia and June..............................193
Chapter Twenty-Three: Air America....................................208
Chapter Twenty-Four: Barcelona..210
Chapter Twenty-Five: Palma De Majorca 226
Chapter Twenty-Six: Time to Face the Music 238
Chapter Twenty-Seven: One Life Over, Another Starting.................245
Chapter Twenty-Eight: Arriving in Southeast Asia................251
Chapter Twenty-Nine: My New Duty Station 260
Chapter Thirty: The Family Arrives.....................................264
Chapter Thirty-One: Adopted by a CIA Case Officer..............267
Chapter Thirty-Two: A Not-So-Routine Line Check...............272

Chapter Thirty-Three: What We Didn't Know Then 276
Chapter Thirty-Four: I Can't Believe She Pulled It Off 281
Chapter Thirty-Five: Hurt, But Not Bad...286
Chapter Thirty-Six: Shot Down and a Trip to Spain............................290
Chapter Thirty-Seven: My Return To Air America and Laos 299
Chapter Thirty-Eight: A Change of Status 307
Chapter Thirty-Nine: One Soul Less 313
Chapter Forty: The Eeriest Flight I Ever Made 321
Chapter Forty-One: Almost In The Worst Possible Trouble................327
Chapter Forty-Two: You Landed Where!?...331
Chapter Forty-Three: A Faux-Pas and More In Cambodia..................335
Chapter Forty-Four: A Landing But No Take-off 338
Chapter Forty-Five: Kicked Out, Black Ops, and Goodbye.................349
Chapter Forty-Six: Back In the USA and Elsewhere..........................356
Chapter Forty-Seven: Stunned Like Never Before 362
Chapter Forty-Eight: Halfway Around the World................................363
Chapter Forty-Nine: Dakar Senegal, and Eureka She Exists! 371
Chapter Fifty: July 74' "Vive La France" 376
Chapter Fifty-One: Back In the States and Facing Reality...................385
Chapter Fifty-Two: At Last, a Respectable Position With a Retirement ..392
Chapter Fifty-Three: The SSL Flight Department and a Happening....400
Chapter Fifty-Four: An Incredible Pairing. A Miracle! 409
Chapter Fifty-Five: Rich and the DEA 411
Chapter Fifty-Six: A Staggering Revelation 428
Chapter Fifty-Seven: Nicaragua 433
Chapter Fifty-Eight: Better Late Than Never 443
Chapter Fifty-Nine: To The Middle East (And How I Saw it) 446
Chapter Sixty: Something It Wasn't Too Smart to Try 456
Chapter Sixty-One: At Last, A Perfect Life, Almost............................463

PROLOGUE

Bread of Shame is a revealing and startling tale of action, intimacy, and final irony. Throughout, whether man or woman, young or old, married or single, the reader will be rooting for Roger, waiting and hoping with fingers crossed.

This is a true account of one man's journey—fraught with terror and excitement, but plagued by a male curse: *Even with the most voluptuous female partner he remains unarmed.* Roger clings to the belief that somewhere out there is that one woman with the "right chemistry" to unlock his manhood. His desperate search to find her dictates his every decision, causing him to repeatedly choose ill-advised undertakings that bring about dire predicaments.

Roger's innocent and unsure teen years lead him to volunteer for the naval aviation cadet program, where he lacks the bold confidence being demonstrated by his fellow cadets. He rashly marries at twenty-two, only to realize that Sara is *not* the woman with the right chemistry. Is it now too late to find that woman who does have it?

As a Marine Corps carrier-pilot in the Mediterranean, Roger stumbles through Europe's most glamorous cities, forever changed by the continental lifestyle. He is whisked through after-hours Barcelona on the coattails of the girls of the Stafford Ballet; has lunch with an exiled king in his vacation home on the island of Rhodes; spends the night in an Istanbul jail cell with a German movie star and a Middle Eastern princess; and accompanies an international arms dealer into Bulgaria to buy guns from the KGB. All the while still tethered to the search for that one woman.

When the Vietnam War intensifies, Roger transfers to the CIA and becomes a Chief Pilot for Air America (portrayed by Robert Downey in a 1990 movie). He is now at the forefront of dangerous Southeast Asian exploits: supplying arms and evacuating wounded in Vietnam and Laos; making covert flights deep into Red China; secretly landing on dikes and tapping the phone lines outside of Hanoi; and losing an eye when shot down in the Mekong Delta.

After nine years of flying foreign aircraft in third-world countries, Roger returns to the States. With no stateside connections, he must accept the least desired and perilous jobs—piloting small puddle-jumper aircraft across the icy Atlantic. After one such crossing, he has an encounter with a UFO. On another to West Africa he has his knees weakened and his soul shaken when he finds himself alone in a Dakar, Senegal hotel room with a beautiful French Supermodel. This life-changing event will have the reader gasping at an unanticipated outcome.

Roger eventually gains a respectable flying position with a Fortune 500 corporation. Alas, after years of exemplary performance, a jealous co-worker deviously has him terminated, forcing him into another kaleidoscope of endeavors. From Bangkok to Khartoum to Barranquilla, he becomes involved in a series of dubious ventures: working undercover for (and against) the DEA; delivering planes to Angolan guerrillas; 2 a.m. flights between hidden Cuban airstrips and dikes deep in the Everglades; dropping guns and ammo to the Contras in Nicaragua; and flying for the Saudi Air Force during "Desert Storm."

You, the reader, will unavoidably find yourself a reluctant arbiter—unable not to levy judgment on Roger's decades-long pattern of questionable behavior, even perhaps morally bound to condemn him, despite his heartfelt efforts to justify his actions and bond with you.

After years of consistent failures and the always-devastating embarrassments, a new woman arrives on the scene. Markedly different in manner, will she be the one who can assuage Roger's humbling male deficiency and hold the key to his future happiness?

Standby for a finality of staggering irony!

Bread of Shame

VIII

Chapter One

RECOLLECTIONS, GROWING UP

Play Acting

Can't remember when I first felt the need to strike people as different—appear special; be someone who deserved a second glance. I *do* know it frequently caused me to be overly concerned with what kind of impression I was making on the new kid in class, my uncle, or even a complete stranger; or why I felt (and continued to feel) driven to be someone or something other than I was; maybe because I was short and not special at all. In any case it started early on.

Mom's birthday was coming up in a few days. I don't remember much about last December, but I'd better remember this one. Everybody was listening to the news. The President made a speech to the whole nation, and the way most grownups were acting since it happened (even talking to us kids) it seemed like Pearl Harbor was something everyone would remember. Right now though—in my world, I knew that as a seven-year old, buying my own present for Mom would be something *she'd* remember. We had a closeness that my father and I would never have. I wanted to buy a really neat gift to show her how much I loved her (and make her love and appreciate me even more). If I could just get some transportation it would be easy, because I already knew what that gift would be. I had seen a pair of ladies' gloves in Woolworth's; finely stitched, tan stretch fabric, trimmed with dark brown leather. I knew these were classy gloves and I wanted to see them on my mother. She deserved gloves like these. She was a special person; you could just tell—real pretty and real smart! She even went to college, a little college up in New York state. And based on the expressions on peoples' faces when they found out, it must have been a really good college. I think *"Vazzer"* or something like that. For a while she was the editor of the *Bergen Evening News*, and two weeks ago they had a party for her when one of her short stories got published in the *Saturday Evening Post*.

Three days before her birthday I asked her for a lift to town—without telling her what my mission was. I think she guessed, was flattered and didn't turn me down. The ride was upbeat and I wasn't even embarrassed to be seen in our ugly green '38 Olds (that we'd gotten in the will when Mom's dad died). I felt noble. Mom would soon be proud of me. With the two bucks I had made shoveling walks and my allowance, I had almost four dollars in my pocket! I was sure that would be enough. We were approaching Woolworth's before I knew it. Everything was going just fine. Mom found a parking place right in front of the entrance. She acted coy, checking her watch and asking how much time it would take. I was excited, proud of this grown-up thing I was doing. I knew it wasn't expected of kids my age. I popped out of the car visualizing the slender-fingered gloves somewhere inside, just waiting for me to snatch them up.

Inside, things would not be so easy. While I was sure I had seen the gloves in this store, they were nowhere to be found. I ran up and down the worn wood aisles, searching the array of sweaters, socks, hats, and nail polish displays. I was sure I'd seen them here; lots of stuff, *but no gloves.* I began to panic. I had no alternative. It was the gloves or I just didn't know what. (It had never crossed my mind to think of a substitute gift.) Heartsick I did one last tour of the store. After doing so, I had to admit it, there were no such gloves in this Woolworth's. Dismayed, I was now faced with coming up with another gift. I examined many possible choices, but nothing seemed right. Quite by accident, I found myself in front of a long counter displaying kids' toys. On it (though it wasn't something I would have bought for myself) I spied a neat Lone Ranger pistol set. The holster was thick leather with real lamb's wool, and a big silver stud in the middle of it. It sure was handsome, but something I could easily live without.

While standing there I noticed I was being observed by a tall well-dressed woman just down the counter; an attractive lady who I'd bet was accustomed to being noticed. She had an interesting sharp-featured face, with an ashen complexion strikingly contrasted by dark red lipstick and a short cut of jet-black hair. I felt a need to add to the impression I might be making; cause her to feel a concern for me. I commenced to first look wistfully at the pistol set marked at four dollars, and then sadly at the three dollars and three quarters in my open palm. I did this several times until I could see she had observed my apparent dilemma and her sympathy had been duly aroused. Having achieved my goal, I was ready to get to the task at hand: find a substitute gift for Mom!

Before I was able to start that search, I realized the tall woman was standing alongside (above) me. Next thing I knew the three bills were snatched from my hand, and she was adding one of her own. "Here, you poor little darling, you just take this gift from Lola." Unable to react, I watched—mouth open, as she gave the four dollars to the sales lady and with a disarming smile *plunked the Lone Ranger pistol in my hand*. I was dumbfounded. I had never considered such an outcome. But based on the convincing nature of my previous charade, I had no recourse but to accept the gift and show a combination of joy and disbelief (the latter being easy), while struggling to thank her appropriately for her kindness. And worse— as if she had just adopted me, she was going to escort me all the way to the sidewalk entrance.

There was a rushing noise in my ears and a sick feeling overtook me. My excitement about the gloves, my feeling of doing something good— *everything*, was over. I wanted to break away, run and hide, start the whole day over again. At the exit, she stooped and gave me one big reassuring smile (that I tried to return) and she was gone, and I was alone. I slunk across the sidewalk and towards the car, not daring to look up at my mother's face. There I was, bearing a Lone Ranger holster set in lieu of those sleek driving gloves. To this day it hurts me to imagine how letdown and disappointed my mother must have been. There was no need to try to describe to her the gloves I *meant* to buy. I didn't buy them. And I didn't dare to explain the scenario inside the store. I was too ashamed of my own part in it. I hated myself and that tall woman who had messed me up.

I guess Mom decided that I was only a kid and what more could she expect; probably thought I couldn't resist the temptation. Maybe she thought it was foolish for her to believe I'd be different than the other kids; capable of doing something so special. Unfortunately this would not be the last time I would "play-act;" affect people's conclusions and actions, and find myself creating increasingly serious responses and relationships.

Conducting a Proper Pet Funeral

I don't think Mom or Dad ever took us to a pet store. We never got to beg for one of those furry, floppy-eared puppies behind the glass, but it seems our house was never without a four-legged resident—usually a cat. Between friends and neighbors and our own discoveries, we were always adopting some big-eyed kitten. Now I don't mean Persians or Siamese, I mean just accidents—splotchy ones and striped ones. That's the only brands we knew. As common as they were, I always ended up loving each of them. I was especially attached to our current all black cat (that we aptly named "Blackie"). I think Blackie was a girl.

The day before my ninth birthday, Mom got a call from the neighbor across the street, that *she had seen Blackie in the street*. I knew that was not too unusual. Mom on the other hand looked worried, hung up and started towards the front door. I was surprised by her concern and followed. And sure enough there was Blackie in the middle of the street—lying on her side. Not a place she'd take a nap. I called her name, hoping against hope. No movement. A realization of the worst overtook me. Heart pounding, I was at her side. She didn't show any evidence of having been hit by a car, but I knew that's what happened. I stood up and remained still; an appropriate moment of silence—challenging any oncoming car to make me move. Before I was finished and without saying anything, Mom scooped up Blackie and started towards our house. Real tears welled in my eyes (giving proof to anyone who might be observing, the effect this loss was having on me). Mom laid Blackie on the front lawn and went back to the garage. I removed Blackie's turquoise vinyl collar and put it on my ankle (where I made a silent vow that it would stay forever). I could just imagine—years from now when I would be in some other place in the world, people asking me about the strange ankle bracelet I wore. It would be my secret (and add to my mystique).

Mom returned with a cardboard box and a shovel, but I was not ready for it to end so quickly and in such a way. Soon my next-door friends joined me. Rolly displayed a visible sadness, but Donnie Bruce didn't seem to understand the extent of this tragedy. Kenny and George Jeffreys from just down the street also arrived. I was determined that Blackie would have a dignified burial with everyone possible in attendance (meaning each of these new arrivals). To assure they understood the solemnity of the occasion, I managed to look as shaken as I truly should have been.

I outlined the plan: We would bury Blackie in the "sand pit"—an abandoned, deep excavation about a quarter mile away (whose original creation and purpose was never explained to any of us). It was isolated in the middle of a mile square block of woods, with only one long path leading to it. Besides being the only place with slopes steep enough to sled, it served us many a day as whatever exciting location we chose to imagine it to be. A quick trip to the attic and I was back out with an old settee cushion. It was perfect! Light blue satin with a gold fringe. I gently laid Blackie across it. We'd make a single file silent procession to the sand pit and lay her to rest in a fitting location.

Everything proceeded with the reverence I had hoped for. Under the noon sun and at the bottom of the pit we found a fitting site and dug a nicely-dimensioned grave. So far everyone had been a respectful mourner and I was grateful for their behavior. Standing side by side at the edge of what would be Blackie's final resting place, ready to lower her in, we all heard the whistle. And sadly there was only one guy we knew that could whistle like that—that loud with two fingers in his mouth. *Spike!* We were in big trouble. None of us knew where Spike lived, but from time to time he would show up, bully us, and then be on his way. We swung our heads up to look at the figure standing silhouetted on the upper rim of the pit. He was motioning to several cohorts to join him. Two or three more roughnecks soon appeared at his side. An ominous profile.

Pointing down at us Spike hollered, "Hey guys look at that. A dead cat!" With these words he and his gang came leaping, sliding, down the sloping embankment. I have no idea how old Spike was, but he was a teenager for sure. He was wearing an old gray tee shirt with the sleeves ripped off, and filthy dungarees (with a silver chain as a belt). He always wore one of those black felt caps with the fold-up brim cut in triangles. Before any of us could move (not that moving was even an option) he was standing tall, directly in front of me on the other side of the awaiting grave. I was worried.

And I was justified in being so. Without another word—just a devilish grin I can visualize to this day, he reached over, snatched Blackie off the cushion *by her tail*, swung her a couple circles over his head, and threw her with a dust raising thud into the recently dug grave. He laughed. His friends laughed. It wasn't funny. None of my friends said anything. I didn't either. We went home. I wanted the best for Blackie, but when it came right down to it, I didn't defend her. I let her be defiled. I should have done something. It was an early showing of cowardice, and I was not at all proud of myself.

A Morning Paper Route

Dad had been right; eleven years old was too young for the responsibilities of a paper route—especially a *morning* route. But I could do it in 50 minutes if I took shortcuts over lawns (and didn't stop in somewhere to thaw out). And it shouldn't be that cold this morning—maybe thirty degrees, although the bent-up corners of my bicycle seat would be frozen stiff, so I'd have to pump standing up the whole way. It was five-ten, the papers should be here any minute. Some mornings, even though I hadn't heard the bundle smack the sidewalk, still in my bedroom I could smell the cigar smoke from the guy in the truck.

And guess what, it was *Christmas* morning! Laura and Hank would be ready to go downstairs by six-thirty. If I didn't want to be holding things up I'd better be on my way. Pulled on a second sweater, put on Uncle Jim's old leather football helmet (and then tucked a folded washcloth inside each ear flap). Down the steps and outside. The bundle was already on the sidewalk. No cigar smoke smell. Maybe another driver on Christmas morning.

The bike tires were good and hard. The route should go quick. It's quiet and clean this early in the morning and you can be optimistic. Even the hills don't seem as steep. The light snow from two days ago was almost gone. I was pedaling my buns off (without sitting down). Forgot my gloves. Not a big deal. With nobody to disapprove I took a lot of shortcuts. I needed a record this morning; didn't take my usual five-minute warm-up in the Ridgewood Arms apartments. (In their lobby was a big heating unit built into the wall, and I could wedge myself into the space above it, for a short "warm up.") Was home at six-fifteen!

And a good thing too. As I came up the stairs I heard Hank calling me from his room. He was ready to go downstairs. On Christmas morning we always went downstairs together, restraining our excitement; especially Laura—almost a reverence in her case, holding her breath, both clutched hands up under her chin. Arriving at the living room door we'd stop, not entering until Mom and Dad appeared and signaled their approval. Under the tree would be an array of gifts—most being school clothes; not all those expensive electronic devices you see nowadays. Before long the floor was littered with wrapping paper and ribbons. Along with a neat 45-RPM record player I had received two records. At the moment Patti Page was letting go with "The Tennessee Waltz." Hank got darts, which I had a hard time believing Mom approved, based on the first several tosses I saw. A few minutes later—after an urgent "look out!" that activity was being discontinued until specific firing lanes could be cordoned off.

Mom made pancakes, and this special morning we were allowed an extra piece of bacon and there were no admonitions about excess syrup. I think Hank was taking advantage of the good will—if not with the bacon, for sure with the syrup. Uncle Jim called, one of Laura's friends called, and uncle Bud called to firm up the deer hunting trip he and Dad were going on. There were non-stop Christmas carols on the radio (which caused Mom to suggest that I give up on the "Tennessee Waltz"). During breakfast I noticed Dad checking his watch and glancing my way. This time he spoke. "Roger, go get your papers ready."

"They're already out Dad. I did them even before Laura and Hank woke up."

He appeared surprised, even irritated. After a couple seconds he said, "Go get them back." Of course this didn't make any sense, but though I often didn't understand my father, I had learned it was best to comply first and ask questions later. I was on my way. My route had twenty-eight deliveries, which for a six-mile route was not good. Seven dollars a week if everybody paid. I was only able to retrieve about twenty papers. Dad would understand (if only I could). Back home Laura was helping Mom, as I must admit she always did cheerfully. Dad was fully dressed and giving Hank instructions on designated fields of fire for his dart throwing. All the wrapping paper was picked up, minus one piece Mom had left for our new gray cat's amusement. I wasn't back five minutes when Dad said, "Okay Roger we're going back out."

Out the back door, down the steps, and into the same faded green Olds. Dad had me point the way for the route. Stopping in front of the first house he grabbed a paper, got out of the car, and motioned for me to follow him up the walk. He pressed the doorbell and stepped back, while I stood there wondering what in the heck was about to transpire. The white wood door swung open, leaving an artificial wreath swishing on the rusted nail from last Christmas. I saw the developing seasonal smile on the face of the unwary resident falter at the sight of this unexpected pair facing him.

My dad, in his red and black plaid wool hunting jacket, large and solid big arm over my shoulders, knowing smile on his face, proudly announced that this was his son Roger, *who had been delivering their paper all year in all kinds of weather, and now wanted to take this opportunity to wish them a very Merry Christmas.* Wow! You should have seen what happened. Every time! Some better than others—but still for me, an unexpected bonanza. Before long I had a pocket full of money, including dollar bills!

The Saltzers were the last house on the route. Mr. Saltzer dug feverishly through his pockets without finding a bill or any change. I could see a measure of panic in his eyes as my dad seemed to loom taller by the second. At this moment—as good fortune would have it (at least for Mr. Saltzer) his son (one of my classmates) appeared in the doorway. He was holding a brightly enameled dump truck, half out of its Christmas wrapping—a loose ribbon still draped across the hood. In desperation Mr.

7

Saltzer shot one look at it, snatched it from his son's hands and thrust it toward me, as his hope-for-the-best peace offering. Dad most graciously accepted it and we continued on home. Dad only went to the ninth grade, but I guess he just picked up a lot of practical stuff along the way.

The Birds and Bees in Five Minutes

I certainly wasn't dating—that was for sure. And even being twelve I couldn't name two girls I spoke to this week. But I *was* a little concerned about what grownup acts would have to take place when you would be alone with one in a bedroom. A little scary. Sure, I heard some of my friends talking, and it surprised me what they seemed to know (or lie about in a real convincing way). This was 1948 and there were no sex education classes, at least not in the sixth grade. I think back then parents were supposed to do it, and some questions Mom and Dad had recently been asking led me to believe they just might be working their way up to this very thing. I was afraid it was coming and that when it would, it would be a very awkward session. One night just before I drew my bath water (we didn't have a shower) I heard my folks whispering, and Mom say something along the lines of "This might be a good time, Kenny."

I was already in the tub when Dad came in, cigarette in one hand, small red pamphlet in the other. He plopped himself down on the toilet and left me to just fiddle with the soap and fear the worst. He leafed through the pamphlet for what seemed like a too-long time. Once having apparently found a good starting point and gotten his thoughts together, he looked up at me and began with a one or two sentence preamble (that I didn't see how would pertain to anything about to be revealed). Satisfied with this he began reading. Word for word. Sentence by sentence. No personal commentary. Lots of male and female plant terms, but no human examples. (Mostly bees and pollen, and things that neither the pamphlet's author nor my dad saw fit to tie together.) I knew all this was supposed to be part of a bigger picture, and I for one was in sore need of some specifics that would help me there.

Halfway through Dad may have recognized that he'd lost me (or he himself may have become unsure about how it was all going to come together). In any case he gave up on the pamphlet, turned on the seat to face me more squarely, and delivered about the most serious, heartfelt cautioning I had yet received—from anyone. The concern on his face was as genuine as I had ever seen, and this uncommon urgency had me "all ears." It had to do with young boys "amusing" themselves (and embarrassedly I think I knew what he meant here). According to Dad, this was something I had to avoid at all costs, *for God sakes!* And he knew the consequences! He had personally seen these guys as adults. *Completely crazy. Out of their heads! Just aimlessly wandering around!* Having given me this warning, it was over. He was up and he was gone. I'd been briefed, and I was *real* worried.

An Old Person Living in Your House

Later in life I wouldn't see it so much, but when I was a kid most of my friends had someone living with them. I mean someone besides their brother or sister—an *old* person! If it was a woman she was always sitting in a rocker in the parlor, near a window; never seemed to be anywhere else. Usually with a shawl over her shoulders, legs straight out, feet crossed. Never spoke to us kids passing through. If it was a man he would speak to us, but usually with a raised finger, cautioning us about our current activity. The old men seemed to spend most their time in the garden, bent over tomato plants, or in the winter telling us kids about blizzards. They always needed a shave, and their trousers never fit right, and they always had a hard time walking—one hand on their hip, the other reaching out for some steadying support.

Well we had one of these house guests ourselves—Grandma Deedy; a tiny, thin, bespectacled, gray-haired woman who lived in a small room in a front corner of our house. The skin on her temples was so thin you could see the veins under it. She had been with us as long as I could remember. But I can't remember the day or week or circumstances surrounding her departure (which was final). I am ashamed when I reflect on my lack of interest, an early example of me failing to recognize something of value; having chosen other things to be more worthy of my time and interest. I never asked Mom if Grandma Deedy was part of her family or Dad's family. Based on her thin frame and sharp features, quiet manners and intuitiveness, I assumed she was Mom's side of the family; could have been her mother's mother or her father's mother, or another relative who had outlived her own children.

The concerns of Grandma Deedy's life rarely gave her reason to leave our property, or even venture outside the house. In fact, except for traversing a short path to and from the kitchen, or short spell in the living room wingback chair, she rarely left her room. It contained only a few pieces of furniture and almost no belongings. I recollect a narrow single bed, a small chest of drawers and a rickety old table holding a small shiny black sewing machine (and an ugly cast iron radiator under the windows). I'm sure she had more than one dress, but if so, they all looked alike—dark with lots of small flowers. Leastways, that's the only pattern I remember. She never went anywhere. Never did anything. She moved about freely while apparently "knowing her place"—making an effort never to be a bother. Never loud. Never sick. On the very few occasions when I took time out of my busy world to share a few words with Grandma Deedy, it was always my gain.

There was one thing she did have—an ornately painted tin box the size of a cigar box. A box which may have originally held spools of thread or some other sewing paraphernalia, but now held Grandma Deedy's few keepsakes; things that few people knew about; things that would not be passed on, things that would disappear. Two of them were old letters. One was from her uncle, written while he was a Union soldier in Virginia during the civil war. It was on a kind of paper I had never felt, and it was written with obvious great care for its appearance. The way he shaped the letters was just beautiful. The vowels were perfectly rounded. Each consonant was taller than we make them now, and sloped at the same angle. (Like you'd see on a certificate.) But this was a real letter done with a fountain pen (maybe done on a dirt mound at night by candle). As she read me the letter, I had a feeling of respect and affection for this young soldier none of us would ever know—for his vocabulary and perfect grammar, and sensitivity. The words were put together in a strange manner, like the writings of famous authors I would later be required to read. It was about battles and cannons full of chains being fired, and people hurt and dying. Grandma Deedy said her uncle was only fifteen when he had written that letter and sixteen when he was killed.

The second thing Grandma Deedy had in the box—Lord knows how she came by it, was one page of an even older letter, written on brown paper and folded in quarters. It was one page of a letter written to Thomas Jefferson by his mother. Like I said, none of this stuff got passed on. Never saw it in any of the boxes when we moved. I wonder where it is now. And I'd give anything to be able to speak to Grandma Deedy again; to have her tell me about her life before our house, about her parents, and how she grew up, and if she remembered when she was a kid like me. If I had that chance, I'd really listen and let her know I cared.

A Face in the Window

Kids generally listen really hard whenever their parents' voices go hushed, and Dad frequently gave me occasion to respond accordingly. He had a way of registering a look of disbelief whenever some information came his way that was outside his data base. He had his own facts; a long list of things that irrespective of their lack of statistical or scientific basis, were certainties to him. An example of one was his explanation for those bright vertical shafts of light created when the sun pokes through scattered holes in an overcast. One time, seeing a few, he pointed them out to me and explained (almost confidentially) how this was *the sky sucking up moisture.* Even at my young age I doubted this could be the case, but his satisfaction in being able to educate me, and my respect for his intent, prohibited me from displaying any misgivings.

The Bruces were our right-side next-door neighbors, though not exactly Dad's kind of people. They had moved in and displaced his good "old-shoe" friends the Fitzgeralds. The Bruces bought a brand-new Buick with electric windows, and sold us their blue '46 Dodge "for a song" It was the best car we'd ever had; at last replacing that ugly-fendered, oxidized, olive green '38 Olds coupe that had for so long embarrassed me. The Bruce's had three sons. The two oldest were in college and just visited from time to time. When I was introduced to them they were very polite, but I sensed that meeting me was not much of an occasion for them. They both wore neckties and their names were Wharton and Dexter. (Sort of gives you an idea right there why this wasn't exactly Dad's kind of family.)

There was a situation within the Bruce household that I never understood (and wasn't supposed to understand) but knew was real serious. One day I overheard Mom explaining it to Dad, and it was evoking one of those looks of shock and disbelief he was capable of. It had to do with Mrs. Bruce. One offshoot was that I was not supposed to speak to her—which would have been hard to do, since it was about this time that she stopped coming out of the house. But I did see her, almost every day. In their house there was a second-floor window at the landing at the top of the stairs. Seems just about every time I came in our driveway and got the nerve to sneak a glance up there; just behind the glass and almost pressed against it (giving me the creeps) was Mrs. Bruce's face, staring back at me. Though our eyes appeared to meet, there was no wave, no smile, no parting of the lips. I never understood why she never came out of the house, or why she was always at that window, but I gathered it was something that it was okay if I didn't understand. The only phrase I could attach to it—that I'd heard during my parents' hushed conversations, was *"change of life,"* whatever the heck that was. As best I can remember, long as they lived there, I never saw Mrs. Bruce out of the house again.

Chapter Two
A SUMMER I'LL NEVER FORGET

An All-Girls' Camp

Mom had been working as the personal assistant for some rich lady who ran a big company in New York and owned a camp in the Pocono Mountains. A few days ago she had asked Mom if she would like to spend the summer as her Camp Administrator. Although Dad wasn't too hot on the idea, since it meant he'd be without Mom for the whole summer and saddled with taking care of us kids. They talked it over and Monday Mom told Mrs. Frey *if she could take her three kids along with her, she'd do it.* Mrs. Frey bought it! Hank and Laura and I would be going on a ready-made summer vacation; or at least Hank and Laura would be. I was fourteen and yup, you guessed it, I'd be *working* at the camp—full time. I'd finished junior high, would be a freshman in high school in three more months. No more just doubling up on the paper routes or stocking shelves in the stores. We made the trip to Camp Teedy-Usk-Ung in our new—well almost new, '46 Dodge. Mom didn't seem as upset about the coming separation as I thought she should. She was still excited, flitting around the premises.

The camp offered lots of activities: swimming, tennis, riflery, archery, badminton and volleyball. But the big deal at Teedy-Usk-Ung was the riding academy. At the far edge of the camp, surrounded by a freshly painted white fence, was a first-class riding arena. To the left were the stables and hay barn, and to the right, the bleachers and judges' stands. Mom said rich people sent their daughters here to perfect their riding skills. And *boy*, was I to find out there were some "horse-crazy" girls. When their camp stay was over and it was time to go home, well you should have seen all the crying and sobbing going on by the stables.

I had assumed I would be the only male on the premises, or at least the only eligible one (and as such was already imagining how popular I might be). But no such luck. Right off the bat I was introduced to Norman.

He was about thirty and good-looking, and six-foot five if he was an inch. Didn't seem fair. Here at Teedy-Usk-Ung he was the head counselor, taught swimming and other sports activities. So now, not only did I have another male to compete with, he was big and good-looking, and a little mysterious. Mom said he was a "conscientious objector" during WWII, refused to carry a gun, and ended up driving an ambulance in India. The second day I was introduced to Harry, and he was exactly my age so I couldn't fudge on comparisons. Harry seemed to know or have done more than a guy our age should have. I got the idea that he didn't have a mother or father living in this area. He had grown up in the nearby town, raised by different townsfolk. Helping my odds with the girls was the fact that Harry wasn't very good looking. He had a bad complexion and bad teeth.

There were just two other guys. Mr. Hale and Buddy. Mr. Hale was in charge of the riding academy and Buddy was his sidekick. Didn't see them much. They lived off the campgrounds in a trailer about a mile away. Mr. Hale was older and bald, and married, but Buddy was a pistol. He was about twenty-five and always telling dirty jokes.

Finally I met Fred, and the moment I saw him I knew I was in trouble. Fred was a large, hunch-backed old man, the year-round caretaker for the property. In the winter months when the camp was closed, he lived here all alone. Now, during the summer he lived in a shack a couple miles down the road. Fred had bowed legs and when he walked, he rocked from side to side like an ape. Several of his front teeth were missing and he only had one eye, or at least one of his eyes was always closed. Never once saw him smile. He had a permanent scowl and stared menacingly, even at strangers. You could just tell life had been hard on him and he bore it a vengeance. He wore the same outfit every day; a blue short-sleeved work shirt and baggy gray pants that hung on wide suspenders. Don't know why, but I was sure Fred didn't approve of the likes of me. (Guys like Harry were okay.) I didn't feel safe in his presence and went to some trouble to avoid crossing paths with him, especially away from the camp center.

I was surprised to find out that just about every camp task there was, was mine! The hardest of them would be taking care of the clay tennis courts, dragging a 200-pound concrete roller back and forth every couple days. Besides that I'd cut the grass (*miles* of grass), collect all the garbage and trash (haul it a half mile back in the woods and burn it) and clean the Admin building. Before meals I'd work in the kitchen for Malcolm, the colored cook. During the meals—all three of them, I'd wait on Mrs. Frey's table where Norman and the other counselors sat. After the meals, I'd be back in the kitchen doing the dishes. After they were finished, I'd sweep the entire dining hall and porch. *Wow*, talk about a full day.

A Bad Start With Norman

The camp was going to open in two days. Lots to do! I was assigned to Norman to help him get the swimming area ready: tow out the raft, string the buoy lines, rake the beach, and set up the lifeguard tower. Norman told me to wear my bathing suit. It was June, but it was seven-thirty in the morning, and up here in Pennsylvania it was a might cool. I was afraid to guess how cold the water would be. I followed three or four steps behind Norman down the path to the lakefront. When we got down to the water, I could see the lake was dying. It was being overtaken with reeds and algae and lily pads. The shoreline to either side of the beach was a swampy area of mangrove-like brush and rotting tree trunks. (Could visualize the snakes sliding through it.) Now wished I had put on some old sneaks.

The raft, which had been beached for the winter, was a ten-foot square white wood platform with four 55-gallon drums mounted underside. Norman had me drag an aluminum rowboat to a spot just a few feet offshore from it. The water was like ice. Norman helped me a little bit (but not much) in securing a rope from the stern of the small boat to the raft. Mostly he gave directions from a safe and dry point up on the beach while I leaned into the raft with all my 119 pounds. As big as he was, I expected he would assume the job of rowing. Instead, he had me sit by the oarlocks and then plopped himself (all 200-plus pounds of him) on the rear seat. This pitched the bow a good foot out of the water, almost launching me out.

I was expecting Norman to give some guidance as to where I should tow the raft; at least point in a general direction. He just sat there in one of his trances. I started towards a spot that I thought was as far out as one could expect the girls to swim and was lined up with where the lifeguard stand was lying on its side. I was dreading the thought of having to get in the cold water. To further discourage me, on the way out I saw a couple wakes near us, as if some type of reptile was moving along just under the surface.

"Right about here. This will do it." (A little proud of myself. I'd picked the right spot.)

Norman pulled the boat up against the raft and climbed onto it. Still on his knees he toppled an oddly formed concrete anchor over the side. A short tug down on that corner, a bob back up, and as best I could tell, we'd secured the raft. He motioned me to join him on the raft, which I did. We sat there together—the two of us, a giant and his small helper in the middle of a dying lake. Silence reigned. I had already noticed that from time-to-time Norman would just stop whatever he was doing and slip into some sort of reverie. A couple minutes of silence and then he'd pick up where he left off. I would wait. An eerie two-foot-thick layer of mist covered the entire surface of the lake.

Through the spaces between the boards I could see the water. Not inviting; a cloudy green liquid that all too quickly swallowed up the shafts of light. *Whoa, what's that!* Something big made a loud splash just behind us. I whipped my head around but too late. Norman didn't budge. I passed some time examining the stainless-steel ladder lying on the raft between us, and the plastic sack of hardware we'd use to secure it to the side of the raft. Norman awoke, grabbed the ladder, worked it over to the edge of the raft, slid it into the water and braced it against the side of the raft.

"Here, hold it like this. Right here." I did, squatting at the edge and holding the ladder so it would not slip into the lake. Behind me Norman ceremoniously began untying a valuable-looking leather pouch. Once opened and each corner carefully flattened, he began to unfold the oily brown paper inside it, exposing the contents: a set of gleaming nickel wrenches. He sifted through the shiny tools, finally selecting one. He held it up just admiring it. He then extended it towards me to a spot three inches in front of my face. "Use this, but guard it with your life." The words were softly spoken, but to my way of thinking, a solemn warning. To me this meant two not-good things: First, I was the one going in the water to attach the ladder, and second, I was going to use that wrench and I'd damn well better not drop it.

"I'll hand you the bolts when you get in the water. After you have them in, I'll hand the nuts down through the spaces between the boards."

What? *Down through the spaces in the boards?* I wasn't just going to have to get in the water, I was going to have to go *under* the raft, which would mean ducking my head underwater! Norman took over holding the ladder. Staring down at the murky surface into which I was about to slide, my imagination ran wild. I lowered my feet into the icy water and a chill went through me. Instant goose pimples. I thought I could make out the tops of seaweed wafting back and forth just a few feet below the surface. I was not eager to lower my body into those environs. But I did, one hand hanging onto the edge of the raft, the other one clutching the nickel-plated wrench from Poland. Both legs were curled up as high as possible, not wanting my feet to be any lower than necessary. Didn't know if it was five or fifteen feet deep (and didn't want to find out). To free one hand and still support myself, I hooked my left arm over the top step on the ladder, which brought a shout of disapproval from Norman, who then had to support me *and* the ladder. Now I'm treading water (and trying to do it with my legs still coiled up). I put the wrench in my teeth. Took the bolts, all four of them, and as fast as I could—one at a time, got them through the holes in the ladder and the boards which formed the side of the raft. Only in the water three minutes and my whole body was shaking.

"Okay, I'll drop the nuts down between the boards. And don't lose 'em!" It was now that I would have to put my head underwater to get beneath the raft. I took a gulp of air and did it. Lowered my head, but not my feet. It was particularly scary under the raft; the off season had left the underside loaded with mud nests, beetle carcasses, and webs with dead spiders. *And* then *I thought I felt my foot hit something in the water!* Wham, both my feet up against my backside.

"Here they come. Gonna give you one at a time." I cupped my hand as high as I could up under the space between the boards. (Still treading water.) The nuts and washers plopped into it. Got em! Uh-Oh, just noticed the two lower bolts were beneath the surface. I'll do those last. Get the two top ones first. I went to work, tightening the nut by hand as far as I could. Would only need the wrench for the last couple turns. Very carefully slid it over the nut. Slow measured turns. There it is—top two done. I was cold, shaking, and imagining all sorts of sea life (like carnivorous turtles and electric eels) circling just below my feet. But I was half done.

The two remaining bolts were only a foot under water and I could see them clear enough. I'd tighten the nuts by hand again—as much as possible. But the ends of these lower bolts were rusty and the nuts didn't go on as easily as the top two. I would have to use the wrench just to begin these. *Very carefully.* Did it a half-turn at a time—the handle of the wrench locked in my fist. Finally got it. *Only one more.* Norman dropped the last nut and washer through. Caught them. Threaded the nut on. This one was not going on easy. Backed it off. Tried again. It jammed again. Even using the wrench I was having a hard time turning the nut. Each half turn took all the strength my thin wrist could develop. Five, six turns—making progress! Almost snugged up. Last turn. While pushing with all my might the resistance quit and the nut (and wrench) spun freely. The force I had been exerting caused my hand to slide right off the end of the wrench. It was off the nut *and out of my hand!* For a second the wrench seemed to suspend itself there, a half-foot under water, not moving. Unfortunately, neither was I.

Another split second and it had recognized its debt to gravity and sliced downward. I took a swipe at it and missed. It flipped and glinted as a shaft of light hit it. It was two feet down. No two ways about it, *I had to go under.* I could still see a fading glint, but it was sinking fast. *This would be my last chance!* In a second I was under, eyes open, moving lower. Another reach for it, but not as deep as I could or should have. (Didn't want my hands any lower in the murk than necessary.) But because of this reluctance *I missed it again!* No choice now but to go deeper. Even if I drive my fingers into the worst type of muck, I've got to do it. Could barely see it. On the bottom now, fingers in the mud, entwining in slick grass. Out of air. Can't see anything. Lungs on fire. Gotta come up.

Even before I hit the surface I could hear Norman yelling. He must have guessed what happened. I knew if when my hand had first slipped off, if I would have just put my face under—right *then*, I could have gotten it. Or even having missed it on the first swipe, if I would have dived then—right then without waiting, I could have gotten it. I was too late making the commitment. It was horrible. Norman didn't chew me out, just sat there stunned, hurt and sulking. Finally into the boat and letting me row him to shore. He didn't say a word to me on the way in, the rest of the day, or much that week.

A Night Out With the Guys

On the weekends Mr. Hale and Buddy (never Norman) went to some backwoods bar; a log cabin-like, draft beer and juke box place not too far from camp. In any case—right now, Buddy was asking me, *Me? Did I want to go with them Saturday night?* I was shocked that they even considered me. While still trying to decide if he was serious, Buddy leaned close and whispered to me that there were always a lot of good-looking girls there. (Well that was one way to get my attention.) Would I find the courage to say I'd join them? I couldn't believe my ears as I heard myself saying "Yeah, sure I can." I knew Mom mustn't find out, but how would she? She didn't hang around with the likes of Buddy.

At 8 p.m. Saturday I slipped away from camp center and up to the highway to wait for Mr. Hale and Buddy, and Harry (he was invited too). Not ten minutes and over the hill came the black Pontiac. I was in and we were on our way. Five minutes (and some awkward joking) later we turned off the highway onto a narrow country road. A few minutes on it and Mr. Hale began slowing down, then made a turn onto an unmarked one-car-wide dirt lane with dense woods on both sides. The headlight beams illuminated no more than fifty feet of ruts and the low hanging branches. It ended abruptly, forcing us to turn into a small tree-stumped clearing that boasted just one poorly lit log structure that I guessed was our destination for the evening's forecast "good times." I was a little disappointed. The *Bear's Lair* didn't look like a place that any girls I'd be wanting to meet (or any girls, period) would be hanging out. Our arrival brought the number of parked cars up to a grand total of three. We all piled out, joking and back slapping (to me a forced attempt to bolster each other's anticipation of a forthcoming good time).

I was last up the steps and across an unlit board porch. Inside there were no more than a half dozen people. And none of them girls! Mr. Hale took over which was good; he was older (and at this point in the evening I still trusted married adults). He strode over to a round table and whipped out a chair. The other three of us circled the table and did the same. I was real concerned about what I was going to order when that time came. No way I was going to get away with ordering a coke.

There *was* a juke box, but no one had put any money in and the silence was doing nothing to enhance our surroundings. Buddy got up and went over to it. After hollering a couple smart remarks over his shoulder, he put in some quarters and made his selections. There were no waitresses at the Bear's Lair, so Mr. Hale set about taking our orders. I knew it was now or never. In a manner I didn't recognize, I replied, "Any kind as long as it's cold." I was a little proud of my quick thinking. What's more, Harry said "The same goes for me." (Maybe the first time in my life I initiated a course of action.)

The tray of beers arrived. *This was it.* Mr. Hale made a toast to some old friends. Buddy laughed and said, "down the hatch." I tried. I tried to take at least two big swallows before putting the glass down. It frothed up in my mouth and burned all the way down. The way the other guys were chugging them down, my glass was only going to be half empty when they finished theirs. I considered lowering the glass below the table edge and tipping some out.

A second mug appeared in front of me even though my first one wasn't near finished. At first Mr. Hale and Buddy were joking about raucous fun times they'd had, then somehow the conversation turned serious, and it didn't seem to me like they were having a good time. Lots of complaining. Oh No! A *third* round. I'd finished my first beer and while making my best attempt at the second one, declined mine. This was an entirely new experience. Up to this point I had only sampled a single mouthful from a rowdy friend of Dad's.

I suddenly realized I had to pee. I spied the men's room door, slid back my chair, stood up, *and got the surprise of my young life!* Almost fell straight back over the chair. I caught myself and was able to avoid a horrible embarrassment. There was noise in my ears and I was light on my feet, as if a cable from the ceiling was suspending me just above the floor. I glanced at the others. *Had they seen? Were they watching me?* I could see their lips moving and expressions changing, but I couldn't understand any words; in fact I may not even have been hearing any words. The room suddenly tilted and I pressed both palms on the tabletop to steady myself. I recognized it: *I was drunk!* In the thirty minutes I had been sitting there— without me noticing it, the alcohol had been doing its job.

I started across the floor. Big job just staying centered midway between the row of bar stools on the left, and the dance floor on the right. Every step was calculated. I was corralling inertia to form a trajectory that would have me end up at the men's room door. Though I couldn't risk looking back, I guessed by now they were all staring at me (probably taking bets on whether or not I'd make it). Almost lost my balance completely on one adjustment. *Thank God I hadn't fallen.* Made it! At the urinal it was a longer mission than I'd had for some time. Being more skilled after my first trip, I did a better job on the trip back to the table.

In my present condition I was an inept outsider, unable to add anything to the conversation, or try as I may—even follow it. I felt excluded but could understand why. May take a while to get in the swing of these Saturday nights out, although so far it wasn't all that much fun, and I wasn't sure I'd even try it again. Things that were happening at the table and alongside us on the dance floor were beyond my ability to register. Don't know how long after that we stayed; could have been fifteen minutes or an hour. Suddenly realized all the other guys were standing up, and I realized we were calling it a night.

Outside now in the middle of the dark clearing, I began to feel a little ill. Took a couple full breaths of the cold air, which didn't seem to help. We must've stayed late because there was only one other car still in the lot.

Buddy was wrestling with me (and it took me a while to even recognize it)! Mr. Hale motioned him into the car, and I think was reprimanding him. Out of the corner of my eye I saw Harry pointing at me and laughing. Next thing I know, Buddy is hoisting me up on the front fender. He held me there a moment, and then before I could figure out what the plan was, *the car was moving!* I grabbed onto a chrome molding to steady myself. Where'd Buddy go? In the car? How did he get there? They *all* were in the car! Of all things, Mr. Hale himself (the one person I considered to be an adult) was at the wheel and laughing like mad. The car yanked to the right and he must've floored it. Grass and dust were flying in the headlight beams. We snarled around the lot in a tight circle. The way the car was turning, I was afraid to jump off. (Was just sober enough to know I could end up under the wheels.) I slipped and slid onto the center of the hood and grabbed the hood ornament like a rodeo rider clenching the saddle horn, waiting and praying for this stupid prank to be over.

Oh No. We're not stopping, we're *leaving!* We're on our way out the dirt road. The car bounced and lurched in the ruts. I was over on my back now. Next thing I knew we were turning onto the main road. The engine roared and I could feel us accelerating. I was hanging on to very little, but hanging on to it for dear life! I was barely staying aboard. The hood was heating up fast. The rushing sound in my ears was now the wind, and my vision was distorted by tears. The night was flying by. Mr. Hale (who I had by now lost all respect for) hit the brakes and I was half down in front of the grill—my shoe on the bumper. Struggled to keep my foot from slipping off behind it (and continuing down to the speeding pavement just inches below). I closed my eyes, squeezed and prayed harder.

The camp—camp center. Thank God! I rolled off the fender and down onto the grass. We were back. I'd made it. Buddy and Harry were laughing and slapping their legs. I was never so happy to be lying on the ground. I'd made it. I never would find out if I had just passed initiation or if this was the kind of things older guys did when they went out drinking. You might guess, the rest of the summer and for sure—Saturday nights, I pretty much stayed on the campgrounds.

A Close Call With Fred

I did venture off the campgrounds one more time. Don't know why (wish I hadn't now), I agreed to accompany Harry into town—his town; the nearby small village of Hawley, which like the camp lake was barely hanging onto life. Shouldn't be too dangerous—still daylight (and without Buddy).

I would finally get to meet some of Harry's friends (who it turned out, all had bad teeth, smoked, drank beer and whose cars were temporarily not running). Still, Harry must have had something going for him, getting enthusiastic greetings from senior citizens sitting on rickety chairs in front of rundown storefronts. There was a wide spectrum that had occasion to know Harry, but they weren't the kind of people who waved at me back in Ridgewood (or even the kind of people in Ridgewood).

Harry wanted to show me the billiards place where *he got beer no problem*. He walked in like he owned the place. I followed, immediately sampling a heavy, damp, old-fashioned odor. The walls were crowded with faded photos, deer antlers, and shelves with stuffed birds. The wood floors were dry and dusty. We plopped ourselves down (like we did it every day) and set about ordering. Several fellows were having a boisterous time not too far from our table. The center of attraction was one young guy about eighteen, in a red plaid hunting cap with those ear flaps hanging down. He saw Harry and gave a big wave. Harry waved back and whispered to me, "That's Lloyd—Fred's son. He's leaving tomorrow." It was 1951, the Korean conflict was growing. Boys were being drafted to go really far away to fight in some police action. This was Lloyd's last day before shipping out. A few minutes later he came (stumbled) over to our table. He began talking Harry's ear off, about the good old times. Don't know how Harry made any logic of it. Lloyd was missing words (and even a couple teeth like his dad) and his sentences just weren't making any sense. Not being Harry, and Lloyd in the condition he was, I couldn't decipher any of it. Lots of old times' stories and I think once, almost some crying. I felt uncomfortable. It was the first time I had been this close to a conversation with a real drunk. I tried to pay polite attention. For me it couldn't have been over soon enough.

Back at camp that evening while we were doing the dishes, Malcolm the Chef asked us about our trip to town. Harry said we had seen Lloyd, rolled his eyes back in his head and smiled knowingly at me. I one-upped Harry, tilting my head from side to side and acting like I was drunk, *not realizing Fred the caretaker (Lloyd's father) was standing in the doorway, watching my charade.* It was the first time in my life I'd seen that much hate, and directed right at me! I knew I had used poor judgment. I don't think I meant to ridicule his son. And going off to war is probably a pretty good reason to get drunk. I was scared and wanted to get to a safe place as soon as possible. I raced through the last few chores and ran up to the

Admin building, where I spent a good hour with mom.

After lunch the next day, finishing up the dishes—everyone gone except Malcolm, he asked me to go down into the cellar and bring up a sack of sugar. I said "Sure." The dining hall's stone foundation served as the cellar walls; a large cold and dark space used for storing foodstuffs. There were three long rows of pallets, stacked almost to the ceiling with cartons and sacks. The original stone walls were crude and cracked. The room itself didn't look real safe—the timbers holding up the main floor were split and rotted. I considered it an act of bravery just to go down there—especially alone. It was like a cave, if you listened hard you could hear water dripping. The floor was hard-packed dirt. It was poorly lit by a few bare light bulbs dangling from a single electric cord that ran the length of the space.

I reached the bottom of the steps and started down the row I knew would lead me to the sugar. As usual I had left the door at the top of the stairs open. (Any extra light you could get down there was always welcomed.) While trying to separate the flour bags from the sugar bags, that shaft of light was squeezed out and I heard the door shut. A second later the dangling lights went out. I was standing there in quasi dark. The meager amount of light filtering through the dirty ground level windows barely silhouetted the tops of the stacked cartons. I was scared.

"Now I've got you. And I've got you where you belong, with the all the other rats in the cellar. I'm going to get you now."

It was Fred! I was petrified. My heart was in my throat. This was it. The acting I had done last night—mimicking his son, must have been the last straw. The loudest thing in the cellar was my heart pounding in my ears. I worked at trying to fix the location of the shuffling noises Fred was making as he worked his way down the aisle. "I've got my rifle here, but I don't need it."

Hearing him speak gave way his position. I backed up carefully making sure not to topple anything, and turned around the far end of the second row. I could hear the sound of cellophane wrappers and debris crunching under his feet. He couldn't have locked the door from this side. If I could just get to it I'd be okay. But the stairway was on the other side of Fred.

"This place was all right before your mother and you came up here. She and her book-keeping and new regulations, and you—you city kid. I know what has to be done."

Fred was now in the third row, halfway down, not twenty feet from me. Didn't know how I could get past him to the stairs. *Oh God.*

"I think as much of you as the other rats in the cellar."

My mind was racing. I was crouched down low. I could hear him approaching the end of the row. I had to go further down the row, further away from the stairs. But I had no choice. He'd see me if I didn't. I wasn't crying but I felt tears in my eyes. I cursed myself for my thoughtless panning of Lloyd. I knew I'd learned an important lesson in life. (It was just whether or not I was going to live to use it.) I heard a low throaty laugh—a not-good sounding laugh. I made it around the far end of the third row. I don't think he knew where I was. I was as still as a statue. I didn't move and I didn't hear him move. Every few minutes I heard another low, mean-sounding chuckle. He was going to wait me out. I knew I had to do something but didn't know what. I was too scared to think well. I was now on my knees at the far end of the room, just waiting to be discovered.

What's that? I heard the door open and a shaft of light shot into the cellar. "Roger, where are you! Get up here with that sugar." *It was Malcolm! He hadn't left. Thank God!* I could hear him starting down the steps. *Thank you God!* I bolted up the row, knowing I would be passing within five feet of Fred on the other side. But I was at top speed and had Malcolm there as a witness. I bounded up the steps and past Malcolm. Didn't have the sugar. Didn't say why not. Out the door! Heard Malcolm exclaiming something about "Damned kids, who can understand 'em."

I spent the rest of the day three feet from Mom. I didn't tell her what happened, but I'm sure she knew something was wrong. I didn't sleep well that night. I was much too worried. Every move I made the rest of the summer was based on my best estimate of Fred's whereabouts.

Chapter Three
IF I WANT A MAN'S WORK, THIS SHOULD DO IT

Hearing About the Perfect Job

Y esterday was the last day of school. For most fifteen-year-olds it meant neat vacations somewhere far away, or one fun day after another at the town public pool, or best of all (my dream) playing baseball in a summer league; on a real team—with uniforms. But not for me, I'd be working. And I guess even if I wasn't, I wouldn't be having all that much fun; probably just end up spending half my time sitting on the curb with Wes or in the back yard with Rolly. My ideal summer would be something I could only fantasize about: first—*not* work and spend every day at Graydon Pool *with those cool rich kids from the Heights*. The guys were always laughing and having such good times, wearing plaid Bermuda shorts and penny loafers, without socks. And the girls from the Heights were all pretty; couldn't miss them in school—sashaying through the halls, in their white blouses and pleated plaid skirts, crossed arms in front enfolding their books (and hiding their emerging bust lines). And now in bathing suits! I couldn't imagine being there that close to them the whole day.

I would have given anything to be a part of that group, but never got close. I wasn't special in any way; not tall, not good-looking, and definitely not a football hero. (Not even a football participant.) Only had a reason to speak with a kid from the Heights when we were together on some class project. And when it happened, to my great surprise they treated me almost like an equal. But this was the exception. There was a difference and I understood it. My dad wasn't like the other fathers; he didn't take the train to Manhattan in the mornings, and I certainly never saw him with a briefcase. Dad worked in an aircraft plant in a nearby town.

But if I was going to have to work again this summer—which Dad would surely expect, I was ready for something new. Enough of paper routes, cutting lawns and odd jobs. I would be in the eleventh-grade next year and I was ready for more prestigious work—*hard work* that deserved some respect. Not sure I ever considered that I could just skip it, Dad was always saying I'd have to learn the meaning of a buck. Wesley Riley said I should check out the celery farms in Paramus. He said they were mostly foreigners and would hire American kids even if they weren't eighteen. He made it sound exciting, although I knew Mom and Dad would need convincing. No one from our neighborhood (even the adults) ever had a reason to cross the highway and venture into the taboo area known as the "truck farms." Still, if I was going to do something different this summer, this would fill the bill. Work hard, bent over, get my back nice and tan, carry a lunch bag, and hang around with older guys who smoked and had tattoos. I'd check it out tomorrow morning.

The Celery Farm

I was excited to begin the four-mile bike ride to the mysterious truck farms. Pedaled east on Lincoln Avenue then turned south on Route 17, past the famous Paramus Roller Rink—a place my parents were not too keen on. (The high school girls who smoked and had older boyfriends with drivers' licenses went there.) Ten more minutes on a gravel shoulder—with tractor trailers roaring by only three feet away, and finally there it was—the turn off that led to the celery farms. It was the first time I'd ever been here without Wes or Skip. I turned in past shanties selling hub caps, old furniture and strange vegetables, whose vendors looked up suspiciously as I went by. Half scared, half invigorated, I pedaled faster. The wind felt good.

I could see it now—the farm Wes told me to check out. A table-flat half mile by half mile bright, wet verdant patch cut out of the woods. Coasted to a stop alongside the only path (not even a road) that led into the farm. Acres of green shoots coming up out of black water, but only a couple small shacks and a half-dozen workers. A couple weird platform vehicles with huge tires were sloshing across the paddies. None of the workers I saw—all shirtless and wearing baggy black leggings, appeared to be looking my way; laid my bike on its side and started in. I had never tackled anything like this before. The nearest group was composed of three, tall, bare-chested men. I steered towards the only one who appeared to have noticed me. Stopped in front of him and surprised myself by speaking right up. "I'm here to see about a job for the summer, if I could work here."

His expression didn't change; spent most his time brushing flies away. He motioned me towards another big guy. Started towards him. Ninety percent of the ground was under water. I had to walk on a narrow, raised dirt path. With each step I sank in and stuck a little. My right shoe got pulled off. Shoved it back on quick before anyone could notice. By the time I got to the guy, both shoes and trouser cuffs were covered with black gook. I pretended not to care. (It wouldn't look good to be overly concerned with one's appearance.) None of the workers—all older men, even *had* shoes on their huge, gnarled feet.

I again explained the purpose of my visit and got no response. The huge man with no shirt, dirt streaks all over his chest, face beaded with sweat, looked down at me in an annoyed manner. He answered with a waving-away motion of his big hand. "No, you much problems. No here." This response could have been enough to turn away an average applicant, and in truth I was becoming less keen on the whole idea myself. It was a cinch I wasn't wanted, I was a long way from home, and it was hot and there were a lot of insects. I'd put forth the effort and tried. And maybe this summer would be the one I'd not work; get to be on a team, or better yet be able to somehow get in with that group from the Heights. *Naw that's just dreaming.* No way Dad would hear of that. He's expecting I'll work full time.

I put on a real disappointed look when he waved me away (though I was aware of noticeable relief at this rejection). Just then another hulking guy grabbed his shoulder. I waited while they hashed something out in subdued tones (although it didn't have to be subdued since only one word in ten was English). A few seconds later and to my great surprise, *I was hired!* I was told to show up at seven Monday morning; thirty minutes for lunch and finish at three-thirty, earn $3.60 a day. They turned back to their work and I was alone. I should have felt better. I had accomplished exactly what I set out to do. But I didn't have a good feeling—not at all. Any hopes for this summer were out the window.

More Than I Bargained For

During the weekend, in contrast to my state of mind, my friends seemed to be in good spirits. But there were no demands on their time. Donnie Bruce wouldn't have to work at all, and Rolly would just help his dad assembling a real church organ (from their basement to the attic). Victor Longo would just keep doing yard work in the neighborhood (friendly surroundings). Wes got a job at Sears Auto and therefore was qualified to be my confidant. We wasted most of Saturday. Sunday afternoon we rode our bikes back and forth past Graydon Pool, hoping to see some kids we might know, but no such luck. Noticeably missing were the kids from the

Heights. They were cool and didn't get too excited about anything (much less a public pool opening). Hit the rack early on Sunday night, knowing I had a six o'clock get-up in the morning.

A quick cereal breakfast, out of the house, and on the road by six-fifteen. This early the day is still what you're hoping it will be, not what it might end up. (The bike ride would turn out to be the best part of the day.) I had two peanut butter and jelly sandwiches and an apple that Mom made me take. At the farm at six forty-five—fifteen minutes early; hoping this early arrival would make points, but it was another thirty minutes before my presence drew any attention. When it did I was told my job would be that of a "planter" (which would turn out to be the perfect job to get that tanned back I was talking about). From 7:30 till 11:00 I walked, better—plodded along, in mud up to my calves, water up to my knees, bent over ninety degrees at the waist, with a long burlap sack full of celery seedlings slung over my shoulder, dragging behind me in the water. My job as I sloshed forward was to use a pointed tool that looked like a thin metal ice cream cone, reach down through the water, punch a hole in the mud every three inches, then reach back, take a celery seedling out of the sack, and jam it into the hole I'd just made.

Not far from me was another operation with one of those strange vehicles I spoke about earlier. On the back of it were two of the biggest and strangest appearing guys I'd ever seen; looked like circus giants. They weren't old, but they were completely bald. They had big heads, thick lips, and wore no shirt or shoes, just those baggy black pants. They spoke no English and as I said, did not look friendly—even to one another. About every fifteen minutes I snuck a "standup" just to see if my back could do it. Eleven o'clock couldn't have arrived too soon.

There was one other young guy working on the farm, but not an American. He surprised me by joining me for lunch. He had unkempt brown hair and bad teeth. He spoke with an accent and didn't have good grammar, but he was friendly. We ate in the shade of an abandoned shed, on a raised dirt bank alongside it. After twenty minutes I wasn't sure I would be able to get back up. The apple was delicious. I wolfed it down (and thanked my mom). Gustav knew a lot about this kind of farm work. He'd had lots of jobs like this. He told me he never went to school. I don't mean he never went to *high* school. I mean he said he never *started*—not even the first grade! (In light of this his grammar wasn't all that bad.) He told me what country he had come from, but I can't remember how to pronounce it. Here in the States he didn't live with his family, or *any* family. He lived with some other young workers he knew. He didn't know where his mother was. His father was working at another truck farm about twenty miles away.

Lunch over we went back to doing the same thing we'd done all morning. I was almost in tears by three-thirty, and as I sped homeward there were tears in my eyes. My neighborhood never looked so friendly. My house never smelled so good. I was just waiting to spill my guts about this new job, but no one was home yet. Finally at dinner Dad asked me about my job and *boy* did I tell him. He didn't look impressed. I think Mom was concerned. I was already thinking of laying the groundwork for the day when I might tell Dad I was going to quit. I could not imagine enduring this for two and a half months.

Each day went exactly the same; every minute, every three inches. Up to our ankles in mud and up to our knees in water, bent over using that strange steel-pointed tool to poke a hole in the mud, then shove one of those green stalks into it. Sometimes I'd accidentally dunk my face in the water. My fingers were worn from the burlap and the mud, and the skin was getting funny from being underwater so much. (It was no longer a priority, but I sure was getting my tanned back.) One week. Made it through. Friday afternoon and payday. The boss made Gustav and I wait an extra hour—until four-thirty, to get paid: $17.60 in cash. They took out 40 cents for something.

Spent just about all day Saturday hanging around with Wes, and did I tell him some stories about his darned truck farm. In the morning we helped his dad who was doing a valve job on their Chrysler. In the afternoon we went to the hobby shop and then walked up the street to the Warner Brothers theater where we read all the *Coming Attractions* posters. And of course we pedaled by Graydon Pool a half dozen times; this time seeing lots of classmates, all apparently having the best of times. After supper we sat on the curb with our eyes closed, trying to identify the makes of the passing cars, just by the sound. Wes actually could do it—almost every time! I have no idea how.

Sunday morning I was awake at seven but stayed in my room till almost eight, attempting to further validate my level of exhaustion. Start of the summer my folks allowed that at fifteen and working full time, I could skip church, at the 100-year-old Dutch Reformed church out by the highway. (We used to be Baptist, but that church was four miles away so we converted.) Sunday afternoon I joined the family for our weekend jaunt to "the property." Dad had managed to buy twelve acres in Upper Saddle River. I had never seen him so happy as when he came driving back with the deed. Each weekend he spent at least one full day up at the property. I'm not sure how much Mom enjoyed these woodsy outings, tagging alongside Dad while he chopped trees, pulled stumps, burned brush, cut roads, widened creeks, sunk wells, and spoke of his plans to build a cabin. She was there by his side on every visit. (I was there behind a wheelbarrow.) Too bad my dad didn't hang onto this property; about thirty years later the adjacent property was purchased by President Richard Nixon.

An On-the-Job Promotion

The Monday morning alarm was a rude reminder of my personally picked punishment. The leisure of the weekend was still fresh in my mind. The thought of all those kids lounging around Graydon Pool, just wasting time with nothing to do, haunted me. Why couldn't I—just *one* year, spend a summer like that? I could visualize the cheerleaders on one blanket, laughing and flirting with the guys, then up and running, being pursued by blonde crew-cut football players snapping towels and tossing pails of water. And here I was on my bike not being thought of or missed by anyone, pedaling my way even further from the good life. The second week dragged by, but I made it, although I was just "doing time" now. The hours came and went. I didn't hear people talking, didn't see things happening. And then (thank God) I'd be on my bike, homeward bound, pedaling like crazy, tears welling in my eyes. Speeding past the shallow and dirty but renown *Duck Pond*. I saw two kids at the edge of the water lazily skipping stones out over the water. Evidently nothing they had to do; were probably there all day.

The third week I was called aside by the guy that Gustav and I called "Big Oop," tall and bald as a billiard ball. He motioned me away from my planting job (which if only for five minutes would be a cherished respite). A safe distance from the other workers he told me in so many barely translatable words, that I was going to be promoted. Not in pay mind you, but by being assigned a choice job. I was going to work in the shade; cool and upright—no longer bent over ninety degrees. I followed him to a three-sided shed constructed of warped 2x4 posts wired together, holding up a battered corrugated metal roof. Inside were two large, galvanized tanks about eight feet long, six feet wide, and four feet high; both filled with dark (not nice, oily looking) water. One of the tanks was against an outside wall below a large opening. The trucks would back up to it and dump loads of freshly picked celery through it and into that first tank. My choice job: Be in that first tank, take one of the hard-bristled wooden brushes floating on the slimy surface, and scrub the incoming celery—every stalk—stalk by stalk. Get all the gook off them and toss them into the second tank. Even at my age and with my limited work experience I wasn't sure that this was any choice job.

After lunch I was in the tank; no shoes or shirt, just wearing my shorts. The bottom of the tank was covered with slim and small objects about which I wasn't sure. *Some were moving!* Sneaks back on fast! I heard a vehicle approaching the shed. Pulled myself up to see over the lower ledge of the opening; saw a dump truck backing towards the opening. I retreated and waited. Another minute, some gears grinding, and *in comes the celery!* I don't know how much celery I thought I'd be dealing with, but I was fighting to stay on my feet. What a pummeling I took. I was never so glad to see anything stop. There was barely room in the tank for me. Even if I hadn't gone under twice, the deluge had my face and hair soaked and dripping, and I had something in my eye stinging like mad. I got ahold of one of the brushes and went to work. Grab, scrub, rinse, chuck it. Grab, scrub, rinse, chuck it. Could have done it quicker except I may be too conscientious—concerned that someone might discover an imperfection in my work. I was resolved to get every speck of mud off every stalk, and determined to get my tank cleaned out, before—God help me—another load arrived. After an hour the knuckles on my brush-hand were aching and my fingertips were raw. I couldn't tell if my hand was open or shut. I'd have to be more careful with those bristles. Thank God for small favors: a second load never arrived. I had the tank empty thirty minutes before quitting time. Big Oop came by and looked surprised. I don't think he was expecting to see my tank empty. He examined some stalks from tank number two; didn't say "good job," but took a couple away with him. I did this job the rest of the week, beginning to worry about a rash I was starting to get all over my body. Gustav saw it and said it was "celery itch"—all the scrubbers get it. He said at the big farms the scrubbers wore rubber suits. Friday I got the whole $18.00. You're probably saying, "That was a long time ago, eighteen bucks would buy a lot." I'm here to tell you it didn't go very far.

The weekend couldn't have been more cherished if I was on furlough from the state prison. The air smelled sweet. Mom couldn't do enough for me and Dad didn't make me work with him Saturday morning, like he'd had me doing each week for as long as I could remember. (I suspected Mom had something to do with that.) Sunday afternoon we went to Grandma and Grandpa's for the weekly roasted chicken dinner. Uncle Jim and Uncle Bob were there, so that was fun. What with the trip to Grandpa's and a couple other family things, I didn't spend much time on my bike this weekend. I missed cruising by Graydon Pool, which may have been for the best. I didn't get to see what I was missing. Those guys and girls from the "Heights" would have been having a fine time, flirting and teasing each other. Sunday night taking a bath I had a chance to see how bad the rash had become. My crotch and the inside of my legs were one big red blotch. I could hardly stand lukewarm water. I put on half a can of talcum powder and set up a table fan at the end of my bed to blow up between my legs. I was real worried about getting back in the tank on Monday. (Knew I couldn't tell Big Oop I wanted another job.) But maybe God *was* watching! First thing upon arriving at the farm, Big Oop tells me I'm being reassigned. Now I'm going to be a "puller." Didn't know if it was because I hadn't cleaned the celery fast enough or because I was doing it *too* fast. The Puerto Ricans sort of had a little union on the farm, and had been giving me real dirty looks and complaining about something to the bosses. (They put *two* of them into the tank afterwards.)

An Unexpected Reprieve

Now—out of the tanks, I'm riding on one of those huge-wheeled vehicles; actually not riding, I was an attached appendage, lying on my stomach half off the rear edge of the flat bed. The back of my legs were wedged under a rusted bar that kept me from slipping off altogether. I was hanging almost upside down off the back of the platform as it moved along, yanking the celery out of the ground and tossing it up behind me onto the truck. (This job let me have no doubt about what my spinal erector muscles were.) There was another worrisome downside to this new job. It appeared that Big Oop—now riding on the truck with me, and the guy driving the truck, hated each other. They were always arguing, and I mean arguing bad! Even as a kid I could tell it was serious, seeing them snarling under their breath. I was staying out from between them, they both looked real mad. I stayed bent over and didn't look back.

A few days later while hanging over the back, clawing the water and snatching stalks, Big Oop and the driver begin arguing more loudly than ever. The truck jerked to a halt, and you weren't supposed to stop in this area, the vehicle could bog down. I raised myself up to where I could see what was going on. The driver was out of his seat and clambering over a railing onto the platform where we were. I was sure he was swearing in some language. In his hand he had one of those worn-smooth, pointed metal tools that I had used to make the pilot-holes. Before anyone could do anything he had driven the tool into Big Oop, who let out a scream and then a terrible noise as he went down on his knees, then over on his side. He tried to get up, but the driver put his foot on him and pushed him off the truck—into the muddy water.

The driver dropped the tool, jumped off the truck and just started walking away; like nothing happened, like it was quitting time. I was standing alone on the flatbed. Big Oop was gurgling in the water alongside the truck. Some nearby workers had heard the noise and were now running our way. The driver kept walking—just normal like. Gustav was nearby shouting that we had to get out of there. I was off the truck and splashing through the water with Gustav. We ran out of the paddies, past the sheds and to where we had left our bikes. On em and going! A mile later, winded and safe, Gustav said he was quitting for sure now. He said he'd seen this kind of thing before and cautioned me, "You won't never get on with another farm if you get tied into this." He said he was leaving for now, but that he was *damn sure coming back to get his two and a half days' pay.* I said, "Me too!" But I knew I had no intention of ever setting foot on this farm again (or even on this side of Route 17).

Twenty minutes at full speed and I was turning onto our street. The driveway was empty, but I spied our '46 Dodge at the end of the street, just about to round the corner. Dad was on vacation this week and they were on their way up to the property. They were headed out to Route 17—about a mile away. Maybe one of them will look back and see me. Or sometimes there was a few minutes delay on the ramp before you could get onto the highway. *Please God make this one of those days.* I was pedaling that Schwinn like never before. Standing. Leaning forward. Bike rocking left to right. *Pump!* I wasn't gaining on them. My only chance was they'd be delayed getting onto the highway. *Luck was with me!* They were and I caught them. I had tears in my eyes but I was with my own family. Mom had tears in her eyes. Dad told me to pedal back to the house. He'd come back and get me. What a reunion we had that day at the property.

Chapter Four
HIGH SCHOOL IN A NUTSHELL

On Being Prepared

It was another humdrum history class until (through the fog of my daydreaming) I realized the kid in front of me was turned around and whispering to me. *...did I want to come over to his house and study? Tonight? For the test tomorrow?* My heart missed a beat, because this was Donald Webster, the paragon of *Upper* Ridgewood (the Heights)! Most days wearing a blue button-down shirt, maroon V-neck sweater, gray flannel slacks, and white bucks. None of the kids from the Heights had ever invited me to their house. Besides, Lord knows a "C" was an okay grade for me, while only once in a while did Don not get an "A". *What possessed him to think I could help him prepare for a test?* But flushed and with no time to think, I accepted. I'd be over at seven sharp.

Knew I'd have to do my afternoon paper route, but also knew I'd better do a bunch of studying before I went over there (or I could be in for a real embarrassing evening). Papers will be here soon, but I can get in a little studying before they arrive. Went to the bedroom, closed the door. This was serious. We weren't just talking about grades; we were talking *reputation*—and not just mine. I'd be carrying the banner for all the other guys on this side of town (Wes, and Rolly, and Vic). This could be an opportunity to gain an acceptance we'd never had.

I read and turned the pages but kept finding my mind wandering. The information seemed simple enough as I read it, but a few pages later I was unable to recite any of the names or dates or places. *Nothing was sticking.* Finally, after coming back from a bathroom break, *at last*—a page that made sense. Good! Maybe we're getting somewhere. Then I realized the pages had flipped back while I was in the bathroom, and I was reading the same page I had just read three minutes *ago!* I'll never remember all this stuff. And there's my papers hitting the sidewalk. Great, did the route in 45 minutes—a record for a Thursday (the day there's a shoppers' section and the paper's too thick to fold). Pedaled the whole route standing up. Was back in my room at five-fifteen. If I didn't eat supper I'd be able to study for thirty minutes more. So much for that idea; Mom and Dad made me join them at the dinner table.

Back in my room, still futile. Don would rue the day he had asked me to help him study. And what's worse he'll know that not only do I live on the other side of the tracks, I'm not very smart. I had to try a different method of studying, even if it took more time. I found a spiral notebook, ripped out the old Christmas wish-list pages and put it on the bottom bunk alongside the textbook. (I was on my knees on the floor using my bed for a desk.) My new idea was: start with the first paragraph, read it carefully, slide the book away, *and then try to write the whole paragraph in just one sentence on a page in the spiral notebook.* I tried it. I read hard, thought about it one minute, and then in my own words transcribed the main point of the paragraph into just one sentence in the spiral notebook. I read the second paragraph; thought about it a moment and then transcribed it into one sentence. Then the third. I was surprised to find myself making good progress. It was going pretty fast. Ten done, only three more pages in the chapter. *6:20: I'm going to make it in time!* The chapter was finished and I had just two pages filled in the spiral notebook. I closed the textbook and lay down on the bed. Notebook in hand I read every sentence, with the people named, the event, the date, and what it meant. It only took ten minutes to review the whole chapter. I was ready to believe I had most the main points. *Might* get away with it. Don might not see through me.

In the Heights. Nervous. In front of Don's. Through large stone pillars and after passing a line of blue spruce, I spied a huge double-door entrance. I felt a chill as I drove up the wide circular drive. I'd never been this close before. Knew I was out of my element. Was pretty sure my yellow-fendered 41 Ford looked way out of place in this driveway. Made it up the wide stone steps and pressed the bell. Don's parents were surprisingly pleasant. My arrival went much better than I had imagined. Inside—wow! There was a room they called *the study*, where his parents recommended we go for privacy. Lots of wood paneling, and I'll bet—real leather furniture. Bookshelves on every wall. Not one, but two huge desks in the same room! We sat in two big easy chairs facing each other. The drill was about to begin. *My mettle was about to be tested.* If I would have relaxed my jaws my teeth would have chattered.

Don said he'd start—be the first to ask the questions. My stomach knotted. I wasn't going to get a reprieve. In the hot seat immediately. Don started out with a simple question first. Maybe he was just being kind and didn't want to embarrass me right off. I held my breath waiting for the second question. Remarkably, I could almost visualize where he was in the textbook—halfway down page two, middle paragraph. Here comes another. *Lady luck was with me!* Maybe by the skin of my teeth, but I made it through. He finished the first half of the chapter and I'd made it! Fortunately for me Don had asked manageable questions about the chapter's main points. (I don't think he was good at digging deep for the small details.)

He handed me his book and told me to have a go at it; ask him some questions. "Okay, sure." I found where he was and began. I was soon embarrassed, because after he had asked me the more obvious questions, evidently I was now asking more complicated ones. The evening went a thousand times better than I could have hoped for. Don seemed satisfied. His parents even acted as if they were pleased just to have met me. But no one was more pleased and thankful than I was. We said goodnight and I was on my way home, singing at the top of my lungs, and giving thanks to the Lord for small favors.

History class was first thing after lunch. Don gave me a big thumbs-up as we sat down, though I wasn't sure that was going to do any good. Last night was one thing, but this was the actual test. Mrs. Payne's briefing was short. The exams were coming down the row. Soon everyone was bent over their desks. The only sounds were an occasional sigh or ruffle of paper. *Please God, be with me again.* He was. Mrs. Payne, who was known for her tough tests (you could never bluff through one of hers), had for once—finally, made up one that was straight forward. For once, each question was in plain language and right at my level.

For once I finished without having made a single check mark in the margin (indicating I should double-check that answer). But there was no sense going over mine. I knew I had already put down the best answer I could think of for each question. On the way to the teacher's desk, I noticed almost the entire class was still bent over their papers. *Maybe there were two pages of questions and I only got one.* She said no, took my paper, checked it briefly, smiled, and nodded me back to my seat. That was that. It was over, for better or worse.

I could hardly believe it when the test scores were posted. I didn't just get an "A," I got every single question right! Don got a "B+" again, like he often did. My personal conclusion was, even though from time to time the teachers might goof and just make up an easy test, I was going to keep on doing my new spiral notebook procedure. Why take chances?

A Spring Formal to Remember

When Mom said it was a *girl,* I thought she was kidding. I was sixteen now, but that didn't mean I was getting phone calls from girls. But it *was* a girl, and a nice girl—Arlene Bradley. Her dad was a lawyer. She wasn't beautiful, but she was okay and smart, and everyone liked her. I often saw the popular kids talking to her. But why would she be calling me? She hardly knew me. She would say something to me if we were squeezing through a door together, but we never walked together in the halls or anything like that. (Of course I never walked with *any* girls.) Although I often fantasized and wondered what it would be like—walking down the hall holding hands with one of those pretty, bright-eyed girls from the Heights.

What? I felt my ears redden and my heart skipped a beat. *Would I go with her to the Spring Formal?* I knew about it alright; it was a "girl ask boy" dance put on by the Junior Class girls every year, and held at the exclusive Ridgewood Country Club. Numbed and not realizing there could be an alternative answer, when asked I said, *yes, I would.* In fact saying no never entered my mind. It certainly didn't seem proper to say no to a girl who got up the courage to call you up and ask you. Actually this wasn't my first time being asked to a "girl-ask-boy" dance. My first experience occurred as an eighth grader, when the Junior High had decided to experiment with such an event. I was similarly flattered when Lucy Ann Clayton had called me. In outlining her reasoning she had said words to the effect of, *"...and you were about the only decent one left."* Prior to later reflection I took that as a compliment.

And something even more scary, this dance was a *Formal.* While I wasn't exactly sure what that meant, from the way all the girls had been talking about it for the last couple weeks, it must have been something really special for them. Mom clued me in: *It meant I was going to have to wear a tuxedo.* Not only did I not have one, it wasn't in our budget to rent one. Mom and I were worried till Dad (of all people) came up with a possible solution. "Herb is just your size, and I know he's got one. He wore it to that thing the Masons had. Betcha he'll lend it to us."

Wow. That would be neat. Except it was hard for me to imagine any adult being as small as I was. *How could I fit in any grownup's clothes?*

Dad asked when it would be and I told him. He said not to worry, he'd get Herb's and bring it home for me to try on. I was at a loss to explain why—on this one occasion, Dad had decided to get involved in something I was doing. This was just a first! And lo and behold, Herb must have been a small guy, because when Dad brought the tux home and I tried it on, it fit me perfectly! Hardly recognized the figure in the mirror. I felt a new excitement to be wearing a grown man's clothing.

When the day of the dance came around I was more than a little nervous. By five o'clock my stomach was churning. Mom had held school on the corsage thing, how to pin it on, and gave me a cram course on the Foxtrot. Think I mastered the basic steps. The Foxtrot was easier, but it seemed to me it would be boring if all I did was those same steps over and over again. And finally I got some tips on things to say. I was sure there was going to be a lot of stuff I wouldn't know, but I'd had about all the last-minute advice I could handle.

Seven o'clock. Arlene would be here any minute. Her parents had volunteered to take care of the transportation. Next thing I knew there was the car in our driveway. They were here—right on time. I checked myself one last time in the hallway mirror, and truthfully I had never seen myself looking so good. I couldn't help admiring the tailored jacket and shiny lapels. I must've looked really sharp, because when Arlene spied me she took a breath—almost appeared startled. And she looked good too, though I would have hated to be surrounded by the material in her dress. It had ruffles all around and made a loud swishing noise when she walked. Mom was great—handled the introductions, even helped me pin on the corsage. I was proud of my folks. It was the first time I'd ever seen them talking to any adults that lived in the Heights, much less socialites like Mr. and Mrs. Bradley. (And in our own house!) The photos and small talk finished we were on our way. I was proud of myself—thought I was acting pretty well composed, although Arlene seemed nervous.

It was dark when we arrived at the Ridgewood Country Club. Mr. Bradley joined the line of cars that were easing ahead and spilling out their young couples to traipse up the wide marble steps. I'd never been in such a setting. Brightly lettered banners and paper lanterns were stretched across the terrace and between the pillars. It was easy to see this was going to be a festive occasion. We disembarked. Arlene's parents wished us a good time and were off. I must've looked sharp in this grownup's tuxedo; would have been easy to imagine I was the center of attention—that people were noticing me. It was a new experience all right, and I must say I was liking it. (For the first time I think I knew why those rich kids from the Heights always seemed to be in such a good mood.) Just inside the door there was a reception line, where Arlene told me it was the girl's job to present her escort to the sponsors. I was feeling even more special; proud to be deserving of her introductions.

By the time we got to the ballroom it was already quite full. The band was warming up. People were milling about. Even before we mingled, still at the edge of the room, I felt as if all eyes were upon me. *And it was then it struck me!* There was a roar in my ears and I felt the color drain from my face. I searched—frantically, my eyes probing the crowd, but not one—not one other guy in the whole place, was wearing a *black* tuxedo! It was a *Spring* formal! *White* jackets! *Now* I understood Arlene's surprise upon first seeing me in the house, and why I had felt as if "all eyes were upon me." I wanted to die, to disappear. But there was no way out, I had to make the best of it. I had two tough hours ahead of me. So did Arlene. She was a real trooper.

A Little Help With a Big Decision

Seventeen, halfway through twelfth grade, graduation just months away, I had given very little thought to what decision that would call for. Certainly my parents cared, but I think they (especially Mom) gave me more credit than I deserved for having some worthy plan. Well I did—for tomorrow night or next weekend, but certainly not involving a career. I've finally recognized I almost never think far enough ahead, and this is just one more thing (big thing) I gave too little thought to. For me it was just another summer about to begin. Hard to believe I didn't realize earlier in the year that I was approaching a significant decision time.

And this was 1953. It wasn't a given that you'd be going to college. Most of our parents (on this side of the tracks anyway) hadn't gone; their well-meaning advice dealt with learning a trade or helping in the family business. Dad suggested I might want to look into becoming a barber. He said they had it made—always closed on Wednesdays, only a half day Saturday, and all indoor work. Not a bad deal he had said, except for the fact you had to spend a lot of time on your feet. Even as little as I thought about a life's work, I was having trouble picturing myself as a barber. To show that I *was* giving some thought to my future, I dropped some hints about maybe (for just one summer—taking July and August off) and then in the fall, start my first permanent job—driving one of those big

38

gravel trucks for *Sam Braen Inc*. You saw his trucks everywhere. Wes's dad told us that Sam gave all his drivers a big turkey for Thanksgiving. With nothing else to go on, this seemed as good as anything to make a career decision on.

By late spring the issue of my future seemed to be coming up more frequently. And whenever it did, I noticed Mom got real serious, to the extent I thought her eyes might be about to tear up (which made me begin to suspect this point in my life might be more critical than I had thought). I always knew that Dad had dropped out of high school to work, but was surprised to find out early on, that Mom had been a high school valedictorian and attended Vassar college in New York, which at that time was the most exclusive women's college in the whole country!

But there was one thing that all my friends' older brothers were talking about: that "police action" thing going on in Korea! True, it was almost over, but if you *did* make some plans, and then the government up and drafted you, well that sure could mess things up. While listening to Dad's occupational suggestions, I often heard Mom mouth the word "college." *College?* I hadn't given that any consideration. No reason to. But if it was an option it would extend my role as a student and postpone the really hard choices. Alas, out of the blue, some direction. None of my doing, but a plan would begin to take shape. The previous summer I had attended a one-week Bible camp sponsored by our small church. It would turn out to have been a key event. The counselors were neat; most of them students from a Christian college in Iowa

Unexpectedly, now almost a year later I received a call from "Digger," one of the camp counselors. He was a sophomore at Central Christian College, and an enthusiastic recruiter. He already knew what *he* was going to do with his life. He was going to be a minister. He told me he had already registered for the fall of 57' semester at New Brunswick Theological Seminary. (About as far ahead as anyone I knew had ever thought.) *And now he was calling to try to convince me to go to Central.* With nothing else on the horizon I listened. And what a salesman! He made it sound just great. I never got to visit Central (or any other college for that matter) but as far as Digger was concerned, I didn't have to. He had more brochures and photos than you could have asked for. And neat stories too—of all the great things about campus life at Central. Even gave me the phone numbers of other Jersey kids who had already decided to go to Central. My parents and I totaled all the costs and came to the conclusion that it could be done. I'd be able to pay the whole year's tuition using my savings and this coming summer's earnings, and my parents would take care of the costs of the dormitory and meal program. For living expenses and spending money, I would do odd jobs there at the college. *Roger Yahnke would be going to college in the fall!*

No idea where I would be today if Digger hadn't called. Personally (and embarrassedly) I did nothing proactively; merely responded in a perfunctory manner to the questionnaires I received from the college, passively going along with how things were proceeding. Here—as would luckily (and embarrassedly) occur often in my life, I would be the undeserving beneficiary of outcomes greatly facilitated by friends, strangers, or situations that presented themselves at a time when I was unaware of the necessity to be decisive and take appropriate action.

12th Grade and Finished!

Waited a long time to say it (though by now you've probably figured it out). My high school days were *not* fondly memorable; not like what I've heard they're supposed to be. Certainly not like the TV series *Happy Days* (although my town, our high school, the kids and their parents, could well have inspired the series). We didn't have a dress code but didn't need one. Most the guys dressed in button down collars, V-neck sweaters, gray flannels and white bucks. The girls (especially the pretty ones from the Heights) dressed the same just about every day: white blouses, plaid skirts, saddle shoes, and ribbons in their hair.

I never mixed with those cool students. Probably my own fault; just didn't think I stacked up. Didn't try out for a team, or a part in the school play, or join any of the clubs. Never stopped in the soda fountains after school (and if I would have I'd never have had the nerve to sit with any of those Upper Ridgewood kids). And that was because I knew I wasn't one of them—not by a long shot. And why? Well besides being known to be on the outside looking in, I was pretty busy. From seventh grade on there was never a year that I didn't have either a morning or an afternoon paper route. (Or both!) And when I didn't have an after-school route, I had an after-school job; spent my whole junior and senior years stocking shelves in the Co-op on Godwin Avenue. Maybe that's one reason I never tried out for a team—couldn't make practices.

Now I ask myself *why* was I always working? I don't recollect the paychecks ever turning into neat things or any great times. I just thought it was expected of me. I knew Dad expected me to earn all my own spending money.

With my daily arrivals two minutes before the first bell and my departures two minutes after the last bell, I was certainly doing my part to maintain a low profile. Though most kids probably knew my name, they didn't have any reason to want to know what I was doing when I wasn't sitting there in class. My mornings remain a pre-dawn image of the clock reading four forty-five, and my afternoons of wolfing down one of those little *Mrs. Something's* pies and an RC Cola before delivering my papers. Seems to me, all I did in high school was work. And this doesn't count Saturday mornings, when by Yahnke tradition a son belonged to his dad to help with the current week's renovation project. (And with my dad, there *was* one every week!)

Well, I did one other thing: *I thought about girls*—imagining myself on a proper date with one of those popular ones from the Heights, or making up more daring scenarios with the ones that smoked and dyed their hair and wore big earrings. (These girls were sort of fair game. I'm not so sure about those nice girls from the Heights.) It worried me because I was pretty sure my friends didn't spend as much time thinking about girls. And I just knew the rich guys from the Heights didn't, but they didn't have to—they were *with* these girls all the time. As I look back (embarrassedly), it seems I spent a lot of time thinking about female bodies. A key time was after I went to bed and before I fell asleep. *Real concerned about that.* But as far as real dates or going steady, nothing was ever put in action. Think I only had three dates in all my high school years.

Graduation
Of the occasions I remember missing out on—being on the fringes of (or excluded from completely), few are more representative than my high school graduation ceremony. I'm sure that's supposed to be a landmark event; a reason for joy and self-indulgence (an excuse for reckless acts). There's supposed to be parties and dances, lots of congratulations, and at least one big gift. I can only remember a few things about mine: A sweltering early evening outdoor ceremony; standing there squinting into a blinding setting sun—seeing only the silhouettes of the parents in the bleachers; and a two-second trip across a rickety scaffold platform to receive my diploma. *That's it.* I'm sure my parents were there; must've been, but I don't remember any conversations with them, before or after the ceremony. Might have gotten one but can't remember any graduation gift.

I do remember the rest of the night—lying on my back on the rear seat of Ralph Harlberg's car, watching the streetlights go by, as he and Skip drove around till 2 A.M., doing nothing, going nowhere. Next day it was over. Like for me it didn't even happen. I remember the envy I felt when I heard that a bunch of kids from the Heights (*girls* included!) had rented half a motel down the shore and were driving down—*to stay overnight!* (Boy did Skip's dad have something to say about *that!*)

Joining the Adult Labor Work Force

The summer following my senior year I knew I had to find an even better paying job (to be able to make a worthy donation to the college kitty). Uncle Jim surprised us by phoning to say he'd found me a job working for a friend of his. We spent all summer knocking down an abandoned old brick-walled building—by hand! I was glad to have had the opportunity to earn some good money, but it was *not* a fun summer. Had to get up at 5:30 each morning, make my breakfast, make my lunch, and then walk a mile to the foreman's house to hitch a ride to the job site. What a ride— dreaded it. I had never met such a pessimistic, complaining adult. Harold complained bitterly about everything, especially his wife and the boss. (And this transportation cost me five dollars a week!)

I was the only kid on the job. All the other workers were grown men, and from a breed I'd never met. They swore like you can't imagine, smoked all the time, never shaved, had bad breath, *and didn't wear underwear.* (I knew that because up on the roof ripping off scalding hot shingles, I was right behind a skinny guy who had a gaping hole in the seat of his pants, and what I saw wasn't a pretty sight!) They drank on the job and were always telling each other about their sexual escapades, the likes of which I had never heard and could scarcely believe. I vowed that whatever I ended up doing in life, it would *not* be something that would cause me to associate with these type individuals on a daily basis. Having now experienced my first permanent job, I said a bigger "thank you" to Digger and Mom, and knew better than ever that no matter what would happen later, it had been a most fortunate happenstance to make that college decision!

Chapter Five

THE BEST KEPT SECRET EVER

Central Christian College

Augost 20th found Digger and I and two other Jersey recruits standing alongside his wood-sided 47-Ford station wagon, waving goodbye. When the last photo, hug, and "yeah, don't worry" seemed to really be the last, we seized the moment and clambered in. The engine caught, some final nervous waves, and we were off for the flat, corn country (though I for one had some second thoughts, praying I had not bitten off more than I could chew). Had no idea what to expect. Went straight through—22 hours; sweating in the day, cold at night. No car radio. No space to get horizontal. But it was a small inconvenience for what would soon unfold before my eyes. When we rounded the final corner and the campus was in sight I was greatly relieved. A beautiful sight. Not threatening at all. Better than the brochures. Just what one would hope for: expanses of bright green grass, old ivy-covered stone buildings, large oak trees, tiny arched bridges, and a network of brick walks. I had an immediate good feeling about what I saw and was anxious to be a part of it.

I'd never met anybody from Iowa, or Wisconsin, or Minnesota. Coming all the way from the east coast, in those days—to those farm kids, New Jersey was almost a foreign country, so we were regarded with a flattering curiosity. We were referred to as the "hoods" and received more attention than we deserved. I realized this could be a new start. *I could be anyone I wanted to be!* No one here from Ridgewood High; no one aware of my mediocrity. I could even be one of those kids from the Heights. I could talk to anyone. Just get up the nerve and do it! If I was ever going to have a fresh start, it would be here.

I Can Be Whoever I Want

During freshman orientation I got an idea. *I needed a cool nickname.* Roger just didn't seem like a cool name. No one knew me here except Digger (who obviously was into this nickname thing). This would be the perfect chance to change my moniker. I wanted something short and cute. I made up a list and spent all afternoon in front of the mirror, mouthing them out loud. Just an hour before the "Let's Get Acquainted" party, I made my selection: *"Dink!"* I would be Dink Yahnke. Sounded cool to me. I was excited visualizing the moment when the ladies at the Welcome Desk would ask me for my name. As calm and naturally as I could, I'd tell them *"Dink,"* like I'd said it hundreds of times (which I almost had). Then I'd watch them scrawl it on my name tag and stick it on my lapel—marking the official beginning of my new persona!

Only three or four freshmen between me and the registration desk. *Only minutes from a fresh start.* Some other freshmen who had already been through the line were standing together drinking cokes and chatting. Among them was a handsome athletic-looking guy from Wisconsin who was going to be our star tailback. Everyone seemed to know and like him. One reason I liked him was because he was only as tall as I was. (It made me feel good when short guys were popular.) True, he was more muscular than I was, and I'll bet he never lifted weights—leastways not as hard as I had. And he wasn't stuck up; in fact he was genuinely friendly. His name was Dwayne Krentz. I could see he was going to be one of the "big men on campus," which was okay with me.

The girl in line in front of me began making small talk, including that she had gone to the same high school as Dwayne, and that they were good friends. And then she asked me what my name was. I was caught off guard. I hadn't prepared myself to mouth my new name until I was officially asked for it. But I rose to the task, took a quick breath and told her that while my real name was Roger, everyone called me Dink. A look of disbelief spread across her face.

"Dink? That's impossible." What did she mean—*impossible?* She pointed at Dwayne Krentz. "That's Dwayne's nickname. Dink!" She said that as a child when he pronounced his first and last name together it sounded funny, so they started calling him that. "Look over there. It's already on his name tag." Incredibly, she was right. I could see it from where we were. The expression of disbelief on my face outdid hers. I was in shock, foiled by a one in a million coincidence. Try as I might, after reviewing the runner-up names, when asked by the woman at the Welcome Desk, I replied, *"Roger."*

An All-Round Great Time

In spite of no cool name, college was a new and uplifting experience. I was accepted at face value (even more) and was (God knows why) regarded as someone to know and say Hi to. I would have liked to do what I had to—to stay that way, but never knew what that was. The school was located in a small Iowa town that had been settled by immigrants from Holland. And it appeared being Dutch was a prerequisite for residency. The phone book was full of "Vander-this's" and "Vander-that'ers." In front of every store were stacks of tulip bulb boxes. Every road into town boasted a sign letting you know you were entering the *Tulip Capital of the USA.*

The town center was a one-block-across, tree-shaded, grassy park, with walkways, benches and a white gazebo. Everyone called it the "square" and it was the starting point for directions to anywhere. The four streets bordering the park boasted just about all the stores and businesses in town. The movie theater was only nine seats across. There was a farm equipment dealer among whose inventory of shiny dinosaur-like contraptions I could not find one whose function I could figure out. Half the population lived on working farms, and as a result, one of the first big surprises for me—something I never saw in New Jersey: it seemed every tenth guy you passed had at least one finger missing.

Each morning started with a short chapel service that had a 100% turn out. Of course that made sense since all the students were from good Christian families, in fact, like Digger, half the male students were going to make the ministry their life's work, and believe it or not, I was toying with the idea myself! (Just thinking I might have *some* plan was exciting.) I had either two or three classes each day, which left me half the day to study or just waste time. Even for the first time in my life, taking a nap after lunch. I was having a hard time not feeling guilty with such an easy routine. I was quite sure my family was envisioning a much more demanding lifestyle.

Mom had recommended a liberal arts curriculum so that's what I signed up for, although I later discovered this was one time when Mom wasn't exactly right. Central had a religion major. (Everyone had to take *Old Testament History.*) The classes seemed just like high school; not harder or more complicated (which concerned me a bit). The teachers were kind and patient. No problem with grades. I was doing better than in high school but wasn't convinced the courses I was taking were practical or moving me towards any defined profession. I just hoped it would all fall in place later. Oh, one other thing about Central: No privileged people from a "Heights" somewhere. I have no idea how these Midwest kids grew up, but they sure turned out okay.

For spending money I did odd jobs at the college. My favorite was the late-night cleaning of the gym. After buffing the floor and being the only soul in the building, I would turn all the lights on full bright, dribble down the shining court, juke the last defender and shoot a lay-up (to the roar of the imaginary crowd). Even with this part time working, my classes, and studying, I had plenty of time left over to do whatever I wanted. I had never experienced such leisure. *I sure was thankful Digger had given me that April phone call.*

Experimenting With Athletics

My beefy roommate had a plan for himself that he thought may as well include me: sign up for the football team! *Me on a football team?* I was the heaviest I had been in my life, but that was just 144 pounds. Being born small was something I fought every day. To better wage this battle, at fourteen I'd begun lifting weights regularly (one could say fanatically) which did make some difference, although certainly not substantial. The first confirmation that I was not of sufficient size occurred in the equipment room. The smallest helmet I could find still swiveled on my head. However, I made all the practices, dressed for all the games, and even got to play in one; was scared and confused on every down and knew I didn't belong out there.

The gridiron wasn't my only ill-advised athletic endeavor. One of the linemen, a big guy nicknamed "Tank" thought we guys from *Noo-joy-zee* must have had lots of fights. Tank was a boxer and this led to trouble. In a soon to be regretted effort to impress him, I mentioned Dad had been a boxer. (He did have a punching bag in the cellar and he did spar with some local fighters.) But the real mistake was adding that I'd had several amateur fights, which was an outright lie. There was no getting out of it, he was bringing me to his gym and I was going to be on his team! *My darned play-acting again. Trying to be something I wasn't.* The club accepted my word-of-mouth credentials from Tank, adopted me into their club, and put me on the card for a big event in Des Moines only three weeks away (without ever having me get into the ring with anyone). I won't go into the details of my boxing career except to say I did win one or two, but was sick to my stomach all day before each fight.

A blessed reprieve: No one had tried out for the pole vault, and several friends talked me into it. I was the vaulter; albeit a completely untrained and lousy one. No one was assigned to coach me and I just practiced the same lame attempts, all alone on the far side of the field. During the first meet, on one vault the pole faltered before reaching vertical. I was stopped dead, short of the cross bar, feet up and going nowhere. The attempt having never taken me to a point over the wood chip pit, I fell back on the hard packed cinder runway, *on a locked-straight left arm!* Dislocated my elbow. It was a heck of a price to pay, but I missed that night's scheduled ring appearance, and my collegiate boxing career was never resumed.

Using Appropriate Language at Central

One evening Digger was driving us around in his now famous old Ford station wagon. Concluding he was doing little more than wasting gas Digger suggested we call it a night; just hit the truck stop for our usual cheeseburger and French fries before heading back to the dorm. Enroute Digger became aware of the "F" word emanating from the back seat and told us that he was not comfortable hearing it. We explained it was doubtful we could communicate effectively *without* using it. Digger—realizing our plight, suggested that instead of using the "f" word, we just use the word "fork." If we said "fork," while he would know what we meant, he could tolerate that.

Inside the diner we took our seats at the counter. The sexiest looking woman I'd seen in the state of Iowa was the lone waitress; large false eyelashes and dyed red hair falling onto large breasts (tumbling out of a low-buttoned green smock). She came over to where the four of us were sitting (our eyes fixed on her and fantasizing). She asked us for our order. We all responded with the standard "Cheeseburger and French fries." A short time later while munching away, I noticed—like me, Digger was using a large toothpick (with a plastic bow attached) to stab and raise the French fries to his mouth. Unfortunately, every other time they'd spin off and fall back down onto his plate. Not only had I seen his toothpick problem, our provocative, bedroom-eyed waitress had also noticed they weren't doing the job. She sauntered over, put her elbows on the counter in front of Digger, and leaning forward with her face directly in front of his, looked into his eyes and said, "You wanna fork?"

My Second Year and My First Girlfriend

My second year of college was every bit as rewarding as the first year; even better, just enjoyed my courses and my still-great spare time. Plus, one brand new activity, *going steady!* At Central every girl was prim. In the dorm there wasn't much gossiping about Central's co-eds. If they weren't some guy's sister, their father was a teacher here or a minister in town. My freshman year had involved only two or three dates—attending completely harmless school-sponsored activities, such as hayrides (in the daylight) and square dances (with half the faculty in attendance). But this second year would be a little different.

By the end of the first semester a certain Minnesota farm girl and I had become one of Central College's favorite twosomes. Constance (who only her closest friends could call "Connie") was a straight "A" student—which you would suspect, seeing her in the library with her horn-rimmed glasses, sitting next to a pile of reference books. My guess is she would have been the answer to any mother's prayers; smart, proper, and seemingly always above the fray. While at first glance her gingham freshness may have suggested a naiveté, anyone who might have tried to pull the wool over her eyes, would shortly learn she was not someone to be messed with. Everybody looked up to her and wanted to be where she was, including the boys. In addition to the attributes previously mentioned, she was sufficiently well-formed to attract attention for some time after passing by. For reasons yet to be explained, she had just "picked me out." I knew I was lucky and went along willingly. It was a first for me: associating with someone who with just momentary eye contact knew exactly what I was thinking, and then passed a proper judgment on it. It was as if I had surrendered to someone. Constance was a junior—a full year ahead of me. It was understood that she was smarter than I was and frequently took charge of our activities. But all that seemed okay.

Knowing Central—with its daily chapels, mandatory Old Testament classes, and parental faculty, the physical nature of our relationship stayed pretty much at the "holding hands" level. Each night after our stint in the library I'd walk her to the front steps of the women's dorm to say goodnight—in full view of the Dorm Mother and a dozen other couples. Before college broke for the summer I began trying a more intimate parting gesture. I advanced to sealing it with a kiss—as best I knew how. They were certainly kisses, but I didn't view them as looking anything like the ones in the movies. And—at least for me, they weren't stirring my soul or my loins. (I prayed they were better on the other end.) And it was a little embarrassing when one of the nearby couples began going at it. To me, those sounds and movement accentuated the perfunctory nature of my attempts. But I was pretty sure Connie wasn't ready for that stuff.

I knew nothing about these kinds of relationships but was beginning to think ours could well be the beginning of something serious—very possibly a long term relationship, who knows, maybe even marriage (though that eventuality never crossed my mind). One tip-off to the possible seriousness of our relationship was the sadness I felt when we parted for summer vacation. And Connie gave every indication she would miss me even more. Real tears. We both agreed that August couldn't come soon enough, and it would be a wonderfully grand reunion!

Chapter Six

A SIGNIFICANT FORK IN THE ROAD

Avoiding the Draft

Two years of college under my belt, but no idea of what I was going to do with them. Not even an inkling of a preference for some life's work. A break might give some time for things to fall in place. And there was a very good chance I would be drafted before I finished my senior year; maybe even before I finished this coming year. The Korean War had only been over two years and the "Cold War" was at its height. Nowadays kids don't realize it (with the current *All-Volunteer Army*), but back then, if you weren't married with kids you were probably going to get drafted. *And that was me.* So if I *was* going to be drafted, maybe I should beat 'em to the punch, volunteer and thus be able to choose my own poison. And God knows why I thought I might like to be (or would be able to be) a pilot, but that's what I was thinking about. It sounded glamorous, would put me in the wild blue yonder and keep me out of muddy trenches.

First week of July I decided to pop in on the local Air Force recruiter to just get some information. Made the drive to the old Post Office in Patterson, where all the recruiters had their offices on the second floor. Tarried in the lobby, realizing I might be getting ahead of myself again. *Well, I'm here, probably can't hurt to get a little information.* Climbed the steps to the second-floor landing where a grimy window was allowing some light to filter into an abandoned dusty hallway. Half way down the hall I saw a floor-to-ceiling wall mural with four gleaming jets in formation. *Yup, that's what I was thinking about.* Eyed it a minute, took a deep breath and entered the office. There was just one uniformed guy inside (who I would have expected to look more pleased to see me entering). In spite of his disinterested expression I told him my reasoning for coming in.

He gave me a quick once-over and spoke. "You got two years of College?" To which I proudly answered to the affirmative.

"How about your vision, do you see 20-20?" Once again the answer was yes.

"Five foot seven?" First time in my life I was ever glad to be five foot-eight.

"Well, you should be a shoo-in, except all our flight classes are filled until the middle of November. But no problem. Take this test here, fill out these enlistment forms, I submit them, and you're in. You'll just have to lie around the barracks a couple months until we contact you."

I was your original "wet behind the ears" kid, but in spite of that, the *laying around the barracks part*, just didn't sound like something a guy could bank on. Hard as it is for me to make a decision (particularly saying "No") I surprised myself by passing on this offer. Head lowered I exited and started down the hallway. Almost to the opposite landing, *what's this?* A poster on an easel on the floor in front of an office was emblazoned *"FLY NAVY."* It displayed a couple on a balcony at the edge of a large body of water. She was beautiful and he was handsome, with a pair of gold wings on his chest. Outlined on the horizon was a large ship. *A what, an aircraft carrier?*

While standing there I felt my upper arm being taken. Looked up and saw a much more hospitable appearing military man. I accompanied him into his office—the Navy recruiter's office. Would you believe—the exact same three questions. Gave the same answers. But this time—no waiting until November. Next thing I knew, I was being seated at a desk taking a long test; the likes of which I had never seen. It included just about every discipline: English, math, geography, history, science, mechanical stuff, and one interesting section that showed large, slotted pieces of flattened cardboard, and the task was to pick which was the correct form if the separate flattened pieces were assembled. Surprisingly it seemed easy to do the required constructing in my head, and I think I got all of them right. Many of the other questions weren't objective, as if they were trying to grade your interests. For example, one question was: "On a Harley, which side is the clutch on?" I knew but pondered: If I put down the right answer, will they think a young guy who rode motorcycles was too reckless, and not the type of young man they wanted. *Would it be better to miss that one on purpose?*

Completed the test and evidently did well. Signed more forms and that was it. Somehow with a mission of "just getting information" I'd gone and done it. Next stop in two weeks would be Floyd Bennett Naval

Air Station in Brooklyn—to be officially sworn in! Lucky I didn't have an accident driving home. It was the most excited I had been in my life (although the excitement was tempered by some *"What in the heck have you just done?"* second thoughts). I couldn't wait to share the news with someone—anyone. (This was way before cell phones were around.) I knew this was a very big thing I'd just done, maybe the biggest thing ever.

Two weeks later, on my drive towards the George Washington bridge and then Brooklyn, I passed an empty field that had a hand-painted sign: *Airplane Rides Five Dollars.* I was still worried about some lurking deficiency that might result in the Navy withdrawing their offer; for example they might ask me if I had ever been up in an airplane. Up till now the answer was no. Pulled over, paid my money and went for a ten-minute open cockpit ride. I didn't suddenly discover the one thing missing in my life. Things on the ground seemed to look normal; just as I would have expected them to look. I was able to keep track of where we were, and I didn't get sick. It was an unemotional, matter-of-fact determination, but my conclusion was (assuming I could learn to properly manipulate the aircraft) I would be able to do this flying thing.

The afternoon at Floyd Bennett went pretty good; passed my physical exam—though not without a hitch; discovered I'm one of those people whose blood pressure can really go up when nervous. Along with one other Jersey kid and two from Long Island I was sworn in as a Naval Aviation Cadet! On the drive home, I couldn't help repeatedly glancing down at the large manila envelope on the seat next to me. It was stamped "OFFICIAL ORDERS" and contained the details of my pending travel to Naval Air Station Pensacola, Florida—the *Annapolis of the Air!*

Pensacola

My trip to Pensacola was delayed a few weeks, due to a Texas recruiter's ambitious plan. He had signed up an entire cadet class from his state (to be called "The Texas Rangers"), except they were one cadet short. Yup, their class was going to be filled by a New Jersey Yankee—*named* Yahnke! No one knows it now, but then—in 1955, old people in the south were still passing on stories about the vicious actions of the Union soldiers, and evidently they made sure their grandkids heard all about it. My Beaumont and Galveston peers didn't just *know about* the Civil War, it seemed like they were still real mad about it! I had only studied it briefly in American History, and am embarrassed to say I had no idea it was still so divisive an event. There were a couple guys (Jim Stremlow from Amarillo, and

Mark Yatsko from McAllen) with whom I initially feared for my safety. I had a real challenge turning their suspicion into tolerance, and finally into acceptance.

The "Texas Rangers" (Class 41-55) was one collection of wide-eyed, "all ears" students starting our Preflight Training. It would be sixteen weeks in a classroom before we would even see a cockpit. It was a comprehensive math and physics review, which for me was more aptly a "Crash Course!" There were also courses on Terrestrial Navigation, Celestial Navigation, Airframes and Power Plants, Combustion Theory, Water Survival, Military Law, and a variety of P.E. (Phys Ed) courses. In class, it sure got your attention when the instructor would start his presentation with "Gentlemen, what you will learn today could very well save your life."

Remember the film—*An Officer and a Gentleman*, with Richard Gere as the cadet and Louis Gossett as his drill instructor. Our DI controlled our every movement; marching us to and from everywhere we went. Once inside he would stand against a side wall, checking for any drooping heads. When he saw one, he would shout out, "Son, that's what the Marine Corps issues you *night* for—sleeping! Now stand up!" (Guilty cadets spent the remainder of the class standing.) More about my two Texas friends: In Pre-Flight there were monthly boxing matches pitting cadets from one battalion against those from another. Jim Stremlow (the Amarillo guy) and I (my big mouth) were going to be two of our boxers. Jim—lanky, squinty eyed, square-jawed, and appearing to be made of 50 feet of pressure treated 2x4's, knocked out his opponent in the first round, and I at least got a decision. My other Texas friend and the most loyal "Texas Aggie" I would ever know, was Mark Yatsko (the McAllen guy); a chisel-faced rebel with dark hair, gray eyes, and a five o'clock shadow by noon each day. He was my roommate for all of Pre-Flight training. He made sure I learned all the words to his two favorite songs: *The Streets of Laredo* and *Ghost Riders in the Sky*. In violation of strict rules against it, Mark was married when he entered the program, and managed to keep this fact undiscovered for eighteen months. While he drank, smoked, failed to avoid fights, and played poker until all hours of the morning, he was "true blue" to his wife the entire time. One day I saw him shaving without shaving cream, and I commented on how much that must hurt. He responded in his emblematic coarse base tone, "Hell man, I usually knock them through with a hammer and bite them off from the inside."

Not sure if it was just these guys or a state-wide thing but being side by side with them (and the others) for sixteen weeks, I developed a great respect for the Texas pride. Jim and Mark were great examples of those wind-hewn men off the prairie (although in the years to come, flying would not treat either of them kindly). I was much surprised (and flattered) to read in the glossy tri-fold pamphlets in the Visitors Center, that we naval cadets represented *"the cream of our nation's youth!"* From what I was seeing I wasn't so sure, but I was willing to give the pamphlet the benefit of the doubt, and hope they were right.

Chapter Seven

MY FATEFUL VISIT WITH CONNIE

An Eerie Midnight Trip

I'd only been in Florida for six weeks when mandatory Christmas leave was announced. My first break from Preflight Training was upon me before I felt I had earned it. But that didn't mean I didn't have big plans. *On the way home I was going to visit Constance!* It had been six months since I'd seen her and although I had found little time to dwell on the relationship, I was excited about this reunion. On this final leg to Minnesota I was wondering what her mom and dad would be like, their farm, and her little town of Grand Meadow. I'd only have three days there before continuing home for Christmas. I was content with my decision to have left college early—at least for the moment. I was proud to be making my way in the world; especially on my way to becoming a Navy pilot. I was no longer just another student wandering a campus. I was older now and even doing something patriotic. And to make sure this fact would not go unnoticed by Connie and her parents, I was wearing my uniform—or selected parts of it that I liked best (and had combined in a completely unauthorized fashion).

It was only my second airline flight—my first one being when I'd flown down to Pensacola to start flight training. The Navy had set that one up, whereas I'd arranged this one myself. I had to change planes in Chicago where I boarded this midnight flight to Rochester. The aircraft was a DC-3, an old two-engine, propeller-driven aircraft. (In ground school we had learned about the engines of the future—*jet engines)!* It carried over 30 people, although on this late-night trip the dimly lit cabin contained only a handful of shadowy passengers, and no flight attendants; kinda spooky. It would've been better if it served a hot meal (or any meal) or had carpet on the metal floor. My feet were frozen. It had been snowing when we left Chicago and the pilot said it would likely be snowing in Rochester. Hard to tell now—pitch black outside. We were scheduled to arrive about one a.m. I had told Connie I'd call her when I got in, and they would pick me up. As we started our descent, I snuck back to an icy metal toilet to take a nervous leak and double-check my appearance. This particular DC-3 must've been a military aircraft because the bathroom walls were still painted olive-green.

Back in my seat I heard the gear come rattling down (which grinding sound seemed to confirm the plane's age). I strained my eyes into the darkness outside, expecting to see the city lights of Rochester. *Whoa!* Jerked my head back; the landing lights were switched on and total blackness was instantly converted to blinding white. The strong beams were being reflected back by a wall of snow. No chance to see anything now; knew this weather would make the approach and landing a little difficult. If I would have known what I would later learn, I would have been worried. In spite of prohibitively bad weather conditions pilots have often succumbed to "get-home-itis." This is aviation jargon for a captain's insistence on getting the airplane on the ground when low ceiling and visibility make a landing attempt inadvisable. Pilots are most apt to do this to avoid missing their anniversary dinner or their daughter's ballet debut. The urgency of those activities persuades them to descend lower than they should and is the main cause of those fiery night-time accidents a mile short of the runway. Fortunately I didn't know about that yet.

In spite of the elements the pilot made a smooth approach and landing. We turned off the runway (the *only* runway) and started taxiing in, the dry snow creaking under the tires. Peering outside I still could see no lights or even shapes. Came to a halt in front of what I guessed—as the only building on the airport, had to be the terminal. Emerging from the aircraft the stairway handrail was an iced rope. I felt the hairs in my nose freeze on the first inhalation. On the ramp I scanned a 360-degree tree-lined horizon; no buildings, no lights, not even a slight glow in the sky to indicate the direction to Rochester. It was as if we had just set down in Antarctica. No vehicles in sight. Zero activity. The terminal was the only structure, and it didn't look anything like a terminal. It was a long barn-like building with wood siding and a shingled roof.

One Weird Terminal!

Entering the terminal I saw nothing more than an expanse of raw gray concrete floor. The interior was barren. No kiosks. No desks. No tables. Not a stick of furniture anywhere in the room. All the arriving passengers had walked straight through and exited through a pair of doors on the far side. I may have been the sole person left in the building. There was no ceiling—you could look right up through the trusses to the underside of the roof boards (where some trapped birds were darting about). At each end of the building I saw what I guessed were abandoned ticket counters, with no equipment or displayed materials to indicate they were ever functional. I kept expecting to see at least *somebody*—like a janitor, appear from *somewhere*. They never did. There was no music, no TV, no PA system. And it wasn't that all the shops were closed, there *were* no shops, no shoeshine booths, no newsstands. Since the four inside walls were also the outside walls, there were no doorways or halls. This was one weird place! I was beginning to feel like I was part of a Rod Serling's *Twilight Zone* episode.

I called Connie's number. She sounded excited and said they were on their way. While waiting for her I decided to get the ticket for my return trip. Behind the counter at the far end of the building, I saw a lone figure. An overhead light illuminated his head like a marble bust in a museum. Hopefully a ticket agent. I crossed the desolate space. Having not spoken a word in three hours and in this cavernous dark space, my voice was barely audible. "Good evening." He didn't look up, but I continued anyway. "I'd like to purchase a ticket from here to New York, leaving on Thursday the 17th."

"You'll have to go through Chicago."

"That's okay."

"Morning or afternoon?"

"How late in the afternoon?"

"Three-fifteen."

"That's fine. I'll take it."

He pulled a ticket out of a drawer, adjusted the carbons, and started writing with a ball-point pen. (This was way before electronic ticketing.) Face up again, but expressionless, he spoke: "Your name please."

I told him I'd spell it: I began: "First letter: Y... Second letter: A..." *Got no further.* After I said "A" the agent glanced up and eyed me strangely. After a second or two of sizing me up, he looked back down, apparently ready to start again. I continued, "Third letter: H..." His head came up again. His expression was a mix of confusion and suspicion. *What the heck was his problem?* We were surrounded by dark silence and could have been the only two living souls within ten miles. He tentatively returned the pen back to the name block on my ticket, ready to make the next entry. But this time he kept his eyes fixed on me. I continued, "Fourth letter, N." With that—for some reason, he laid the pen down and took two steps backward from the counter (out of arm's reach) never taking his eyes off me. During this awkward standoff, I happened to notice the brass name plate over his pocket; a "one-in-a-million" coincidence: It read, "YAHNKART"! *He thought I was the nut!* (The first four letters of my name being the same as his, he thought some crazy passenger was buying a ticket using *his* name.)

Together and Trying to Measure Up

About my visit: I would like to have told you it was, but it was *not* a great three days. It could have been. Lord knows I *wanted* it to be. We did take some short walks. Watch some late-night TV. Visit a couple of her high school friends. All that went okay. Her mom was nice—real nice. Her dad: seemed to me he was overly cynical, particularly when it came to my military status. A couple times he went out of his way to say something "to get my goat." Hopefully it was just because he wasn't ready for his daughter to be getting serious about some guy. I don't know. I hadn't given him any reason to disapprove of me. In any case I never felt comfortable with him. He was a big man, and one time he took my small-sized hat and plunked it on top of his large, wavy gray-haired head. The hat looked like a piece of doll's clothing. The evening of my second day he asked if I would like to join him for chores the next morning. Ever since my morning paper routes I've hated early get-ups, but you can bet I said "Great!"

I was up and ready to go before first light. And I was a real trooper—up to my ankles in manure, wet to my armpits milking, having my teeth rattled on the back of his feed cart. I was wholly and vigorously involved, lifting barrels, shoveling grain, and tossing hay. I went at it like it was my own farm. Anyone arriving on the scene would have been hard pressed to tell which of us owned the place. It was a matter of credibility—he already knew I was from New Jersey and that wasn't in my favor. In view of what I thought had been a great attitude and a laudable effort on my part, I was surprised (and disappointed) when later at breakfast, he jokingly—but only half-jokingly, described my contributions as ...*what you would expect from a city kid.* That hurt, but it was far from the worst thing to happen on my last full day in Minnesota.

The Worst Possible Finale

Talk about shocked, I was caught completely off-guard and reduced to befuddlement. That night at quarter to eleven, sitting on the cold board floor in her living room, only fifteen feet from her parent's bedroom door, this wonderful young woman, the light of her mother's eye, *wanted to have sex!* I was numbed, struggling to believe what was about to take place. Sure, this is how these things end up—eventually (*I know*) but I never thought about *when* it would, or where it would be. At Sunday School and from my folks I'd heard it a hundred times: *A girl saves herself. She waits until she's married.* And Connie? God sakes, *Connie?* Other girls maybe, but not Constance Luedeke with her thick glasses and long-sleeved, high-necked blouses.

But there were no two ways about it. She had decided she was going to give up her body tonight! And from the way she was wildly undressing, she wanted me to take it in the next two minutes. And what I do know is—*I wasn't ready for it,* not by a long shot. I might have been planning vacations and buying my own airline tickets, but I hadn't been hanging around with any single women, and never had occasion to consider that they might "want it" too. I was twenty years old but had not yet lost my virginity. Sure, I had *thought* about it a lot. (In fact I fantasized a great deal more than I felt was normal.) But I hadn't *done* it! This would be my first time, but oddly enough I wasn't preoccupied with that. I was concerned about everything else. At the bottom of the list was any possible physical pleasure that might be in store for me. I was in no way mentally prepared for this. But there was no altering the course of events she had scheduled. *I was going to have to perform, and soon!*

What followed was probably the most awkward, unskilled, and unsuccessful effort ever devoted to satisfying a woman. I think I started out okay, nuzzling, stroking, and kissing her now exposed female body. I did all the things I thought were expected and would be arousing to her; though to me they seemed to be artificial, contrived, mechanical actions. Finding myself in this situation, with its definite requirements and larger-than-life expectations, I was *not* feeling confident. *And why?* Well for one thing, after a goodly time of conducting the aforementioned activities, irrespective of what Connie might be feeling, *I was aware of a frightening numbness precisely where I should have felt some activity.* And worse, there was no reason to believe that five more minutes was going to make any difference. An even greater fear began to overtake me. I knew I had to consummate this act. *I had to.* I was striving and straining, pleading to the gods of lovemaking, and swearing under my breath, beseeching myself with desperate urgency. *C'mon. C'mon. Please!* But not a bit of progress where I needed it.

This lack of arousal was in stark contrast to the daily if not hourly (and often untimely) hard erections that had plagued me from the time I was twelve. God knows I had spent more time than I should have thinking about being in this exact situation. In bed at night I'd made up exciting scenarios (such as myself and some voluptuous woman being forced against each other) and every time—in a matter of minutes (if not seconds), I'd find myself in possession of a rigid device that demanded satisfaction.

Due to my lack of readiness, I delayed "going for it," continuing to position and reposition, avoiding and postponing. All the while my pretty Connie lay there, twisting and moaning in anticipation. I looked down at her—head back, eyes closed, mouth raised, and cursed myself. Embarrassed and ashamed, and becoming more so with every minute, I prayed she was not aware of my deficiency, and that some miracle would occur. Some minutes later we were a mass of tangled clothes, elbows, perspiration, and floor burns—with me in no better condition. I could have cried. I was ready to scream. I could have wrung it off and stomped on it. With jaws clenched tight, lest I fill the air with profanity, I was now wildly distraught. I tugged her this way and that, transmitting stupid instructions (when I was the one who needed help). I got her to allow me to slide a pillow under her hips—which some guy had told me positions the woman's pelvis just right. (As if the previous angle was part of the problem.) But she did it. She was going to try anything to get this thing on the road. She tugged it under her full white buttocks, wiggled a bit, and indicated she was ready. *God, if I just was!*

Almost impossible to imagine I was not overcome by her warm, damp body, and round, heavy thighs. I wasn't in the slightest overcome with the lust and desire that I knew should be consuming me. I was just a man on a mission—his own project, totally dedicated to overcoming his inability, wholly concerned with it; a preoccupation that left no room to savor the moment and let nature take its course. I lessened the touching and kissing I had been doing. How could I continue without being able to consummate it? And I'm not sure Connie needed any more foreplay. Her movements and utterances indicated she was ready for ignition. I was exhausted, devastated, and more embarrassed than I had ever been.

The mental anguish, futile contortions and flailing about was abruptly interrupted by a resounding loud metallic clang! My foot had kicked my heavy Navy brass belt buckle into the base of a metal floor lamp. With the sharp noise reverberating in my ears I could visualize her father (in the next room) bolting upright in bed. Like a boxer in the throes of a hopeless loss, I would be "saved by the bell." *This was going to be my reprieve.* I scurried for distance in mortal fear that any second the bedroom door would come flying open and I'd be looking up at her father. Connie must've had the same thoughts, as I saw her arms up and several articles of clothing all in the air at the same time! Any pending activity was going to be curtailed.

I was quite sure in the days to come she would spend a fair amount of time reflecting on this non-event. (I knew I sure would.) I was afraid that after this, my male attraction would never be the same, never have the same allure. And I guess I was right. The big fade began soon after. From down in Florida—with letters, flowers, telegrams and phone calls, I tried desperately to win her back. She had begun dating another guy at college. I knew him; an older guy there on the GI Bill. He'd been in the army, been overseas, smoked, drank, and almost immediately seemed to have some kind of mysterious hold on her.

Chapter Eight
EARNING MY GOLD WINGS

Finishing Up Preflight

Christmas with the family was great and I was now back in Pensacola—the memories of my Minnesota visit still too vivid. First time I'd felt so helpless. I spent valuable time and energy trying to win Connie back (including phoning college buddies still up there, imploring them to make personal appeals for me). One night after a wrenching phone call to her, and with mounting desperation, I went out into the pine grove behind the barracks. Standing on a bed of needles, looking up through an opening in the canopy, I pleaded for help from above. *Please God, give me some sign that you hear me, and you'll help.* No sooner had I gotten the last word out of my mouth than the opening above me was sliced in half by the white trail of a meteor arcing across the night sky. This caused an excitement I could barely contain, though time would show it to have been just a capricious celestial coincidence. It became harder and harder to reach her on the phone—finally not at all. I never saw Connie again. In spite of this weighty preoccupation I finished Preflight okay. Never fell asleep in class and passed all the tests. Earned ninety-eight dollars every two weeks (and had money left over). Spent my share of Saturday nights at the infamous Trader Jon's in downtown Pensacola.

One slight problem: For the sake of eye appeal in formations, individuals are positioned by height—from the tallest to the shortest. This way there's not more than a half inch difference between the tops of any two side-by-side heads. At five-foot eight I was third from last. Arriving at the chow hall for meals I was number 37 in a queue of 39. I usually was just picking up my tray when the DI hollered for us to "fall in" outside. But a possible reprieve! Halfway through Preflight he recognizes this inequity in the order of eating times, and is going to alter the eating formation. "From now on gentlemen we are not going to fall in by height. We are going to line up alphabetically!" *I was now next to last!*

Initial Flight Training

I was transferred to Naval Air Station Whiting Field, where we would finally get in the cockpit. Here cadets underwent twelve weeks of initial flight training, culminating in the most revered entry in any pilot's logbook: *"Cleared for Solo."* I got mine, although concluding there was an aptitude for flying (or maybe just an abundance of bravado) that I was not blessed with. I had to do each maneuver over and over again before I finally had the sequence and amount of control inputs that were required to have the plane perform on cue. When I did succeed, I knew it was not as a result of any natural ability; just the "playing-back" of memorized mechanical actions. It was not apparent that any of my friends were having the difficulties I was having. (Or if so they weren't talking about it.)

The Dreaded Check Rides and Other Neat Things

At the end of each phase of instruction and before advancing to the next phase, we had to demonstrate a competency for all the flight maneuvers taught thus far. These check rides caused me to pay my "worrying dues." A cadet friend of mine was a week ahead of me in the syllabus so underwent his check rides before me. His terrifying narrations of the untaught maneuvers he was asked to demonstrate, and the unreasonable expectations of the check pilot, caused me many a sleepless night and nauseous morning. I finally concluded: *nothing is ever as hard to do as the guy who just did it tells you it is!* Except for a few unconsciously bold souls these "check rides" were rightfully feared.

I was impressed by all the "fail safe" systems in the airplanes. For instance, if a pilot is landing and has forgotten to lower the wheels (yes that does happen) when the aircraft slows down to landing speed (well prior to touching down) a loud horn blares in the cockpit. Hearing this sound the pilot realizes his omission and quickly puts the gear handle down. *Neat!* Well you'd think so anyway. A cadet on his first solo flight made a "Gear Up" landing (forgot to lower the wheels). During the resultant accident investigation, a tower controller said that he saw Ron's wheels not extended and was shouting this to him over the radio. The Accident Board chairman hearing this looks at Ron and asks him "Why didn't you heed those transmissions"? Ron replied, "Never heard him. A loud noise in the cockpit was blocking everything out."

Instrument and Night Flying Training

Graduated from Phase One at Whiting and moved thirty miles to Cory Field, where I'd undergo the next two phases of training: night and instrument flying. At night there is no horizon or visual reference to assist the pilot and he can easily become disoriented. To avoid this, a pilot must be able to interpret and rely on his flight instruments. Therefore, instrument flight training preceded night flying. You cannot fly at night "by looking out the window" as was tragically demonstrated by John Kennedy Jr. who exposed himself to the pitfalls of night flying before instrument training.

One could move on to night flying only after passing one of those dreaded "check rides" for the Instrument Phase. This one was worse than any of the others because it was administered "under the hood." The pilot had to wear a visor-like device on his helmet that prohibited seeing out of the airplane, leaving only the instrument panel in sight. The hood simulated flying inside the clouds or at night, and you had to convince your check pilot that using only your flight instruments, with no view of the horizon, you were able to keep the thing straight and level. This task was sufficiently challenging to cause some cadets to cheat. They would put that visor hood on at a slightly raised and canted angle, providing a small space under one side of the hood and they would be able to get a sneak peek outside the cockpit to orient themselves. I never did.

Once finished with Instruments we started our night flying training. On the nights you were scheduled, you always hoped for a full moon. On dark nights the cadets would joke that *they felt like they were in an ink bottle, inside a coat pocket, in a closet.* I was impressed by whoever selected the cockpit lighting, because they chose red, which I thought was cool esthetic touch. (That was before I learned the frequency of red light does not destroy night-vision, and every airplane ever built has red cockpit lighting.)

Before night flying ourselves, we were trucked out to observe a standard night-flying landing pattern. During the one I was observing, an airplane lost an engine and went down. After the plane had bull-dozed a hundred feet of dirt and shrubbery, skidded another hundred feet along a concrete culvert, and then flipped over onto its back, the cadet was able to unstrap and drop to the ground—*without a scratch!* An emergency vehicle containing the usual cadre of super-motivated Crash Crew personnel was dispatched to retrieve him. They found him, threw him into the truck and peeled out, sirens wailing. Halfway to the base hospital the vehicle flipped over. Checking into the hospital an examination found the cadet to have multiple contusions plus a broken left arm and collar bone (causing him to miss two months of training).

Formation Flying and Tactics

The most common formation angle used is called "Parade." The second and other aircraft achieve and maintain a precise 45-degree rearward bearing off the lead airplane. The one way to know when you had successfully maneuvered your aircraft onto the proper angle would be when—to your line of vision, the lead plane's wing tip light was superimposed over the head of the pilot flying that aircraft. Once this "sight-picture" was achieved, geometrically your plane was on the required 45-degree angle. All you had to do then is hold it.

I viewed this formation phase as downright dangerous. Piloted by cadets as untrained as I was, were jockeying their aircraft to within a few yards of each other! While perhaps the other cadets were up to the task, I recognized early on that formation flying required a certain visual perception and motor skills that I did not come by naturally. While I graduated okay from this phase of training, it was my conclusion that there had not been a single day when—due to my own lack of skill—I had not narrowly missed colliding with another aircraft; some misses due to a frantic last second correction and some due to pure luck. Fortunately, I don't think my friends were aware of my deficiency.

Cadets were advised not to bring their car to Pre Flight, so I had not brought my shiny black 1941 Desoto; an old classic car that I had spent many an hour washing and waxing; a car I would someday bring to those classic car shows. But now—down here, to quit hitch-hiking and improve my chances of dating, I needed some wheels. I found a really cool, couple year old, coral and cream Mercury Monterrey hardtop convertible. However I was seventy-five dollars short. *Where would I get seventy-five dollars?* The guys said I should just ask my dad. *My Dad?* For the first time in my life I decided to try it. I phoned him and couldn't believe it, he said yes! And though it took a few days, he wired me the money. The car was mine! Maybe my dad was mellowing in his old age. (More about this transaction later.)

Training For Carrier Qualification

Next stop Barin Field, just across the Alabama border. The one revered aspect of being a Navy pilot (not available in the Air Force), is being a *Carrier Pilot*—having landed on board one of those "flat-tops" and eligible to be a member of the infamous "Tailhook Association." Here I would undergo six weeks of training in preparation for the day I'd fly thirty miles out over the Gulf of Mexico and try my luck aboard some WWII carrier. On that flight I'd need to make five successful "traps" to earn my carrier rating. "Trap" is the word used to describe a carrier landing, in that your tailhook catches a wire (ideally the third of four wires) and traps you—violently yanking you to a stop. Without catching a wire you would continue over the bow, brakes locked, and plunge down 50 feet to the water. Then while slowly sinking the ship would churn over you and likely grind you to pieces.

Landing on board a ship is the epitome of aircraft control. Unlike landing on a long runway where your touch down point can vary considerably, in a carrier landing you absolutely must touch down at a precise location and be at a certain slow-enough speed. Day after day we cranked up our WW II propeller aircraft and practiced carrier landing approaches. We used a grass landing strip on which a carrier-sized, rectangular touchdown zone was outlined with white lime. To assist pilots in making their carrier landings (here in practice and on the actual carrier) the Navy utilizes a Landing Signal Officer. This experienced carrier pilot stands alongside the intended landing point with arms outstretched left and right—each hand holding a brightly colored paddle. He adjusts his arms up or down as necessary to signal your deviance from the optimum glide path. (This has since been replaced by a high-tech optical mirror system using colored lights.) During training this fellow graded our landings to be sure we were progressing; consistently touching down halfway between the beginning and ending lines, and halfway between the side lines.

To have the smoothest air, carrier landing practice was conducted at dawn (before the ground could heat up and cause convective turbulence). Now in November it was still dark when we got to the ramp. Some mornings it was still below freezing, and it was necessary to use a piece of thick rope to scrape the frost off the wing's leading edges. (The airlines don't use rope. They spray the surfaces with hot alcohol.) You *never* takeoff with any ice or snow on the wing. It changes the *shape* of the airfoil and thus changes the amount of lift the wing can generate. (There are airliner accidents every winter as a result of this.) The whine of the starters and the sounds of back-firing coincided with the first pink glow in the eastern sky. (We referred to our ungodly early wakeup time as "O-Dark-Thirty.")

The BIG Day

I completed the *Carrier Qual* land training and the day to give it a real try arrived. You might imagine I woke up with more than my share of butterflies. My four-plane flight plus two other flights would fly out into the Gulf and land on a real carrier. This was the flight we had all awaited;

the one where we'd get our five shipboard traps and be qualified to call ourselves *Carrier Pilots!* The mood in the hangar was cautious and quiet. (Didn't see any of those overly confident cadets I had mentioned earlier.) This check ride would be different from all the rest: *We had never actually done what we were going to be asked to do.* Our on-land practice sessions were just semblances; nothing like what was about to transpire. I for one was worried.

And there was another problem: *Time!* We were going to have enough of a problem with the landings, without being told *we had to get them done in a hurry!* They told us we had to get out there quick, set up quick, fly a tight pattern; not waste any time. The USS Saipan would only stay out there for one hour and thirty minutes! You either got your landings in or you didn't. Computing it in my mind: *three flights of four aircraft equal twelve aircraft, each needing five traps. How are we ever going to get sixty carrier landings in ninety minutes!* And to make things worse, my flight drew the short straw—we were to be the third of the three flights. And the Yahnke curse, I was the fourth (last) aircraft in our flight. If we ran out of time, *I was the one that was going to get screwed!*

The trip out went okay. Approaching the ship the first flight descended to the pattern altitude of 500 feet altitude. The second flight orbited at 1,000 feet ready to drop down to pattern altitude when the last aircraft in the first flight had his fifth trap. My flight was orbiting at 1,500 feet, stuck there until the second flight was cleared down to pattern altitude. My heart was racing. It was surreal from above, looking down at the daisy chain of miniature yellow airplanes over the bright green water; strung out on the downwind leg, turning base, on final, and hitting the deck. And there were plenty of sound effects. Non-stop throughout this continuous loop the LSO (Landing Signal Officer) was screaming instructions and condemnations over the radio. I watched the planes hit the deck and be yanked to a stop, or hit too long and miss a wire; looked like most of them were getting their five. *Please God help me when it's my turn.*

Being the last aircraft in the last flight I was real concerned about time. Since I had not marked our arrival time, I was at a loss as to exactly how much time we had remaining. I did know we were well into it when the first flight completed theirs. Big shuffle now—musical chairs in flight. The second flight was now descending to the pattern altitude of 500 feet, while we descended to 1,000 feet. The first flight climbed to orbit at our just vacated altitude. This took a good five minutes. Finally, after what seemed like way more time than it should have taken, the second flight completed their landings and my flight was cleared to pattern altitude. *Finally*—we were set up in the circuit. Number one's already on final. Number two was turning base. Number three was halfway along the downwind leg, and I was just entering downwind. Hooray! First's got a wire! He made it. Second guy's on final. Number one off the bow, airborne. Number three on base. As number four, I was almost to the base position.

Turning base I made the required call, "Gear Down, fuel 1200 pounds." (Pilots have to make this fuel quantity call so that the ship can set the arresting wire resistance for the total aircraft weight.) Number two is getting unhooked. He made it too. Three on final. I'm right behind him. I was experiencing an exhilaration I had not yet come close to sampling. Even in this incredibly focused maneuver I was aware of the clear blue sky, the expanse of emerald water beneath me, and the clean—sweet smelling, fresh air. For these carrier landings, our cockpit canopy was slid all the way back—an open cockpit! It was an aura of being in a very special place at a very special time. I filled my lungs and squeezed the grip on the stick.

The ship left a pure white foam trail in its wake, that I was now just lining up over. Wings level. Altitude okay. Didn't know exactly what my control inputs were, or why, or where my eyes were looking, but somehow the plane stayed lined up and was descending at what seemed to be just the right rate. Shoulder harness locked. Airspeed... *about ten knots too fast.* Little power off. Little nose up trim. Double check the gear. They're down. Off center. Gotta slide a little left. That should do it. Looking good. What's that? The LSO was screaming something at me. Couldn't decipher it. Words but no meanings. He still was showing good paddles. Feels okay, but not sure what it should feel like. Ship looming up. I'm under control (I think). I'm gonna hit harder than on land, but that's how it's supposed to be. Ship under me! No green. All gray. *Wham! Kerunch!* First the impact noise when the tires pounded into the deck and the wheel struts compressed, and then the screaming ratchet whine as the arresting cables were pulled out. Head snapped forward. Helmet hit the dash. Hand slipped off the stick. *I got a wire! I've made a carrier landing!* It was then I realized another voice was screaming at me. *Oh yeah, gotta reduce the power.* Gotta let the wire pull my aircraft back until it has enough slack to drop out of the tailhook. "Go! Go! Go!" *The hook must have come loose.* They were screaming at me to add power and take off. Number One was behind me on final, about to touch down. If I didn't get back in the air in two seconds, they would have to give him a "Wave Off" (deny his landing attempt) *because I was in the way!* This is called a "fouled' deck" (and the *last* thing you want to do is be the reason your roommate doesn't get his trap)!

I made my second, and my third, and then—a monkey wrench in the plans. A wind direction change, meaning the ship had to change course. (Carriers always turn into the wind before recovering their aircraft.) *Another five minutes wasted.* We had to climb back up to a higher altitude and orbit until the ship was established on its new course. *This delay could do it. I may be screwed!* Finally back down. Back in the pattern. On the downwind. Turning base. On final. Made it! Got my fourth! Only one to go. *Just do it one more time!* Climbing out off the bow, lowering my left wing for the turn to downwind I heard the words I'd been dreading: "Flight Three. Everybody. Flight Three rendezvous at 2,500 overhead. That's it. We're all through."

I was ill—sick! We were going back and I'm one trap short. Could've done it. I *know* I could have gotten my fifth, but just didn't get the chance. On the return flight I couldn't stop shaking my head and could hardly muster the strength to make the normal radio calls. The elated voices of the other flight members were in stark contrast to my depressed state. The flight to shore was one of the most discouraged fifteen minutes I'd ever spent. I didn't cry but felt I could have. What's worse, back on the ramp you should have seen all the back slapping and congratulations. It was just one big celebration all the way to the hangar. Except I was not part of it.

Back in the hangar the instructors debriefed the flight, but with no indication of future plans for me. No mention of when I might be rescheduled. I was assuming I'd be dropped back to the next class; lose a week (or two) and go out with them when they went. I wondered whether at that time I would only have to get my fifth or do the whole five again. Unable to remain silent and needing some consolation I shared my great disappointment in not having qualified with Alf Rylander, who had been a close friend since Pre Flight. Seemingly taken aback he answered "Whattaya mean, not qualified?"

Evidently he hadn't (of course) been counting my traps; that made sense—he wouldn't have known that I only got four. I told him, "Only got four Alf, I was in the upwind turn when they cancelled the period. We ran outa time before I got to shoot my fifth. I was screwed by that hour and thirty thing."

69

"No way. We all qualified. Look at the blackboard."

What? All he thinks? I knew I only got four. Afraid of what I might see (yet praying Alf was somehow right) I weaved my way towards the blackboard, waiting for the annotations to come into focus. *Could they possibly have not noticed? Could the instructors have lost count?* Lo and behold, I *was* checked off as a completion! To this day I'm not sure if they knew I only got four and just figured I would have made it on my fifth try, or if *I was the one* who lost count, and *did* get five. In any case, regardless of the reasons I was now a full-fledged carrier pilot and that was a recorded fact; one that could never be challenged or revoked.

As you might imagine, there was a great celebration at the Cadet Club that night. The place was rocking. The Fats Domino hit *Blueberry Hill* had just come out and was being played on the juke box every other song. I don't know if I'd ever felt so relieved, so elated, so euphoric from any single day's accomplishment. I wanted all my family and friends to know (and wished I still had a certain Minnesota farm girl to tell). Got a pocket full of change, found a pay phone and called everyone I could think of. Unfortunately, only once did I get someone on the other end—my sister Laura, and although I'm sure she failed to grasp the scope of this accomplishment she did manage to sound real excited at the news.

Remember Dad Wiring Me Money?

Carrier Qualification was the last phase of Basic Training and I was finished with it (and a little proud of myself). In one week I'd be off to Corpus Christi, Texas for Advanced Flight Training—and *jets*! In the few days off before departing I decided to catch a flight up to Jersey and personally bring Mom and Dad up to date (okay, brag a bit) about my training stats. Got into La Guardia late but got home okay and got a good night's sleep. Spent the morning filling in the folks on all the details. Just before lunch— I'd already put it off too long, I went to the garage to pay my respects to my classic 41' Desoto. I was anxious to sit in it and admire the neat dash, old radio, gray felt seat upholstery, and feel the steering wheel in my hand again. But the garage was empty, and both Mom and Dad were home. *So who's where with the Desoto?* On the way back to the house I met Dad coming out the front door. He'd know. "Dad, where's the Desoto?"

He looked at me like I had said something stupid and replied, "What? Where do you think I got the seventy-five dollars for the Mercury?"

Advanced Training and Becoming an Officer and a Gentleman

Advanced training had the same segments as Basic Training: *Instruments,*

70

Night, Formation, and two new ones: *Tactics* and *Gunnery*—all done in jets! And once again we were pretty much overwhelmed. You'd think I would have had some memorable flight experiences to relate, and I'm sure I did, but to this day the details of Advanced Training are a too-fast, blur of briefings, flight lines, more classes, studying for tests, worrying about check rides and frantically asking each other for tips on how to pass them. It was as if I was a pin ball the whole time, ricocheting crazily from bumper to bumper until finally tumbling into the bottom hole—graduation! Hard to recount a journey like that.

I remember more about what little free time we did have; catching an hour at the pool, discussing cars, the latest pop hits, and mostly the local girls we'd met. It was a hot time for American cars—especially the big Olds 88 Rocket with the first wrap-around windshield, and the new 57 Chevy Impala with its great sweeping tail fins. I one-upped those by purchasing a 1955 Thunderbird; aqua with a white leather interior, whose future collector's value I failed to anticipate (congratulating myself two years later for having sold it for almost the same price I paid for it). For the songs of the day, I particularly remember (maybe because I was in cowboy country) Marty Robbin's "A White Sport Coat and a Pink Carnation." As far as girls were concerned, they certainly got their share of conversation and speculation. The barrack walls were plastered with *Playboy* centerfolds. I doubt anybody was more lustful than I was, although embarrassedly I admit, while I did get two girls into the rack I won't dwell on the outcomes.

Completed my Advanced Training in June, and since it was all in jets, I was now not only a qualified pilot, but moreover—a qualified *jet* pilot! (At this time—a still small and esteemed group.) A graduation ceremony was held at Naval Air Station Kingsville, Texas—a small town right next to LBJ's ranch in the town of Alice (where records indicate Lee Harvey Oswald stopped on his way back from Russia). I walked across the stage and stood there questioning reality and mentally shaking my head as a tall, balding Admiral smiled and pinned on my coveted Naval Aviator's wings. I still had no handle on what it was I had accomplished; didn't grasp what it meant, or have any idea what would be coming next.

This graduation not only meant that we were fully qualified pilots, but also qualified to be Commissioned Officers—each of whom receives a certificate bearing the president's signature. (In my case he must have had no idea of my lack of qualifications.) *A cadet yesterday and an Officer today.* For most cadets this meant they would become an Ensign in the

Navy. But there was another option: one could, and I did—apply for a commission as a Second Lieutenant in the United States Marine Corps. This was available to cadets who had the grade point average and then had then been able to favorably impress a stern-faced board of Leatherneck officers. (I had undoubtedly been lucky on both counts.)

Chapter Nine

ON MY OWN, AND SOMETHING NOBODY EXPECTED

My First Duty Station

For any new Marine pilot, the choice duty station was El Toro, in Santa Ana, California (just thirty minutes from Hollywood) and I got it! It was *the* place for new and daring activities. There were movie stars, health nuts, cool surfing dudes, and most importantly, hard-bodied, honey-haired females wherever you looked. It was everything and more recanted in the lyrics of the *Beach Boys'* songs; everything a young bachelor could want. This would be my best chance yet to break out. And I would not be totally among strangers, my best flight training buddies—the Animal and Mark Yatsko (the Texas "Aggie") had also gotten El Toro. In addition to rooming with Mark all through Pre Flight, based on our names beginning with "Y" he had been lining up next to me in every formation. The Animal was assigned to my squadron while Mark went to a historic WWII fighter squadron on the other side of the base.

My Place of Work

My new squadron was an Electro-Countermeasures and Aerial Photography squadron, and as such our aircraft did not have any armament. We were the brunt of jokes about a "kinder, gentler" Marine squadron. Many of the senior officers had flown in World War II, and all of them had flown in the Korean conflict. Back then we were not fighting ragged Third World civilians that we had declared terrorists; we were fighting armies that actually had uniformed soldiers and air forces with operative aircraft. The Animal and I listened attentively anytime the combat stories got going.

The squadron had two types of aircraft. One was a powerful propeller driven aircraft—the AD-5N *SkyRaider*. During the Korean conflict it had been an "attack" aircraft (dropping bombs and shooting rockets). Ours were modified with specialized electronic equipment to find enemy radar sites. The second type aircraft was a jet—the F9F-8 *Cougar*. It was a swept wing, photo-capability version of the famous F9F-5 *Panther* that

Harry Brubaker flew in the classic William Holden film, *The Bridges of Toko Ri*. Animal and I began training in both of them. This phase in the life cycle of a Marine squadron is called Phase One and lasts twelve months. Phase Two is the tactical phase, which in our case would be an overseas deployment to Japan. There, we would do the same type flying, except there we would do it for real, up and down the coast of the Soviet Union.

In addition to flying duties each young officer was assigned a collateral duty. I was the Survival Officer. I gave weekly presentations on ways to survive a crash at sea or some remote land location. During one presentation I was explaining the use of the Rescue Signal Mirror—a 4x6 inch sized mirror with a see-thru aiming sight. A pilot dangling in his parachute would never be seen, so to attract attention he would aim the mirror to reflect the sun's glare into the cockpit of the search plane. Since the mirror was not simple to use, I told them they should memorize the "Instructions for Use" *in case they needed to use it at night.*

Not bold enough to get a place in town, I opted to live in the Bachelor Officers' Quarters on base. It was like a college dorm. Most single guys leapt at the chance to move into a bachelor's pad in the notorious nearby town of Laguna Beach. From time to time I was invited to dinner at one of my braver cohort's cool digs on the beach. One night on the way back to the base I stopped at a local restaurant for a piece of pie and a cup of coffee. Just finishing the pie, the entrance door swung open and in walked what had to be a "lady of the night," open blouse, bra showing, short tight skirt, (wrinkled and twisted off center), tousled dyed red hair, with badly smudged lipstick and mascara. Whew! Evidently she had allowed various papers and receipts to accumulate on the front seat of her car, because—you remember those adhesive-backed *Green Stamps* that the grocery stores gave out for discounts on future purchases when you had spent enough money, well as she passed my booth I saw a whole sheet of them stuck to her backside.

A Glimpse of Married Life and It Looks Just Great
After only a few months at El Toro—just discovering the challenges of living an independent life, and not yet having given any thought to a next step, *it's hard to believe the commitment I let myself in for.* Mark Yatsko and his lovely wife Caroline invited me to dinner at their stilted wood home, perched on a cliff overlooking one of Laguna Beach's most beautiful hidden coves. Here they had a life that I felt they deserved and could only be envied; one beautiful, stress-free day after another, with

only a two-minute descent down to their own personal beach. She the happy, stay-at-home wife, and he the swaggering "top gun" of what used to be Pappy Boyington's *Black Sheep* squadron (and later popularized in a made-for-TV series).

Along with me they had invited a fellow Marine we had both known in flight training. Tom had been the starting quarterback for the University of Missouri; a sturdy, fireplug guy, with freckles and close-cropped red hair. Tom was there with his super-tanned fiancée—an absolutely knock-out gorgeous local girl. Up till tonight I had never seen Valerie not in a bikini. And I hate to admit it—a bikini that was never quite up to the task of disguising its contents. Tonight she was wearing white shorts which seemed to be lifting her off the ground. (Stealing a glance at them it made me feel as if I should give a tug down on the hem of my own boxer shorts.)

The evening went swell—couldn't have been better. Caroline made a terrific tomato and basil spaghetti dish. A good time was being had by all (helped along by one delicious innards-warming glass of wine after another). Caroline jumped to her feet at any request from Mark, did it quickly, and returned with a loving smile. And Tom and Valerie while finalizing the plans for their coming wedding were getting along just fine. She was sitting on his lap with her shapely tan arms around his neck and proud breasts pressed against him; never letting thirty seconds pass without planting another long kiss.

Talk About a Single Pivotal Moment

About ten, the room was full of contented smiles (and the sink was full of empty Chianti bottles). The world was a wonderful place to be. I was favorably impressed by this married and "about-to-be-married" lifestyle. It was my first observance of such a husband-wife relationship among my peers; apparently a union to be highly sought after. In the midst of this warm conjecture I realized Caroline was speaking to me. "And Roger, how about you, you must have a girlfriend somewhere."

Understandably no one came to mind. But then, "Yes, yes I do." I began to tell her about Sara, a girl I had met at a church summer camp back in high school, and to whom I had written a couple letters (mainly because she was the only girl I knew). They all chimed in with "so what's happening now." I obliged, for some reason enriching the relationship. Frequent sips of an after dinner Mexican liqueur may have helped me manufacture a not yet existing romance. The other four were all ears. I heard the at-best casual link between Sara and me turning into something way more than it was. I can't remember who suggested it or why I went along with it, but after fifteen minutes of this dialogue, I was directed to the phone and was dialing Information for Sara's number. I don't recollect any details of the conversation, but when it was over I was being roundly toasted and slapped on the back. I had somehow said, or at least allowed Sara to think that I was not just calling to touch base, but to rekindle a relationship.

An Unwarranted Union

Once again, not just things of mass, but situations can have an inertia—a momentum of their own. Similar to the succession of perfunctory responses that led to my college enrollment, and those that allowed my successful progression through flight training, a couple months later, after many unclear phone conversations, *a diamond ring was in the mail.* And the subsequent forever-binding event materialized just three months later. In December 1957—two months after my twenty-second birthday, *I let myself become a married man!* This without having gone steady with, or been engaged to, (let alone slept with) my bride-to-be. I had never even had a crush on a girl, ever. I'd heard about that "loving couple" thing, but my only simulation of it was my pairing up with Connie. And now I'm married! An act in retrospect that I was definitely not qualified for. I knew nothing of myself or my possible place in the world. I did it without realizing the first real thing about what being married would mean; had no idea of what it would put an end to, and its *permanency!* My second thoughts were not long in coming—they hit me within two minutes of exchanging the vows. To this day, looking at the last photo in our wedding album—the one taken from behind the getaway car, where the bride and groom are smiling over their shoulder out the rear window, I can see the befuddlement (downright fright) in my eyes; the "*what on earth have I just done*" look in them.

There were a couple of family get-togethers, two or three rehearsals, and then the wedding—a wonderful old-fashioned Eastern European wedding. Everything went smoothly. No drunks. No fights. No relatives pulling you into a corner for lengthy counsel. During the reception I observed a traditional event from the old country: *The dance with the bride.* Any male (regardless of age) who wanted to dance with the bride, had to put whatever he could afford into a hat to do so. There wasn't a man or boy present who did not avail himself of this opportunity. You should have seen the loot we pulled in!

There was one embarrassing occurrence at the reception. Sara's immigrant parents had arrived in the States via Canada and many of her relatives in attendance lived there. Someone had the great idea for Sara to introduce me to all her uncles and aunts from Canada. In a lame attempt to appear more quick-witted, I endeavored to greet each one with a different salutation: "Pleased to meet you." "How are you today." "Thank you for making the trip." Well after the fifth or sixth original greeting, I was out of new ones. A dapper man in a gold-buttoned, double-breasted blazer was in front of me when I thought of a new one and blurted it out: "Hi, I've heard a lot about you." *The place went dead.* You could have heard a pin drop. Later Sara informed me: That uncle had recently left his wife and run away with his secretary.

California Dreaming

My folks' wedding gift to us was the airline ticket back to Los Angeles (albeit a late "red eye" flight). We spent some time in the terminal counting the ones, fives, and even a ten received from *the dance with the bride.* Heard the call for our midnight boarding and stuffed all the loot into our carry-on. During one of the delays while taxiing to the runway, Sara said she had not even felt us go airborne. I explained why. Got into LA about seven a.m. It was a fun drive south to Laguna Beach. Since this was Sara's first trip to California (if not her first time out of New Jersey) she was awed by typical L.A. sights. "Roger! That car is pink!" "Wow, look at that crazy palm tree!" "That person is walking four dogs!" "Roger that woman is wearing orange stretch pants and she's eighty if she's a day!"

Regarding our first marital digs, I had been real lucky. It was a cute, multi-colored cottage designed and built by some Swedish guy. Soon as I saw it I signed a rental agreement. The real estate agent told me it had been featured on the cover of *Better Homes and Gardens* (now framed and mounted on an inside wall). Sara was mightily impressed. The house was located high in the hills just east of the famous Coast Highway, in an elevated and exclusive area of Laguna Beach known as *Top of the World.* Many of these homes have since had the earth beneath them give way, causing them to cascade into the ravines below.

Couldn't Delay It Any Longer: Bed Time

I was a little nervous (more than a little) as the sun set on our first day of life together, knowing we would soon be joining our bodies for the first time. During the afternoon we did some grocery shopping and paid a visit to Mark and Caroline. In the evening we tried to make it seem old shoe by making small talk and watching some TV—I think both of us delaying just a bit (aware of the scope of the forthcoming event). But now it was after ten and in view of the day we'd had, neither of us could think of a reason to stay up longer. I was already in my recently purchased silk pajamas. Sara got her night gown and went to the bathroom to ready herself. I passed the time stretched out on a batik print couch in the living room (feigning relaxing when in truth I was actually shivering). She was out all too soon. I met her in as romantic a way as I knew how, kissing her forehead, putting one arm around her waist and taking her hand. I escorted her into the bedroom and to the huge platform bed (which had been brought over from Sweden). The solid side walls were three feet high and adorned with hand painted Scandinavian winter scenes. I helped her up the few steps of the attached ladder and then joined her under the sheets.

I lay still for a while, so as not to appear too anxious (and muster the assurance it was going to require). When there was nothing left to warrant a further delay I leaned over and kissed her, and then began what I hoped would be pleasurable foreplay. I continued, not rushing, and found it this time to seem appropriate. This was my wife—clean, sweet, innocent; ready to give herself to me. It would be a wonderful physical and spiritual union. After a reasonable time of stroking and kissing, I was again concerned as I was not yet in possession of what would be necessary. Sara laid there quiet and wonderfully patient (and thankfully refraining from giving me instructions or encouragement). I did this and I did that, but I didn't do "it." In spite of several awkwardly futile attempts to do so, I was unable to enter her. I was enormously embarrassed and discouraged. Sara was very supportive and (thankfully) had evidently been warned (by some unknown great friend of mine) about this possible occurrence (or non-occurrence). Lying there afterwards she continued to reassure me that this was not at all uncommon, and not to worry.

But of course I *was* going to worry—not having forgotten my fateful late-night experience with Connie. For the first time I was fearful that at least in my case (now with a 0 for 2 track record) it might not be so uncommon. My hope being: both times I had tried with a woman with whom I had no chemistry. All through high school the mere sight (or thought) of the inside of a woman's thigh would produce a prompt and embarrassing response. The end-of-period bell would often find me sneaking out of class holding a notebook so as to hide an untimely protrusion. I knew there would be other nights. I was just hoping and praying they'd be a lot different. But twice, two times in a row!

Chapter Ten

SEVEN YEARS LATER

A Recap of Our Time Together So Far

Our life in the Marine Corps had gone smoothly, in fact great. I was given challenging assignments and we were stationed and lived in three different states. We had new and exciting experiences and made many close friends in the Corps. The only downside was six months into our married life—a major interruption: they sent me on a one-year, unaccompanied tour in Japan. ("Unaccompanied" meaning Sara could not come with me.) Not good. Here, we usually lived in very nice base housing. Now we were living in our own small home. No husband could have asked for a better wife than Sarah; a loving partner cheerfully turning-to on every kind of task, rarely if ever registering disapproval of my often-foolish ideas. And our marriage? I'd like to say that it was typical, providing the expected contentment. But I will admit there was a problem, in fact two problems—both mine, both weighty, and either capable of destroying a marriage.

First: my inability to carry out my male partner role did not correct itself, resulting in a rarity of even attempting it. Mercifully, Sara did not seem bothered by the infrequency or ineptitude of the encounters. Perhaps she even thought this was normal for a married couple. Of course I was sorely affected; daily humbled by an awareness of this deficiency. I concluded I'd just married a woman with whom there was no chemistry. And I have to confess that (especially after a chastening performance) *I could not dismiss the idea that somewhere out there, waiting to unlock my manhood, was that one woman with the right chemistry!* (Where she might be and how I would find her I did not know.) But too late now. I'd gone and done it; gotten married.

And the second curse affecting my commitment to the marriage, and maybe even worse: I was unable to overcome the conviction that I had closed the book on my life too soon; that I was destined for something else; *that there was another more fulfilling, more exciting life awaiting me!*

(Though I had no idea where or what it would be.) But again, too late now. I'd married Sara and selected this military life, and would have to do my best to adhere to it.

However, we did experience two blessings. Miraculously, in spite of my inability I managed to impregnate her twice, gifting us with an adorable and very-sure-of-herself, daughter—Samantha, and a cute and smart beyond his years son—Mark Adrian, who you may have guessed I named after my flight training buddy Mark Adrian Yatsko, who was killed in a midair collision during a *"scare the Chinese"* show of force in the Taiwan straits. (I sent Mark Yatsko's parents the birth announcement and they sent us a silver cup engraved *Mark Adrian*.) Nuther subject: Remember that unaccompanied one-year tour in Japan I mentioned, well the Marine Corps was going to do something like that again!

July of 64 and Going to Sea

Besides the previous separation from my wife, the Marine Corps now had me scheduled for a ten-month carrier cruise. This first involved two months of "dry land" carrier landing training. The grading on our hundreds of simulated carrier landing attempts had been tallied. The much-awaited meeting was held and the top fifteen pilots who would be "going to sea" were announced. I was one. For most it was a real macho celebration. The *Armed Forces Times* article was pinned up all over the base. *"Marine Attack Squadron 331 was Combat Ready, going to put to sea on board the USS Forrestal."* We were going to cruise the Mediterranean as part of the awesome Fleet Marine Force! But I for one felt mixed emotions, including a "not-for-the-best" premonition.

Now—still in port, about to cast off, standing high and alone on the non-skid flight deck of this ocean splitting behemoth, I had a strong suspicion I'd have been better off if I'd never seen it. Just *miss* the damned cruise and stay in the states. Weed the yard, clean the carport, watch Sara cooking supper, be on my hands and knees with the kids. The sky was gray and an annoying wind kept flipping my tie up into my face. I was in an unfamiliar world, one lone figure in an old black and white photo—charcoal water, pewter ship, and leaden sky. But there was nothing I could have done to avoid this; never had an option. All around me people who should have been here and knew what they were doing were carrying out their critical casting-off duties. Apparently no one felt as misplaced as I did.

Within the hour we would be heading towards the Atlantic—into the open water outside the Chesapeake Bay Bridge, with Norfolk sinking over the horizon (along with my heart). Thirty minutes now and I could still visualize Sara's face—holding back tears. And she wasn't the only one. I was feeling a new sadness. Shamefully, up until about a year ago I was still sure of having too-soon "closed the book" on my life; that I'd foolishly allowed a marriage to happen. But recently I had begun to shed that mindset, finding a new contentment being with my wife and kids in our own little home. The yearning for the yet undefined but adventuresome life I always thought I was destined for may have been lessening. I think I had finally accepted the situation and knew where I belonged, *and now I wasn't going to be there.*

Like the final scene in a movie I had watched our Ford station wagon leave the pier parking lot and blend into the patchwork of other vehicles. I hung onto the visualization of Sara's face as long as I could. Sammy and Mark were fascinated by everything happening here on the ship, but of course had no idea of time and what this would mean. It was high up here. I could see forever, but no longer my car. It was gone and I was part of this. The activity was almost frenzied now, causing me to move and watch from a safer distance. From stem to stern, time-critical tasks were being undertaken by obedient young sailors responding to the hoarse commands of the flush-faced senior petty officers. As a Marine it's traditional to poke fun at the Navy. This carrier cruise would put a stop to any of that. I would discover operations at sea to be a demanding, precise and unforgiving campaign, run by a group of dedicated professionals (albeit they were sailors).

It was happening—right on time. Our seventy-five-thousand-ton gray monster began to creak and lean. Thundering vibrations erupted from deep within as she strained to move. Mammoth brass screws at the stern pounded the water into froth. Tiny tugs crouched then lunged forward into wet and shivering lines. But the ship was a slumbering giant, appearing to ignore these efforts in favor of one last effort of her own. A final shudder and we were away from the dock. Swirling dark pools filled the gap between the concrete pier and the straight steel hull. For better or for worse, I was on my way.

The entire squadron was now up on the flight deck, and no horseplay or joking going on that I could see; every man silent—left with his own thoughts, feeling the tremors up through his feet and beginning to sense the permanency of this event. Alone on the port catwalk I gripped the railing and took a deep breath, determined to hang onto the sight of the

Norfolk skyline as long as possible. I couldn't keep back the tears. But no one could see, and I suspect I wasn't the only one. In fifteen minutes we were past the last rock breakwaters. Another fifteen and we were into open water; just a handful of guys on deck now. Only the bay bridge and some tall loading cranes broke the horizon. Soon I was the lone sentinel. All the other officers had gone below to begin exploring the maze of passageways and compartments we would get to know so well. In defiance of the unavoidable fate awaiting us, I blinked into the wind, staring eastward—2800 miles towards the Azores. We continued to plow ahead determinedly, bashing the dark water to either side, leaving the continental states further and further behind us.

For me—from the day the cruise was announced I had an ominous feeling about the coming separation. A couple carrier training periods I did so poorly I could have been cut from this prestigious team, irrespective of my wishes. I even considered not trying quite so hard—actually fail to qualify *on purpose*, but Jim Stremlow—our LSO (Landing Signal Officer) and my old Preflight friend, was running the show and would not have tolerated that. He was an Alpha male if ever there was one. Long and angular, from Amarillo, Texas, he appeared to have been made out of pressure-treated-pine 2x4s. I had never seen him in doubt about anything for more than ten seconds. And some guys have all the luck, not only was he big and tough, he was smart! I never could imagine verbalizing my reservations to him. Darker than dusk. Stars out now. Noticed I was shivering. Rubbed my arms and decided it was time to go below. Surrender.

The Ship's and Squadron's Complement

We forged across the Atlantic in a fearless manner, devouring mile after mile of helpless waves. The ocean was no match for the ship. The water ran over itself trying to get out of our way. Of course we weren't alone on the ship. There were five squadrons on board: two Navy fighter squadrons, two Navy attack squadrons, and a Marine attack squadron (us). ("Fighter" aircraft have air-to-air weaponry—to shoot down other aircraft. "Attack" aircraft have air-to-ground weaponry—to destroy ground targets.) There were also two rescue helicopters and a propeller mail-plane. In addition to these tactical aviation units there was the "Ship's Company"—the hundreds of departments and thousands of "hands" (Navy commissioned officers, Petty officers, and enlisted men) whose job it was to keep the ship itself up and running. They do their stuff and we do ours. The enlisted ranks sleep in large, barrack-like areas, in side-by-side, three-tiered bunks. The officers sleep in private staterooms—two to a room.

Our squadron commanding officer (called the "Skipper") was Lieutenant Colonel Cunningham. An alright guy. Big—well over six-foot and bald. (Looked just like *Mr. Clean.*) He hadn't gone to flight training until midway in his career—which is difficult and rarely attempted. (Flying is something it's best to tackle before you've learned much about caution.) The second-in-command is called the Executive Officer, and we had a good one— Major Keith Johnson. He was one of those few senior officers who could do anything the hot shot lieutenants could. Besides him we only had one other major—Major Burnham, the Maintenance Officer. Major Johnson could have been "one of the guys" without trying. Major Burnham would never quite make the bond (though I give him credit for trying). Besides me there were three captains, one of course being Jim Stremlow, who would be my roommate for the cruise.

The lieutenants were the cream of the crop; all cool, good-looking, athletic guys, most still bachelors. I envied them—not being able to recollect that "single" phase in my own life. It seemed every one of them had owned a Corvette before we deployed, subscribed to *Playboy* and *Forbes,* and came from good families in South Hampton or Beacon Hill. The world was their oyster and as a captain in this outfit, I knew any performance less than admirable would not go unnoticed by these guys. On the crossing there was no flying. If there was, and you broke a hook trying to land, you'd not be able to reach a land airport, so you'd have to pull up alongside the ship and eject, hoping the rescue helicopter got you before you drowned.

All the junior officers were assigned collateral duties, usually as an Assistant Officer-in-Charge in one of the squadron's departments. The assigned junior officer's duties would be at the discretion of the more senior Officer-in-Charge (OIC). Perhaps the most vital department in the squadron was the Aviation Maintenance Department—responsible for the condition of all our aircraft. Major Burnham was the OIC of the Maintenance Department, and yup, I was assigned as his assistant. Within this department were: the Engine Shop which repaired all the engine components, the Electric Shop which repaired and replaced the generators, wiring, gyros and radios, the Metal Shop that did all the repairs on the aircraft structure, the Hydraulic Shop that took care of the pumps and filters that provided power to the landing gear, flaps and brakes, and the Flight Equipment Shop that issued and maintained all the parachutes, life vests, rafts, and survival kits. I would devote an hour or more to each shop each day; sorting out the reported malfunction reports and listening to the problems of the young enlisted men working in the shops; providing a sympathetic shoulder when necessary.

The Infamous "Ready Room"

Each day started with a 0800 *All Pilots Meeting* in the squadron Ready Room; a place designed for official squadron meetings and flight briefings, but more often serving as a hangout for any otherwise unoccupied pilot. It was an olive-drab cross between an all-metal schoolroom and a pool hall. Eight rows of steel-framed chairs (cockpit seats removed from retired transport aircraft) were bolted to the floor ("deck"), a few pieces of Naugahyde furniture against the walls ("bulkheads"), and a raised platform with a podium and blackboard up front. Not well lit. The key attraction was a closed-circuit TV mounted high on one bulkhead, where pilots could watch real time video of actual landings. The camera recording this hair-raising footage was embedded in the flight deck near the desired touchdown point (arresting wire three), and aimed back up the final approach. Stenciled on the TV screen was a crosshair, which—if the aircraft was in it, meant the pilot was on the ideal glide-path for landing. Since it's no small task guiding ten tons of metal at 140 knots to a spot the size of a kitchen table, few pilots would be in the crosshair the whole time. They'd be either above it (high) or below it (low). If you were above it you would land long, miss the "three wire" and be hoping like hell to catch the "four (last) wire." Miss that one and you'd be cursing the gods and adding full power to go around for another try. If you were a little below the desired trajectory you might catch the "two wire" (hopefully). Or lower yet—the "one wire" (please God). Or short of that, the aircraft would hit the aft edge of the deck *and cartwheel down it in a disintegrating fiery ball.*

Sitting in front of the TV in the Ready Room became a popular pastime, provoking loud and well-animated commentaries (interspersed with a fair share of "Holy Shits"). After each landing session (called a "recovery") the pilots who had just landed would come down to the Ready Room and watch a replay of their own landing. Entering the Ready Room, pressure suit hose swinging, smelling of sweat, hair plastered to your forehead, helmet in hand, and hearing what your buddies had to say about your landing, could be a humbling experience. Besides the oft filled Ready Room, we had our own squadron work areas (the shops), and our sleeping quarters (staterooms). A person could be in any of these three known areas, or a hundred other nifty hiding places on board. You would be assumed present without being present.

What Was I Doing in My Spare Time?

Writing letters to Sara. And, to add some size to my slight frame I had lugged a set of barbells onboard and found a neat hideaway for them in a rarely visited cranny of the upper forecastle deck. It became my own secret place. Whenever I wasn't there, at the desk in my stateroom, or touring my shops, I was on the flight deck—my solace, sixty-five feet above the racing water. The expanse of the horizon was inspiring. The warm sun piqued my skin and the air was so fresh and clean I could actually smell its sweetness. In light of my exhilaration, I could imagine how the old sailors must have felt and why they put to sea. If it was this inspiring atop this noisy, vaporous steel factory, I wondered what it must have been like a hundred years ago, standing on parched decks, hefting a wood wheel and listening to the snapping canvas above.

Arriving in the Med

Lo and Behold on the eighth day—Gibraltar! We'd made it! It looked just like the logo for the insurance ad. *Were we going to try a launch before putting into port? What was our first port going to be?* Once again it seemed as if I was the only one for whom this was a first trip. The squadron and all the ship's company were acting like they did this every summer. We would be replacing the *Saratoga*—another carrier on its way back to the states after its ten months over here. There would be a big change of command ceremony tomorrow afternoon, on the north side of the island of Majorca. The captain of the *Saratoga* would be relieved of duties, our ship's captain would receive his orders, and then when the *Saratoga* steamed westward we would be the new good guys in the Med.

The "Change of Command" Ceremony

1300 hours, 22 June. Pollensa Bay: Now *this* was what I was imagining. We sailed through a fjord-like cut into an emerald green bay and dropped anchor (which process emitted a bone jarring steel rattling that could wake the dead). Chalk-stained charcoal cliffs rose steeply upwards from the water's edge. Unlike Norfolk, the sky was cloudless and the golden sun was doing its job. Nestled on the beach was a dazzling white village. Luxury yachts and sleek speed boats began to hurry out to investigate this huge visitor. Each one as it entered our monstrous shadow would throttle back and settle in the water, apparently awed by the immensity of this hobbled giant. One by one as they gained their composure, they'd rev their engines and begin to circle the ship or race back and forth alongside. The well-tanned beautiful people reclining on their glistening teak decks waved up at us with great enthusiasm. I was flattered by this greeting. Maybe we Americans onboard *would* be something special over here. Everyone whose duties would allow (which appeared to be everybody) was topside gaping in awe. The change of command ceremony held on the *Saratoga*, was completed by 1600. Our captain had just been piped back onboard after the short passage in his private boat (although not looking like one, was referred to as the "Admiral's Barge"). We watched the *Saratoga* pull colors and grind out of the bay—homeward bound. The *Forrestal* was taking over. Now it'd be us cruising around, flexing, just waiting for the order to devastate some eastern European Soviet site, or whatever else for miles around we might accidentally destroy.

Chapter Eleven
MY FIRST LAUNCH!

The Day Arrived

Starting today there was going to be a one week at-sea flying period before putting into port. We spent our first day east of Menorca running alongside two tankers, taking on fuel. Besides the thick black hoses there was another cable stretched between the ships, with gurneys hanging from them—carrying people! That completed we steamed south all night for today's flight ops. Based on our demeanor this morning, I think we all were a little apprehensive (though no one was saying as much).

Each day of flight ops would consist of four launches. The first launch (as all launches would be) was composed of three flights of four aircraft—twelve total. It had been shot into the air at 10:00, for a standard hour and a half flight. We had been in the Ready Room, three decks down, when they were launched, and wow, those catapults are something else—raw power. Their heart-stopping explosive jarring made you wonder how long the ship was going to stay glued together. On an upper deck—nearer the tracks, the noise made you fear for your life.

The Crew Scheduler had assigned me as a Division Leader for the second launch—leading a flight of four. The Ready Room was air conditioned, but the back of my flight suit was soaked. Was having a hard time imagining ten straight months of mornings like this (at least the way my stomach felt now). And I heard flight ops were going to be scheduled every day. Only when the flight deck rose and fell over thirty feet, would flight ops be cancelled. 11:10—I'd soon be leading my guys up to the flight deck. Those 10:00 first launch guys were up there now, milling around and nervously waiting for the completion of our second launch. One minute after the twelfth plane of our launch was off the deck, the first returning plane would hit the deck (and one every minute for the next eleven minutes)! That's how each and every launch would go.

I noticed a minimum of wise cracking this morning. Would've bet I wasn't the only one feeling queasy. Not sure how good my briefing would be I led my guys to the furthest corner of the Ready Room. You need to have some worthwhile training objective. Though I didn't state it in my briefing, I had at least one: *get out and get back safe!* I outlined a profile for a basic navigation drill, done without the use of our electronic navigational aids. This navigating by just flying headings and times (with no electronic or satellite positioning guidance) is called "Dead Reckoning." My flight would be that sort of drill, in case one day our aircraft's navigational devices failed, and we were forced to go back to the basics. Today we'd fly a big triangle with three 180-mile legs, and hopefully at the end of the third leg, spy the ship! A nice safe kind of first try. No daring exploits. I *look* like a pilot and *talk* like one, but in all truthfulness—my little secret, I wasn't one of those guys who "could fly the box it came in" (like Jim Stremlow). I had to pay attention the whole time and had my hands full with whatever maneuver I was doing. I wasn't that keen on looping or rolling it (that most the other guys lived for). I was content to do things methodically and within the envelope. We'd have to be back at 12:50, ten minutes before our "Recovery Time." Our launch would be a four-squadron launch: three Navy squadrons and us—sixteen planes! I was already concerned about someone screwing up the landing order when we all came back at the same time.

The Trip to the Flight Deck

Finally the dreaded announcement came: "Second Launch, man you're aircraft." The looks exchanged in that instant indicated none of us were carrying an excess of confidence. Rising and looking as nonchalant as we could, we picked up our helmets and kneeboards, and for better or worse, were on our way. We got a round of cheers from the guys whose names weren't on the flight schedule and were now casually strewn around the Ready Room. They knew that thirty seconds after the last plane in our flight was catapulted off, the first plane from the ten o'clock launch would be starting his approach. The second show—*ours,* the one I was worried about, would be at 13:00 when *we* came back, when all our squadron mates would be in front of the Ready Room TV. Glued there, amongst gasps and slaps to the forehead they'd observe our landings. The TV was irrefutable evidence of a good approach or a porpoising, skidding, slipping, lunging, diving, *Thank God for small favors* landing.

We were out of the Ready Room and beginning our trip up to the flight deck. Had to remember to step high enough through each "hatch" (doorway on a ship) to clear the ten-inch steel lip above the sill (known as "shin splitters" to those who failed to lift their leg high enough). The Ready Room was two decks down, along with a multitude of other shops and offices. Hundreds of them (called "spaces"). No daylight ever gets to this lower mid deck, whose bulkheads are a pea-soup-colored enamel. (Not a great color when you're already slightly nauseous). They barely reflected a dim glow from the not closely spaced incandescent 25-watt bulbs. The mid deck is the level used most frequently to travel fore and aft (from bow to stern), or left to right (port to starboard) across the ship. And the maze of passageways makes one of these journeys no easy trip. In our ten-month cruise, with a hundred trips to the flight deck, I don't think I ever took the same route twice.

I hoped I was leading the guys on a proper route, but you could be traipsing along on a seemingly sensible route, yank open a hatch and step through it into a hot and steamy, slick-floored galley, and be face to face with a big Filipino cook; or through the wrong hatch into the sheeted jungle of the sailors' bunk area, now face to face with a pale-skinned, tattooed guy wearing only baggy undershorts. *Oops, took a wrong turn somewhere.* A sheepish "Good Morning," a U-turn and on your way again.

We straggled through several ship's company areas full of faces and uniforms we didn't recognize. Each tactical squadron and each ship's company unit had their own work areas, eating areas, recreation areas, and sleeping quarters. The ship was like a county full of small towns, connected by narrow, winding, unmarked roads. Once you got the right paths memorized, you could avoid the aforementioned intrusions. If you were lucky you could make the trip without bumping into anybody other than your squadron-mates. I stayed the course, only making lefts and rights where absolutely necessary (trying to keep the compass in my head from spinning). You could be on the starboard side of the ship, trying to go forward, have made a wrong turn and transition to the port side of the ship, going aft. What a surprise when you'd scamper up a ladder into daylight, fully expecting to see the bow of the ship, and find yourself peering over the stern.

Success! Only three turns and two ladders later we emerged onto the hangar deck (one deck above the Ready Room and one deck below the flight deck) where all the airplanes that aren't "topside" are undergoing repairs. It's a crowded dangerous place. On the starboard side of the hangar deck are two elevators—fifty-foot by fifty-foot steel platforms protruding out just ten feet over the treacherous racing water. Aircraft after having been worked on are towed onto these elevators, to be raised to the flight deck. Almost every cruise, something or someone goes over the side off one of these elevators, never to be seen again.

The Spot Where It All Happens!

I'd never buckled-in off dry land. This would be my first launch. (No wonder my knees were shaking.) Hugging the port side of the hangar deck away from most the confusion. I found the ladder which would take us topside to the flight deck; a place for launches and recoveries; pure flying business, nothing else. It's either abandoned or a furious pulpit of screaming, steaming, lashing, cable-slapping activity. Forget the *flying* part, a guy could get killed real quick just by standing in the wrong place. Objects of horrendous tonnage would be hurtling by just yards away. Seemingly chaotic but urgent activities were being carried out on all sides.

Understood by me but not sufficiently anticipated was that the carrier was steaming at 18 knots into a 15-knot wind—resulting in 33 knots of wind across the deck. Popping out of the hatch and onto the flight deck, I wasn't prepared for the gale-force wind that all but blew me back inside. Eyes watering, cheeks buffeting and spit being sucked out of my mouth, I scanned the gaggle of aircraft trying to locate where our Marine A-4's were stationed. All three of my guys were out of earshot, but one of them was making a pointing motion straight ahead. Squinting forward I recognized the shape of our Skyhawk rudders, all but masked by the taller tails of the Crusaders. In 30-plus knots of wind a man has a hard time just standing up, and here we are carrying all our stuff, weaving around stacks of equipment and moving vehicles—taking giant steps and little hops to avoid the tie-down cables. Almost every aircraft had several of these stretching out at weird low angles, just waiting to snag a foot and send you sprawling.

And if you didn't trip, you had a real good chance of being run over. The most dangerous thing to lookout for were the eighteen-year-old Mario Andretti's driving the tow tractors. These low flat tugs were screeching everywhere, popping in and out of gear, surging ahead or rearward at full speed. Their job was to hook up to an aircraft and pull it onto the catapult. And besides these tugs and going just as fast, there were at least a half dozen motorized Volkswagen-sized mobile power units zipping all over the deck. (Airplane batteries alone can't start their engines.) Like a hummingbird going from blossom to blossom, they would zoom up to and away from each aircraft, plugging in their power cable to provide the high amps necessary to start a jet engine. Later in the cruise after a night launch, a Navy pilot would be hit by one of these power carts breaking both of his legs.

Kha-wham! The first test shot on the number two cat went and my heart almost came out of my mouth. The piston tracks were only a foot below the surface of the flight deck, and I had been walking right on top of number two. I popped into the air like a drop of water off a scalding grill, and was now trying to hover there to avoid the bodily damage that would surely result when my feet returned to the deck. I continued towards my assigned aircraft (which was doing its impression of a young sapling in the wind). I could see it shifting and leaning as the ship listed and pitched. The steady gale was trying to thrash the flight control surfaces and twisting the fuselage—so much so that the skin on the side of the aircraft was actually wrinkling. And the small open cockpit ten feet up didn't look like a safe place even here tied down.

Standing by the side of the aircraft and awaiting my arrival was Sgt Parker—the assigned "Plane Captain" for my aircraft; the mechanic responsible for giving my plane the necessary care and assisting me in and out of the cockpit for the next ten months. Once assigned to an aircraft, that aircraft is his and his alone. He greeted me, apparently not noticing my doubt and hesitancy. *That's good.* No reason for him to know how scared I was. The first never to be omitted ritual: the "Exterior Pre-Flight Inspection," a quick, crouching, kneeling, neck-craning examination of the aircraft struts, tires, brakes, hydraulic lines, visible connectors, hinges, flight control surfaces, fluid levels and pressures. Today they were all just fine—*no reason not to accept the aircraft.*

Manning My Aircraft and Doing It!

Up the rickety ladder. Whole plane rocking now. Standing on the top rung, the last thing before getting in: check the ejection seat for *two* "safety" pins, and pull out *one*. With one pin remaining in, while strapping in if I accidentally hit the ejection seat handle, the seat wouldn't fire. Over the canopy rail and into the seat. *Whoa*—I saw most of the canopies already closed, I was a little behind. Gotta hurry. Into the cockpit. Seat belt. Parachute harness. Shoulder straps. Sgt Parker was handing me items, helping me adjust and tighten them. He's handing me my helmet. It's on. Where's my gloves? "Thanks Scott." He took care of the final step—

removing the remaining seat pin. *Seat's armed. Gotta be careful now.* The canopy's coming down. It's down. Lever forward, lock it. This is it.

Geez! Sgt Parker was shoving the power unit into the side of the plane with such force, the whole airplane was rocking. It's in. There's the indication. Got the voltage. Got start clearance from Air Ops. Light-off. It's winding up. Exhaust gas temperature okay. Stabilized. Radios on. Listen for the sequence. The first two Navy Crusaders were being towed onto the number one and two cats. Larry and Tripp were somewhere behind me, couldn't tell, they weren't in the mirrors. Searched ahead for my signal guy. The windscreen is an inch thick and has a fair amount of distortion (which isn't too bad now but can be real dangerous at night).

The ship's flight deck personnel were responsible for a variety of critically important, rapidly occurring, sequential steps during the launch. They worked in highly specialized, well-coordinated teams, and to indicate their specific task and identify themselves to the pilots, each team wore like-colored vests. Beneath, in front and to the sides of me were fast moving patches of green (catapult and arresting gear handlers) and yellow (the signalmen we searched for) and obeyed. No red vests today, that's what the ordnance crews (bomb and rocket loaders) wore. From the cockpit it was a coded blur of color as the various crews scurried here and there, unhooking cables, waving signals, shouting, hauling away tow bars, and finally attaching the catapult-connecting halters to the aircraft. *What an operation.*

There goes the first F-8. *Wow.* Now the second. Clouds of white steam and hot oil vapor poofed skyward, and then blew back over the waiting aircraft (smearing my previously clean windscreen). Two more fighters were being pulled up. I was trying to do my post-start instrument and engine checks (in my opinion more important than that exterior inspection I had done a few minutes ago). Checked the gauges for the critical "go, no-go" readings. Everything okay. Lifted my eyes back up and outside. Yeah, there's a yellow vest waving at me—in fact frantically. Didn't see him before. The wheel chocks were out. Got the signal. Tug's on me, towing me to the number four cat. Going to the number four cat. Got that. Can see that. The whole plane shook. What the hell was that? They pulled me over something big. *Bang! Klunk!* Felt like the struts were going to buckle. On the cat. *I'm on the cat.* Christ, I'll bet I'm not five feet from the edge of the deck. Could look almost straight down at the water. If the ship lists, if I started sliding, in just a few feet I would be over the side. *Geez!*

I could hear noises and feel the vibrations up through the rudder pedals as the unseen crew beneath me was attaching the halter to the nose gear (connecting me to the catapult). *Holy Shit.* Only a matter of seconds now. The launch officer was out there. Saw him. He was looking forward. Back to me now. Looking forward again. Arm up. Waving it. Faster. Tight circles. Giving me the turn up signal. I'm doing it. All the way up. At full power. The engine was roaring, the plane was shuddering, the radio was blaring, my eyes were watering. There he goes! He dropped to one knee, twisting his torso towards the bow and throwing one hand forward.

Whoa! Neck snapped back, helmet pinned against the headrest, hand half off the stick, visor cutting the bridge of my nose. *Ride er' out!* I saw the end of the angle deck racing towards me. Airspeed 110 knots. Need another 20 knots! Only fifty feet to go. *Thunk!* The halter's off. On my own. Over water. Power at 100% but sinking—losing altitude. Nose up! *More.* Get ten degrees nose up. Hold it. Wings level. Looks good. *We're flying!* Vertical speed indicator showing a 500 foot per minute climb. We're accelerating. *I did it!* I'm airborne. We're flying. *Jesus Christ, we're flying!* I think I'm going to be able to do this. I think I'm gonna like it!

Chapter Twelve
WHEN THE MOON HITS YOUR EYE LIKE
A BIG PIZZA PIE

Our First In-port: Naples

Had already gotten a couple letters from Sara, and they were great. It was almost like I was still there. She gave me all the details about Sammy and Mark's activities, as well as the latest on our friends and neighbors. As for my writing; my goal was to make sure my calendar showed two days a week marked as "LS" (letter sent) days. In view of this, the activities related in this chapter are perplexing, and would leave me on an unchartered path.

We pulled into the port of Naples about midnight Sunday, where we would put our feet on European soil for the first time. We were on the flight deck observing the city lights and hearing the sound of a ten-ton anchor dragging out chain links as big as 55-gallon drums; the sound we'd grow to love (meaning no more flights for a week and time to recreate ashore). When in harbor, half the personnel are assigned to a "port" duty section, and the other half to the "starboard" duty section. One section stays on board while the other is free to "hit the beach" (time ashore is called "Liberty"). The old hands had warned us not to expect too much in Naples. Jim Stremlow and I took them at their word and signed up for the three-day Chaplain's Tour of Rome.

Moored a half mile out, the only way to get to shore was by using a "liberty" boat, and our tour group was on the first boat. In port they would run 18 hours a day, bringing the wild-eyed expectant revelers to shore, and the weary, out-of-money souls back to the ship. These boats were open, so lots of wind and salt spray. Just rows of benches, no protected area, carried about fifty guys and offered a usually soaking and always bumpy ride. Viewing the shoreline, I could see why the old hands had said what they did. The scene was not uplifting: debris-strewn water, rusty tankers, dilapidated piers, and fume-spewing trucks chugging up and down the wharves.

Roma! (and Another Person)

Wow! This city was something else. Monday afternoon and most of Tuesday we availed ourselves of the scheduled stops: Trevi Fontana (the fountain from the famous movie *Three Coins in a Fountain*), the Coliseum, the Forum and the Catacombs. Ten miles outside the city one could easily imagine the twelve disciples or a Roman legion coming around the next line of cypress trees. Wednesday—our next to last day, we visited the Vatican. I'd seen hundreds of photos but had no idea of its grandeur or being inside it. And that's where my behavior startled me. I don't know how I came to notice her, but what I remember mostly about the Vatican is Ardith—one of the ladies in a tour group alongside us. It was difficult not to notice this lone, proudly upright female person in a bare-backed, pink-checked sun dress. As Jim and I plodded across the pavers of Piazza San Pietro she appeared to be gliding across it, with a long strong stride and her head held high. She wasn't a young girl; couldn't even call her a girl; must've been at least thirty. She was not mixing with the other members of her tour group, and for some reason, I felt a concern for her.

While waiting to get our souvenir envelopes franked at the Vatican Post Office, she happened to sit down on the base of a huge column directly alongside Jim and I. Sandals off she examined her feet (most likely for developing blisters). She tilted her head back and closed her eyes. Thick auburn hair contrasted a fair-skinned, slightly freckled face. Rejoining us in line Jim nodded her a polite hello. She responded with a disarming smile. I suspected we had just met a proper European woman, to whom we hoped to appear at least halfway intelligent and counter that "Ugly American" image. We introduced ourselves as pilots off the carrier, presently anchored in Naples, just up here for a three-day tour. It was lunchtime and Jim surprised me by inviting Ardith to join us. The meal consisted of tasteless dry sandwiches (with one incredibly thin slice of ham) and a soft drink called *Orangina*. We told her about carrier life, maybe even impressing her. She was from Scotland but now lived in Knightsbridge (which I later learned was an exclusive suburb west of London). She added she worked at Whitehall—a complex in Westminster where many classified government agencies were located. (Jim surprised me by having heard of it).

Making our way along Via Della Conciliazone, and listening to her, it was obvious Ardith was well schooled in the arts. And once again I was deservedly embarrassed by my lack of knowledge in that area. Jim was doing considerably better than I was. Made a silent vow to learn all I could as fast as I could, about the well-known artists and composers. (I would discover if you're going to make it in Europe this is a must.) Our contacts with the vendors made it clear she was fluent in Italian. I heard her tell Jim she was unmarried, which was difficult to believe. Jim told her about his family. Not sure why, I found myself remaining silent.

Ardith was courteous and respectful, perhaps speaking more with Jim than with me—which was understandable. He was a John Wayne-looking kind of guy and could be very pleasant in short social meetings. And maybe she felt equally comfortable with me, recognizing my innocent appreciation of having a conversation with an educated English woman. Anyone would have been flattered to be seen with her. I was beginning to suspect the rest of our last day in Rome might coincide with her planned activities. And it did (though my intent evaded me). I only observed Rome as it went past out of focus, while listening to what she was saying. At Whitehall she was an assistant to one of Britain's most renowned nuclear scientists. But "Enough of that" she said, "Today is my third day of a short holiday and I don't want to talk about work." (I would learn "holiday" is used by all Europeans where we would say "vacation").

Our tour would be over in another day and we would be heading back to Naples. I was now beginning to feel that might be too soon. I was almost startled when Jim suggested the three of us have dinner together. But it wasn't going to happen. She had a previous commitment: a dinner engagement with a Count. *With a Count?* She was quick to brush it off, but to my astonishment she agreed—no, *volunteered* to meet us for a coffee or a *gelato* after her dinner engagement. I was surprised (and flattered) that she had even considered this. To give her an out, (or to back out myself as a married man on my very first trip ashore), I added, "But wouldn't that be a little late, with your earlier engagement and tour activities tomorrow morning?"

"No, no, it's fine with me, I'm accustomed to late hours. Dr. Whitehead calls me into the lab at all hours." (Yes, a Dr. Whitehead worked at Whitehall.) Fortunately, the cafe she suggested for a meeting place was one that we remembered seeing at least several times. It was set. Jim and I arrived back at the hotel—a couple of sweaty, foot-sore, weary travelers. Inside my room and "out on my feet" the bed looked inviting, and I was having second thoughts about the evening's plan. Take a shower, lay down and think it over. I did and dozed—easily. About seven-thirty Jim and I ate at a pasta place next-door to the hotel. We did consider not going, but since we had told her we'd be there, we were pretty much locked in. If she were to show up and we didn't, that would give American men (and commissioned officers) a bad name.

At nine-thirty Jim and I stepped onto the terrace of the Caffe Della Parma. Neat atmosphere. Cellophane lanterns swaying in the breeze, lots of small metal tables with red paper table clothes (held down by large wooden clothes pins), and great music playing. Lots of families with young kids, enjoying themselves to the max. We'd gotten there early. Ordered Cinzano with soda. We'd seen this drink combination on billboards all over town. Sipping it would make us look less like the rank tourists we were. Was half hoping she'd show up and half hoping she wouldn't. Perhaps for the best. I was questioning my motives; why I accepted this meeting. Ten o'clock and still no Ardith, and Jim had already dozed off a couple times. But as late as they dine in Italy, her estimate of nine-thirty had seemed too early. Ten-fifteen and still not here. I was thinking of leaving, and Jim was doing it. He'd had it. I told him go ahead back. I'd give her another fifteen minutes and if she wasn't here, I'd be right behind him.

The fifteen minutes passed. Time to call it a night. I'm leaving tomorrow. Guess she's really running late; in fact may not be going to come home at all. *We'd lost to the Count.* He'd be toasting her now, in his silk smoking jacket and ascot, his glass of sherry held high. I could picture his balcony doors open, a breeze coming in from the terrace. Lace curtains wafting across a polished dark floor. *Who was I to be getting involved with this type thing?* And what could I contribute to her Rome vacation? I certainly couldn't add anything to what she already knew about the city. And I was married. I'd be real temporary in her life (in fact momentary). The Count would be able to provide a lot more interesting conversation and lasting companionship than I could, and she deserved it. In fact, no doubt *he* deserved it more than I did. I decided to head back to our hotel and just rest. *Rest and forget this craziness.*

Then it hit me... *Caffe Della Parma?!* No wonder Jim thought we had seen it several times, there were *two* of them! 11:00. If by some chance she's still there, we're the ones who will be late. I kept telling myself it was a matter of two Americans having to keep their word (even if only one showed up). A matter of courtesy. *Although I was not wholly assuaged by that reasoning.* The night scenery was flying by. Now past a gaggle of foreign-language-speaking kids wearing rucksacks covered with patches from Sweden. One more block. Via Del Corso. It's on this street. I saw it! The Caffe Della Firma (different last word). Looked just like the other place, same Cinzano umbrellas, striped awning, and paper lanterns. *There she is! Sitting alone.* I begged her to accept my and Jim's apologies, and recounted having been at the wrong café. Ardith didn't seem irritated that I was late, in fact seemed really happy I had shown up. Out of such relief to have avoided being a "no show" and found her, I reached out spontaneously and took her hand with mine. As soon as I realized I was holding her hand, I quickly let go.

After our coffee and sherbet we left for her pensione, meandering like time meant nothing. She mentioned she had graduated from Queen Mary University with a post graduate degree in physics. (And me with 60 semester hours.) Up and down tiny streets, through deserted parks and along high wrought iron fences surrounding official looking buildings. We ended up at Piazza di Spagna—the famous Spanish Steps. We made the long climb, trying to count the steps, but lost track at over a hundred. We took a much-needed rest on the terrace on top, in front of the Trinita dei Monti church. From there it was quite a sight. The sparkling night majesty of Rome beneath us, spanned the horizon.

Ardith was standing close, smiling and appearing very comfortable with me—for what reason I can't imagine. It was a strangely easy and natural time, which was for me not appropriate and unusual considering we had just met twelve hours ago. I sensed I was lucky to spend these few hours in her company. I never could have imagined being part of an evening like this. Yet here I was, viewing it as a disconnected, momentary diversion that would have no effect on my marriage. Realizing the way-too-late hour it was time to start back to her pensione. I was taken aback at how trusting she was—as if she would have let me do as I wanted. I wondered what might have transpired if we would have been another couple, in another private place. We didn't kiss goodnight, not even a peck on each cheek, and that was proper (especially for me). But it was a long parting handshake. A few more of the unsure, separating niceties you might expect, and I was (shakenly) on my way.

A long run and I was back in the hotel. I lay there exhausted but mind churning for a long time before a much-needed sleep overtook me. Just a few weeks ago I was in my home, in bed with my wife. *And look at me now.* Did I let it happen, or did I make it happen? Why had I found so much satisfaction in such a foolish mini adventure. What good could possibly come of such a thing? Starting with the innocent few words at the Vatican it was a weakly based, no—a baseless endeavor. Stupid. The bus ride back to Naples (to the carrier and my real life) was like the one up, except my head was full of "what ifs" and "maybes."

Back to My Real Life

Awake at 0600. Had multiple dreams of which I could make no sense of, though Ardith or something about her may have been lurking. Jim had already gone down to the wardroom for breakfast, and I was in the stateroom alone, and for once used the time wisely: I wrote a long letter to Sara—three good pages bringing her up to date on the things we were doing (not counting most of Rome) and what I had learned about carrier-based aviation operations. Would have been easier without the guilt I was feeling as a result of the events of the previous day. Luckily, having experienced my first launch and recovery I did have a lot to say about that.

The non-flying duties assigned to the younger officers were frequently in title only, but not mine. Without having attended the USMC Maintenance Officers School, I was still a big help to Major Burnham. My schedule here in port was just about the same as while at sea: visit each of the five shops in the department each day. Go over their pending repair work, read all the aircraft discrepancies—written by the pilots, to make sure that what they had written, was really what they meant to convey. (Often the write-ups were ambiguous or barely decipherable.) I'd then edit those write-ups and elaborate on them with the men tasked to take the corrective action. In so doing, more efficient corrective actions were taken and the outcomes noticeably better. Besides that an important part of my job was to take as much time as it took to listen to the men and *their* problems. Let them know we officers cared about them!

Working hand in hand with the Officer-in-Charge there is always a Staff Non-Commissioned officer directly in charge of the enlisted men (but below me in the chain of command). Ours was Gunnery Sergeant Baldwin. Out of a respect for his age and many years of service I never issued any directives to the men without first bouncing them off him. (Make it appear as a procedure we came up with together.) The number one objective of the department was to have an Operational Readiness of one hundred percent at 0600 each day. This meant all twelve of our aircraft would be in an "Up" status (ready for flight without a single "grounding" discrepancy).

Another Liberty Day

Woke up early the third day, an off-duty day for me. My section—the port section, had liberty. Spent as I was, I still decided to go ashore. Give Naples a try. Once again, in the open, thumping liberty boat, my main goal was to stay out of the cold salt spray and keep my teeth from chipping. What I saw once on the pier caused me to reflect on the grandeur of Rome. *Could I? I guess I could.* I could hop a train and be up to Rome in an hour or so, and on the Via Veneto, which would be a lot better than watching the fuming trucks here. Jogged to the train station in ten minutes. Found the schedule board and scanned the flipping black metal cards, searching for the trains to Rome. (No LED readouts yet.) According to the schedule board there was a 0928 *"Rapido"* (I guess meaning the "express") to Rome, leaving from *pista nove*, and my plan was to find track nine and be on that train.

Hard to believe this was a *Rapido*. We stopped two dozen times. Finally arrived at the Rome Stazione Termini. It didn't seem the same; a million tourists and the same great surroundings but lacking the excitement of a few days ago. I sat on a bench in Piazza Republica enjoying a myriad of interesting sights. But had an empty feeling. It was then that it hit me: *Ardith,* that's what's missing. *Should I try to find her?* I would. Found a pay phone and had the right tokens. Dialed her number. Ringing. Still ringing. Nobody answering. Well-meaning people from tour agencies overhearing my efforts kept approaching me with hotel brochures and good deals. Gotta check for myself.

The end of July—middle of the day and I'm tear-assing down Via Nazionale again. Shirt wet straight through. Into the Pensione Venezia. Got her room number from a bespectacled, ornery old codger on a stool behind an unpainted plywood counter. Up the stairs to Ardith's room. "Ardith, it's Roger. I was able to get back to Rome. Are you in?" Two seconds later the door swung open and out she came, with a great big smile. She did a spin and as her dress swished around her legs, I observed long muscular calves. An even bigger surprise, she gave me a quick kiss on each cheek. I broached an idea—a ridiculous idea that had just popped into the space normally occupied by a brain: a picnic. If it was going to happen I'd have to get things going right away, because at around 10 p.m. I'd have to catch a train to Naples and be on the dock by midnight to catch the last liberty boat back to the ship.

I rented a scooter. I'm sure Ardith was a little scared on the back of our beat-up Lambretta. I was fortunate to get the bread, cheese, and wine in a single stop (but no wicker basket or checkered cloth). Getting out of downtown Rome was a real challenge. I wanted to get to the outskirts and start searching for some grassy hill. *Senso Unico*—one-way streets, kept tossing me back into the thick of things. Finally we were out of the city, but not in a nice area; nothing but weeded lots with trash, abandoned commercial buildings, and people fixing cars in the streets. *Please God, give me that grassy hill!* Two-thirty. The sun is way past the halfway point. My afternoon is disappearing in front of my eyes. All Ardith can have by now is a sore rear. Finally, maybe this'll do! It wasn't a grassy hill, but it was an empty lot on which stood the remains of an old monastery-type structure. Hopefully somewhere on the premises I could find a picturesque spot. Off the bike and into the ruins. Found a wing of the building with two walls gone and a half grass half dirt floor. Things were almost falling into place; not as I had visualized them, but it could have been worse. We ate. I drank my share of the Chianti.

We were finished but the afternoon had turned cool, in fact chilly. I don't know how much Chianti Ardith had. (For this project to fly she would have needed a lot.) Ready to leave, probably out of respect for all the effort I had put into this afternoon picnic, she wiped off her dress, walked over to me, and gave me a nice big hug. The firmness of her body against me scared me. Two seconds like this and I felt her suddenly tense up and could sense her discomfort. I pulled back to see a dismayed expression on her face. After observing something behind me, she looked quickly down at her feet. I spun around. Ten yards behind me some vagabond was noisily relieving himself against a wall. We were out of there. The motor scooter ride back was no great time either, but she hung in there. I tried to return the scooter, but the damned place was already closed; left it outside against their fence. We started back to her pensione.

You've felt this way before: You'd give anything to lie down and close your eyes. I was beat. Suspected Ardith was as well. It was now seven. Another two hours and I'd have to be on my way to the Stazione Termini. A train ride back to Naples, a mad dash to the dock, and catch one of those liberty boats out to the carrier. Hard to imagine what was left in my day before I would be back on the ship in my rack. In my condition and the late hour, I knew what I *should* have done. What I *did* was different. "C'mon with me, I know a fun place." She was off the steps, up on her strong legs, and we were on our way. The other day I had passed a restaurant with happy music flowing up the steps from a lantern-lit room underneath it.

Looking down the stairwell leading to it I'd seen a bunch of laughing, singing, dancing, leg slapping locals. It looked great last night. Here's hoping for tonight.

Arrived and good fortune was with me. The place was the same. At first Ardith was a little apprehensive, but soon gained her confidence, and in thirty minutes even just watching she appeared to be having the time of her life. One little boy in shorts ran over and pulled her onto the dance floor. She was thrilled. The two of them reeled around to the cheers and clapping of the crowd. I was happy for her. Her eyes were shining. So attractive and intelligent, you would have thought she would have had lots of happy times. But it was like all this was a first time for her, and she was thrilled to finally be part of something. We were both drinking the Chianti from a bottle given to us *"complimenti della casa"* (free) which was certainly appreciated by me, my cash running real low about now.

Finally the Chianti was gone, my feet were aching, and my legs were being crushed under Ardith's weight. (Fifteen minutes ago someone sat in her chair and I had motioned her over to sit on my lap.) I was afraid to check my watch. When I did: 2200 hours! *No way now.* I'm in big trouble. Too late to get to Naples in time to catch the last boat (at midnight—the "Cinderella" boat) out to the carrier. But I had known what was happening and I let it happen. But now what? If I could be on board a train in the next hour I could be in Naples by one, where I might be able to talk the Shore Patrol guys into letting me on one of their shift-change boats. That'd at least give me a couple hours sleep before my 0730 hours meeting with Major Burnham. What in the hell am I doing up here? Don't know what I was thinking, or if I was even thinking.

The owner and half his family walked us out. Lots of handshakes and promises for another time. Maybe for Ardith. I doubted I was going to see Rome again and was sure I'd never see her again. I knew I had done a foolish thing (lots of foolish things) in the last two days. We walked silently, and it wasn't going to be just a simple good night, it was going to be a goodbye. Another guy might have tried that *Can I come in for a cup of coffee* thing, in hopes of you know what. Even as fascinated as I had become with her that just wasn't an option. I was married. In fact, I knew I shouldn't even be standing here in this hallway! Our time together had been innocent, almost playful. She was like a little girl and I doubt me spending the night ever crossed her mind. If I did, would she turn out to be that woman with the right chemistry and I'd perform? She thought we had lots of time: the fall, the winter, next summer, visits to London, who knows—perhaps a whole future. *Me? Play-acting again.* My heart hurt. This goodnight graduated from a handshake to a hug.

Just before turning to leave, she blurted out that she would be leaving tomorrow and was there any chance *I could I go with her to the airport.* (She had no idea the hoops I was jumping through just to get to Rome.) I asked her what time her flight was. "I'm leaving from Fumicino at 8 p.m." She lowered her head and looked sad. I dared not to believe it was because we would be parting company. I was sure it would be better not to come up at all, yet found it impossible to say no. I heard the words coming out of my mouth: "Yes Ardith, maybe I can." The look on her face indicated she would be pleased.

I knew any number of things could come up aboard ship to squelch those plans, not to mention the realistic second thoughts I was already having; so I added: "I'll try, but if I'm not here by five o'clock, just plan on taking a cab without me." Gave her a hug, turned and left. Outside I broke into a run, intending to sprint all the way to the railway station. Not knowing when the next train would leave, I knew five minutes could be critical. Tried to keep the feet flying but couldn't do it. Slowed to fast trot. After midnight. Almost on my revised schedule. Exhausted.

My Return to Naples

At last—Stazione Termini. *But it was deserted!* Hard to imagine having had such a mass of humanity all day, it could be absolutely soulless now. Eerie! Not a moving thing in sight. All the newspaper stands were shuttered up. The cafeterias too. *Oh no, what's this?* The ticket windows are closed too! The *Partenze Informazione* was dark. Now I *am* worried. Quarter to one. There were a couple thousand tourists here six hours ago. Somebody must still have to get somewhere. I'm a prisoner in Rome. A stanchion with a framed timetable showed the last train to Naples left at 1205 and the next one wasn't until 0443 with an arrival in Naples of 0622. And I had that 0730 meeting with Major Burnham! That was going to be real close. Three hours to wait.

I found an empty baggage cart and pulled it behind some pallets for privacy. Located a few clean cardboard boxes, flattened them, and layered them on the metal bed of the cart. Glad Ardith (*or for God's sake—my wife*) can't see me now, curled up on a baggage cart, my clothes all wrinkled and needing a shave. Even the baggage check was locked up tight; like the place was quarantined and somehow I got in. Almost afraid to nap, lest I sleep through the 0443 train. (Assuming I could even fall asleep.) If so, I would bank on the noise of the early shift coming in to wake me up in time. I was in a state of dismay. We had been talking about meeting each other on another vacation. About me visiting her in London. There had been little I could say that was true. I did not feel good about my conduct and the actualities I had failed to mention. I knew my life, my future, who I was and who and what I could never be, no matter what my fantasies or temptations I was now exposing myself to.

While still positioning and repositioning, trying to get away from sharp corners and hinges, at about three-thirty the early-shift workers started coming in. All manner of banging and shouting commenced, along with the prompt loss of my bed. The train station was an old fossil erupting into a live creature. It was the end of any chance of sleeping. I checked my watch, waiting and praying. Outside the black sky was turning a light gray over the tops of the buildings. A bundle of newspapers came flying out of a passing truck, tumbling past me on the sidewalk. Guys with trays and boxes of bread and rolls were running in and out. The shutters of the newsstands and coffee bars were clattering open. Cabs and buses were suddenly everywhere. A new day was beginning in Rome, but I wasn't going to be part of it. And I shouldn't be. I didn't deserve it. I had been on borrowed time. I was leaving as I should. I winced again at the thought of my wife being able to observe me right now, or worse—last night! I didn't care that the cafes still weren't serving. Thirty minutes more. Hard to believe that I'll be on the carrier at 0700.

At 0440 I climbed aboard the train. An hour and twenty later I was in Naples. Caught a cab to the dock. 0625. Got the first liberty boat returning to the ship. I'm going to make it this time, but how many next times? I can't imagine going back to Rome tomorrow—will have to let Ardith get to the airport on her own. What was I thinking of doing? Could these past few days be part of that search for that one woman with the right chemistry, or, an introduction to that life I might have been destined for? I was allowing myself to do things that are more than just inappropriate. It was possible I could become more involved in my temporary "play-life"—an impossible fabricated one, than in my real life—the carrier now, and home shortly.

I struggled up the least used ladder to the flight deck, praying I wouldn't run into any of the other pilots (let alone the Colonel). Jim—

my roommate would know I had not come home, but he should be the only one. Made it across the hangar deck undetected. Snuck through the narrow and dimly lit passageways. My shoes had trod a million steps and my feet in them were aching. My collar was wet around my neck, and I'm sure, badly soiled. I probably shouldn't even wash these clothes, just throw them away. Made it into my stateroom; confused, weak, shameful, yearning for safety. Fortunately Jim was already gone. I'd rather not face him right now. A quick shower and shave. Dressed again. Might look okay. I had to be careful, first in-port and I had almost relegated the ship to just a place to change clothes! Could I already be grudgingly co-existing with it; my first time ashore having teased me with another existence. Was it a woman like Ardith that would have shown me that other fulfilling life I felt I was destined for.

I made it to my meeting on time, explained to the Major my plan for a new maintenance procedure; a way of tagging suspect aircraft parts that had been removed, but that may not have been bad. This way they could be identified for further checking, and possibly even reinstalled. The Major was impressed with this innovation; wanted me to hold meetings with all the shop heads right away, explaining to them how we would implement the procedure. It was just about noon when I exited the last shop. And then—took it better than I thought I would. I admitted to myself that neither physically or mentally could I handle one more round-trip to Rome. And I mustn't see Ardith again. No way—not right. Although that afternoon at five, a melancholy came over me as I visualized her checking her watch and knowing I wasn't coming.

Chapter Thirteen

A NIGHT LAUNCH AND BIG TROUBLE

What It's Like Flying at Night

We would be at sea a full week (and not making us feel any better) we would commence our first *night flying* operations! This was something that would test our nerve and mettle, and I was scheduled for the midnight launch! Back home strolling around at night you're usually within fifty feet of a lit house, or a hundred feet of a streetlamp, or a mile from a shopping center, or 5 miles from town. Well that's cheating. You have no idea how much light is emitted from these sources—reflected back from the clouds and trapped in the lower atmosphere. Here in the middle of the Med, there is no reflected light. It's black, black! Even before you launch, still on the Flight Deck (no ship's lights on) you can't see much outside the cockpit. You're looking through a four-millimeter plastic visor and a solid inch of stressed acrylic canopy. Together they mostly just reflected your own gawking head and a slew of distorted double images.

And after launch, in flight—worse! You could be right-side up, sideways or upside down. You're in your own little thirty by forty-inch cozy warm world, and just eight inches outside each of your elbows, was a harsh and hostile foreign environment. Tonight there was no moon, no stars, no water, no horizon. No outside reference at all! *I would have to be able to interpret the myriad of gauges, rotating dials, and pointing needles, and then, equally important: trust them!* But even in the best of aircraft, equipment still goes on the blink. If you lose your *flight* instruments, you may not be able to keep the aircraft right side up! If you lose your *navigational* instruments, *you have no way to find your way home.* Here at sea, even flying in the daytime there are no identifying ground features, no railroad tracks, no Super Domes, no highways to follow. And if this equipment failure occurs at night, forget it! Absolutely impossible. Total blackness. No way to find your way back to the ship!

So If You Lose Your Navigational Instruments, What Do You Do?

You call the ship on the radio and ask them for a "Radar Steer." There is an electronic device in each aircraft that continually sends a signal back to the ship. The guys in the radar room see this as a small "blip" on their radar scopes, and if needed can give you headings to fly back to the ship. The alternative to not finding the ship, is—before you've run out of gas, pull up and eject. Out you go into a screaming, sub-zero, lip-ripping wind that could tear your arms out of the sockets. With metal buckles bruising your chest, hard straps ripping at your crotch, nylon cords cutting your hands, and the wind buffeting your face, you plunge down towards a cold sea just waiting to swallow you up. All the way down you're praying you don't get knocked unconscious on impact and drown immediately. If you make it through that, start praying all over again that you don't die of exposure before dawn (when the first miniscule chance for your unlikely rescue occurs).

A night bailout over open sea is the one terrifying and statistically fatal event no pilot wants to contemplate. The guys up in the radar room—all nice and comfy, sitting in armchairs and eating their late-night snacks, don't have any idea what it's like for us out there. They cannot appreciate the frightening and all too real possibilities facing us when they hear our call for a radar steer. (They know where *they* are.) They watch their scopes in a safe, warm and friendly environment, munching sandwiches and listening to the *Top-Forty* on the Armed Forces Radio.

And if these guys are successful in getting us to a position where we can visually spot the ship, we still have to maneuver our aircraft into a position that we can land on it. And as hard as it is to land aboard a carrier in the daytime, it is many more times woefully challenging at night. The pilot has to interpret and react to constantly changing yellow, amber, and red lights projected off a mirror located just to the left of the desired touchdown point. When he has these lights in sight he hollers "meatball" and uses the changing colors to guide his flight path. All this culminating with a teeth jarring slam into a completely darkened, lurching, listing, wet and windy deck, blessedly catching a wire and walking away. No small task, frequently causing what we pilots call a "leemer"—*a cold shot of urine right through your heart.*

The Launch

Almost midnight, was sitting in the Ready Room with my wingman, Tom Krimmings. (Wondered if he felt as queasy as I did.) I had briefed for a rendezvous after takeoff—on the ship's 045-degree (northeast) radial,

50 miles out, at 25,000 feet. We'd join up there, practice night formation flight, and then get back to the ship for our recovery. "Recovery" is an easy word to say, but it means controlling every axis of your aircraft down through the night sky, into an increasingly narrow chute, at hurricane wind speeds—without varying more than five or ten feet in altitude or left to right—to a spot the size of your kitchen table! To preserve our night vision, there are no white lights allowed on the ship, just low-watt incandescent red lights (as mentioned earlier, red doesn't affect night vision). In the resultant muted scarlet glow Tom's facial features were barely recognizable. We looked more like a couple of sallow ghouls than hard-charging Marines.

There it was: The PA boomed with the now familiar announcement: "Attention. Pilots man your aircraft. Man your aircraft." I nodded to Tom and he fabricated a weak smile. We rose with our flight paraphernalia and started what never did become an organized journey, the always adventuresome trek up to the flight deck. Once there in the pummeling cold wind we stumbled and searched, finally locating our aircraft. I was two back for the number three catapult. Engine running, going through my checks. *Oh no, may have a problem here.* The magnetic compass was not showing the proper heading. But I'd heard the maintenance guys saying that there was so much metal in the ship's nearby superstructure, it could affect the compass, causing a temporary false indication. Only trouble is, on all my previous day launches I had not yet seen this error. The ship is heading due north, and even though I was pointed straight off the bow, my compass was showing a north-westerly heading. I might actually have a defective electronic compass—a *really* bad thing for a night launch. *Should I shutdown and ground the aircraft?* Maybe. But canceling out of a night flight was not good for your reputation. (One pilot ended up with the nickname "Strep," since he claimed a sore throat every time his name appeared on the night flying schedule.) And this compass discrepancy had recently been described as "to sometimes be expected." Don't have too much time to mull this over. If I cancelled out and it turned out there was no discrepancy, I'd never live it down.

I'm on my way onto the cat. *Uh-oh, what's this?* I don't think my direction-finding needle is pointing where it should either. *Geez!* Don't tell me it's malfunctioning too. It should be pointing to the location of the ship's radio beacon, but it's not. Wait a minute. Yeah, that could be correct. Oh well it better be, cause I'm getting hooked up right now. There's the launch signal. W*hoa!* I'm going! Head pinned back. Halter's away. Off the deck, supposedly due north. On my own. Sinking just a bit, holding my own, nose up ten degrees. On the gauges. No horizon. Hold it, hold it. Got flying speed! I'm accelerating. Cheated death again. I turned right to intercept the 045 degree (northeast) outbound radial. Climbing 4000 feet per minute. Tom should be off in thirty seconds. Ten miles out, twenty, thirty miles out. The distance measuring equipment was working okay. There, established now on the 045-degree radial (according to my instruments). But other instruments weren't adding up. My position indicators weren't agreeing. Level 25,000 feet. There's fifty miles. Set up my left orbit. Nav lights on dim for Tom. (Full bright would blind him when he tried to join on me.) *Don't have a good feeling.* Five minutes. Seven minutes. No Tom. Where the hell is Tom? Geez! My DME (Distance Measuring Equipment gauge) just spun up to 100 miles, then back down to zero, and stayed there! Now I have no way to monitor how many miles I'm out. Gotta call Tom.

"Fast Fleet 505, this is Lead. Where you at Tom?"

"I'm where I should be Rog, dead on the 045 radial. 50 miles out and twenty-five grand. Where are you?"

"Not sure. I may have a problem. Standby." *Goddarn compass.* Wait a minute, lemme try something. *Shit,* that's what I was afraid of. This is not making sense. With where I am (or should be) the needle pointing to the ship's beacon should be directly behind me, but it was off my wing. *If you left Oklahoma, going to Georgia, you know that Ohio should go by on your left side. If it went by on your right side, you couldn't be on course!* According to my navigation instruments, that type of thing was occurring. My high-tech gadgetry was contradicting itself and not meeting a simple test of logic. I double checked "old faithful"—the not-too-accurate but reliable, non-electric "boy scout" compass mounted on the windscreen. It's an original *Spirit of St. Louis* instrument still being installed in every new 757. But it was not agreeing with the new, state-of-the-art gyro-driven electric compass. This is the bad, *two* kinds of trouble at the same time: A *directional* error—my compass system, and combined with that, a *positional* error—my navigation receivers not working properly. I take that back—*three* kinds of trouble! My DME isn't working either, so now I have no way of knowing how many miles I am from the ship! I was in *big* trouble. *Three* instruments were lying to me. My CDI showed me on the 045 degree radial—northeast, which made sense (since I had taken off due north and made a quarter turn to the right). Gotta be near it but couldn't know. I was wings level (which causes an airplane to go straight) but my Directional Gyro showed me slowly turning left! My DME now showed me 117 miles from the ship, but I knew that was crazy. *No telling where I was.* Holy Shit! My first night flight and I'm having the troubles I just described to you a page ago.

I called Tom: "Fastfleet 505, lead here. I've lost all my Nav. You may as well go back to the ship."

Tom answered: "Roger 504, You sure there's nothing I can do?"

"Naw, you'll never find me. I'll get a radar steer back."

At least that was my intention—shouldn't be too difficult for them to find me. Just stay here, keep circling right here. If I stay here, at least I'll know I'm still northeast of the ship and somewhere near 50 miles out. This way the radar guys only have to search the top half (northern area) of their scopes. I switched my exterior lights to full bright. One of the other guys *might* see me. (Hah.) If so, I could join on him and he could lead me back. The one thing I *did* have, was my radios. While I had no way of determining my position, at least I could talk to the ship, explain my predicament, and ask for a steer back to the ship. Remember? From those radar guys back on the ship, listening to music on the Armed Forces radio, munching on midnight snacks and drinking coffee. Once they found my "blip" on their scope they could give me vectors to fly back to the ship.

First things first: *Fuel!* No gas stations in the sky. Pull back the power. Stay at a high altitude where fuel consumption will be less. Only when the muscles in my jaws started cramping, did I realize how tightly I had my teeth clenched. *Relax Rog, relax.* My whole body was tense (and soaked). All alone in the middle of nowhere. All alone in this small capsule zipping through 56-below-zero ethereal blackness. *Time to call the ship for help.*

I called the ship. "Pancake, Pancake, (the ship's call sign). This is Fastfleet 504. How do you read. How do you read?" Silence. Nothing. More silence. *Shit.* "Pancake this is Fastfleet 504 how do you read? Over."

"Aircraft 504, this is Pancake, go ahead."

"Pancake, this is Fastfleet 504, I'm about 50, maybe 60 northeast. Lost all my nav, need a steer back to the ship."

"Say again 504, sorry, busy. What do you need?"

"I need a steer. Lost all my nav. I need a steer back to the ship!"

"Roger 504, Squawk Emergency for fifteen seconds." (This meant switch my aircraft position transmitter to a position that would cause my blip on their scope to appear brighter.)

"Okay. Doing it!" One minute of silence, nothing, still nothing. *Come on you guys!*

"504, say again your approximate position"

"Yeah, Pancake, I'm northeast of the ship. Gotta be. Somewhere near the 045-degree radial, about fifty to maybe eighty miles out."

"Standby, we're changing operators here. We'll be back with you in a couple minutes.

Jesus Christ!

"504 (mumble) this is Pancake, we're not painting your squawk. (mumble) try emergency again."

"Wilco you got it." *(Godammit!)* "And Pancake, you sounded garbled on that last transmission. I had trouble understanding you."

"Yeah 504. Sorry, my mouth was full. Still nothing, are you sure you're southeast? What's your fuel state?"

"No Pancake, not southeast. *Northeast!* I was on the 045-degree radial just ten minutes ago. Couldn't have drifted too far from there. My fuel state is 2,200 pounds...only about forty minutes more." Whew! This thing was getting serious! *Where did they get southeast from? I told them northeast!* They shoulda had me by now. Really black outside. No horizon at all. Even when there is no moon, you still have starlight. (They *do* make a difference.) But tonight, nothing! No moon, no stars, no up, no down.

I could almost *see* the fuel gauges going down. It was October, the water would be cold. Pilots who don't drown in it, freeze in it (in fifteen minutes). I was circling to stay in the place I thought I was. But maybe too much bank. (Takes more power to maintain altitude in a bank—got to shallow the bank angle and save fuel!) Fuel, that's the thing. Power's set at max endurance.

"504, I think I got you, turn due west and hold it."

West? That didn't compute, but: "You got it. I'm turning to—I think a heading of west, but I'm only using my wet compass so the heading may be off just a little."

"We're looking for you. We got a target. Got ya! You're southeast of us 504. Got you eighty miles southeast."

Eighty miles, southeast? *That doesn't compute.* I couldn't have gotten southeast of the ship—no way! I'd launched to the northeast and stayed on that heading. Had to be northeast! Now I *was* getting worried—real worried.

111

"504, turn to the northwest. Fly 330 degrees and we'll bring you in."

"Roger I'm doing it, but I don't like it. Double check. Double check that target on your scope. The position you got on me doesn't compute!"

"Rog 504, are you steady up on 330 degrees now?"

"Yeah, I'm dead-on as best I can tell, but my wet compass is bouncing around in the glass and the light in it is so dim I'm holding my penlight in my mouth." "But close as I can see I'm on 330 degrees."

"504, this is Pancake."

"Yeah, 504 here. Go ahead."

"Uhm, ...um, you still maintaining that northwesterly heading?"

"Affirm, Affirm! Just like you said, 330 degrees, as best I can tell. But I don't like it!"

"Ah, 504, reverse course, turn south to 210 degrees, start letting down to five thousand feet."

"*South!?* 210 degrees? Now you say turn south? You mean now you got me northeast of the ship like I thought?"

"Yeah, yeah. You're north. We got you now."

"What happened, how did you paint me southeast?"

"I thought I had you on the bottom of my scope sir, but it was a speck of mayonnaise."

Once safe back from this white-knuckled flight, having survived it, I think I considered myself "bullet-proof," destined to survive the cruise. The rest of this at sea period went pretty good. Was feeling confident and part of a worthy effort, but not so enthralled that I wasn't looking forward to a break from flight ops and our next in port stay. We'd be arriving in Cannes in eighteen hours.

Chapter Fourteen
THE FRENCH RIVIERA

Wow!

No place in the world would leave a more indelible mark on my life than the Cote d'Azur. Seeing it, feeling it, smelling it, one could never be the same. Who could forget the fresh early mornings; the redolence of freshly baked croissants and café au lait; seeing the men raking the beaches and washing the streets, and the old ladies setting out their flowers on the sidewalks. I know I for one wasn't ready for it. On the outside it was crisp and clean, light blue, golden, and white. Inside it was crimson with sequins and eye shadow. I had been to stateside seaside resorts, but I had never ever been to a place like this. When I think back to it a provocative array of intense and sensual images whir past my eyes. Cannes was an exquisite lady, leaning back on her elbows against the cliffs of south France, exposing her body to the Mediterranean sun, knees drawn up, offering herself to those willing to pay the price.

There was a great deal of excitement as we steamed north toward Cannes. Those who had been here before were more than willing to prepare the first timers. While the ship's PA system played old songs by Edith Piaf and Charles Aznavour, the seasoned voyagers described their previous adventures and romantic encounters. Hearing all this we were lucky some of the young sailors didn't just jump overboard and swim for it. We knew that Cannes was the site of the renowned World Film Festival and a hangout for international cinema celebs. We'd heard about the French movie stars (Brigitte Bardot and Alain Delon), the topless beaches (St. Tropez and Antibes), and the gambling (the Palm Beach Casino). The air was electrified. We were going to be there—smack dab on the Riviera, with who knew what adventures in store for us.

We didn't arrive in the harbor until almost midnight. When the anchor chain made its usual bone-jarring plunge, half the ship was on the flight deck ogling the shoreline's twinkling night lights. You could just imagine the music and laughter. As usual we were mooring a mile out—directly off the hotel beaches. A real paradox we were—this bunch of crew-cut regimented worker bees inside their huge gray hive, about to come face to face with a complete lack of discipline. Talk about "off the turnip truck." Good thing we didn't realize our naiveté. If we would have known how outclassed we were going to be, we might not have been so hip on venturing ashore. I hit the rack, anxious for the morning.

Saturday 0900 hours: This was going to be a good group: Bob Harmon, the "Goffer" (Don Goft), Nick Cassopolis, Mike Ballard, and yours truly. If there was a liberty party to be in this was it. (Seriously doubted there would be any museum trips for us.) Bob and Don were tall and good-looking, and always an asset. Nick with his dashing good looks and flashing smile was a good magnet to have in the group. And Mike had the chase in his blood and would find himself venturing out frequently. Major Burnham (my boss) never recognized the extent to which he didn't fit in and unilaterally attached himself to our party. I think the plan was to play along for a respectable time, and then lose him when the sun went down.

It was a brilliant postcard morning with clear skies and sparkling colors. The liberty boat was quickly eating up the distance to the dock. Unable to take my eyes off the magnificent view of the shoreline, I reached out like a blind man—groping for the gunnel to steady myself against the boat's jolting. The closer we got, the whiter and more luxurious appeared our destination—the beautiful and prestigious *Marina de Cannes!* And of course, it didn't let us down, picturesque and replete with multi-decked yachts and large sailing vessels.

The engines cut back our boat swung nicely against the seawall at the far side of the marina. I felt a little apprehensive clambering up onto the dock, already sensing that we could well be uninvited guests. We falteringly made our way past a panorama of dazzling white hulls, lacquered teak decks, colorful pennants, shining stainless and gleaming brass; passing only a few yards from the privileged people and their valuable possessions. (Much closer than I would have imagined ordinary citizenry would be allowed.) On the stern decks the proud owners and their guests (in navy blazers and coral ascots) were casually seated or draped just right on pastel deck cushions. Twirling their glasses and throwing their heads back, they seemed to me to be laughing and joking artificially (almost for our benefit). On almost every boat, at their feet lay one or two strange looking dogs that appeared equally aware of their station in life. If this place wasn't going to be prohibitively expensive, I would be surprised.

I had my first exposure to the melodious and manipulative *langue Francais;* an obviously superior method of communicating (if the demeanor of those wielding it were any measure). I was worried about what my voice would sound like. Bountiful as it was I would discover Cannes was not that anxious to welcome Americans, particularly those who did not speak French. The mile long, immaculate and arcing grand avenue in front of the big hotels was called La Croisette. This beautifully manicured, divided boulevard bordered a long and carefully gussied beach. It boasted three separate lines of hundred-foot tall Royal Palms. One along the sidewalk in front of the hotels, one on the center median between the opposing traffic lanes, and one along the raised walkway (the Esplanade) that ran the length of the beach. The traffic crawled by to see and be seen: black Porsches, silver Jags, and open red Mercedes. All occupied by well-tanned handsome men and alluring women behind dark glasses, who seemed dedicated to taking little notice of the foot-bound population. We walked the half-mile long La Croisette from end to end—several times, never quite being able to become part of the revelry; instead I suspect, continuing to appear to be just what we were—overwhelmed gawking aliens.

From the elevated esplanade alongside La Croisette we ogled the beach below. The women-watching was of dizzying proportions. There appeared to be little doubt these jeweled and lotioned females had come to be seen. They coyly maneuvered to attract any male who might have them in sight. Everything was a charade of vanity. They strutted, sat, bent over, turned, and crossed and uncrossed their legs artfully. Each apparently innocent movement designed for effect—to produce the best possible exposure of the parts of their anatomy of which they were the most proud. But this was the south of France and this was what they did best. One of the guys said, "All of Europe can't be like this. Who would ever live in the States?"

Most in their 30's, but many in their 40's or 50's—*even 60's,* the vainest of all women came here to flaunt. They caught your eye and stared you down. Never had I seen so many apparently refined women wearing such outlandishly undersized shorts and bikinis (along with all manner of raffish bangles—to include seductively draped gold waist chains). Even in the hotel lobbies when these bodies were more appropriately clothed, it was an arousing exhibition. And I must admit the European men hanging around this beach were no slouches either, though they all looked the same: imposing heads of wavy black or salonized silver hair, bright red silk shirts open to the navel, white slacks, and blue suede moccasins. (Not a single guy was wearing socks. Guess that's the fashion.) On the beaches, they strutted their stuff, their muscular abdomens well exposed and their thin nylon bathing suits leaving little to the imagination. These men were not at all embarrassed about advertising their bodies. (And I'm sure they didn't have to be home at midnight like we did.)

There were three big hotels: The Carlton, stately and sovereign it was obviously the most exclusive. It towered well above adjacent structures and there for mere mortals to ogle from a safe distance. A half block down— the Miramar, which also was no average lodging. Another two blocks, the Martinez Hotel, where we might have been able to afford a room. All three had large hedge-bordered terraces in front, for dining and special affairs.

On the water side of La Croisette, every hotel had its own private beach with showers and change-rooms underneath the elevated esplanade. Barely any sand was visible, just wall-to-wall chaises and umbrellas. Bow-tied attendants squirted between the bright cushions and towels, ready to bring an iced Cinzano or a steaming cappuccino. For another hour (and what a crude foreign sight we must have been) we plodded up and down the bricked esplanade above and bordering the beach, taking in the brilliant aquamarine and gold, and spellbound by the endless glistening copper carpet of shameless female sunbathers below. We were like the proverbial rabbits in a lettuce patch. Never had any of us seen on display so many well-tanned and well-oiled curves. It was public eroticism. I personally—painfully aware of my own masculine deficiency, was unable not to envy the confident gigolos just waiting to pounce (and had no doubt about what their capabilities).

Finally, feeling like the absolute voyeurs we were we decided to take a break. Some went to check out the beach shops, others to explore up the hill behind the hotels (into the real world of dry cleaners and grocery stores). I chose up the hill, returning thirty minutes later with a strange cache: a pair of hardwood shoe trees, a neat tortoiseshell hood emblem for a Ferrari, and a pair of gray suede Italian loafers. (The last representing the first part of my future Continental disguise.) We met back on La Croisette at one o'clock and decided it was time to tackle lunch. As boldly as we could (now well aware of our limitations) we set out to find a friendly place to do this.

Outside and below La Croisette, on each hotel beach, was a restaurant where sun worshippers could take the noon meal and get their rays at the same time. Under umbrellas an array of small tables with pastel-colored linens were set to accommodate the most discriminating patrons. Since there were about ten hotels there were ten of these restaurants, side by side, spanning almost the whole length of the Cannes beach (separated only by colored ribbons). Leaning over the railing on the esplanade we peered down at the sea of flamboyant diners. Large-mouthed and sun-glassed women of status were tossing their heads about and sending out throaty laughter. It was not immediately apparent where we would fit in best (if anywhere). We finally picked the lemon and turquoise restaurant belonging to the Miramar, stoked up our courage and invaded it.

It was a delightful lunch. Avocado stuffed with shrimp then a croissant sandwich of shaved country ham and melted cheese (and authentic Dijon mustard), and then for a *postre*, the world-famous *Fraises a la creme—* strawberries and fresh cream. All of which was abundantly washed down with ice cold Amstels. The food and the surroundings were great, but this was my first experience with service in a French restaurant. I have sampled it many times since and my opinion remains the same: The waiters are there at their own convenience, preset to their own speed, at serious odds with both the management and the diners, dedicated to the art of showing complete disregard if not disdain. All of which (according to the unwritten rules) the diner feigns not to notice, and then upon leaving, professes to have enjoyed immensely. During this lunch (with all the nearby female diners half naked) I couldn't help noticing a lady at the next table in an ankle-length dress. She had long dark hair and fair skin, and was reserved and gracious in her actions. One time I think I caught her looking straight at us (probably in disbelief), but hard to tell since she too wore those super-sized dark glasses.

Afterwards, back up on La Croisette we were getting that downer that follows a couple beers at lunch. I knew I for one could use a nap, especially if we were going to be back here tonight. Jim suggested we get a hotel room convenient to the beach, where we could rest or change clothes without having to go back to the carrier. A couple guys agreed and left to do just that. Below us on the beach we heard some music coming from a circular, thatched roof bar. It was presently surrounded by fifteen or twenty of the previously mentioned beautiful people, who all seemed to be reveling in brazen social indulgence. Didn't know about the other guys, but I was feeling a little inadequate. Our JC Penney sport shirts and polyester trousers had looked reasonable when we got into the liberty boat, but here on the beach, we looked like a delegation from the Country of the Nerds. I was afraid if we went down there we would likely be no more than the recipients of dismissive glances.

Still—down we went. We weren't the brunt of any dismissive glances, but in a way it was even worse. Sitting only two yards from them we couldn't have been less noticed if we were transparent. Engaged in thespian-like orations and then exaggerated laughter, they acted completely unaware of their recently arrived audience. I've since learned, on the Continent this behavior is called "theater" (and it's endemic in France). We set about rating the bikinis. And there was some assortment: white silk, gold lame, knitted with pearls and sequins. All of ridiculously inadequate coverage; many being worn by women—who based on their age and body type, you would have thought would not have been caught dead in something like that.

Ordering and sipping our drinks we were complete aliens. My preparation for all this was two years in the Boy Scouts and three paper routes. I looked exactly like what I was: "Just off the ship." We spent the waning hours of the afternoon there watching the crowd thin out. (Many I'm sure, to hotel rooms for ardent "afternoon delights" while we told old jokes.) We saw our share of topless bathers but agreed the farce and taunts of the preposterously dressed (underdressed) older women strolling the esplanade and staring you down, were the best. I was toying with the idea of maybe doing some exploring on my own, but Major Burnham was already organizing a dinner party at a special restaurant he was touting. What the hell—these are the guys I live and work with. I'll stick with the group. Secretly I wondered if I had the courage to split and test the waters on my own. If so, it would have to be after a rest. I was ready to collapse now and it was only five. Got two hours rest in our new hotel room. We'd meet at Le Bistro at seven-thirty.

My First Night in Cannes

Have to admit the dinner at Le Bistro was great. Major Burnham insisted that everybody try the onion soup. Had my first Chateau Briande and first taste of Béarnaise sauce, and a bottle of old Bordeaux. If I wasn't hooked on Europe at 3 this afternoon, I was a goner now. And it felt good to be with the guys and doing something normal. About ten-thirty, the day's accumulated fatigue overtook us and the party broke up. I was alone. I started back down La Croisette, past the Carlton which seemed to be cautioning passersby *Think it over very carefully before you start up my steps*. And I'll admit, I for one wasn't ready to challenge it. In its circular drive was a line of expensive cars, spilling out the *creme de la creme*. Past it. Past the Miramar. *Hey, what kind of music is that?* Great sounds were wafting up the street from the Martinez.

I jogged to the Martinez not wanting to miss another minute of it. The large terrace in front was surrounded by a tall hedge. Peeking through it I was surprised to see only twenty or thirty people in formal attire. A live group on a small stage (set up under the awning where dinner had been served) were singing their brains out, and in English! A funny looking set of kids with weird hairdos. I didn't see an entrance into the terrace so I squeezed through the hedge. No one anywhere to collect any money; must be the last throes of a private function. Although they only did one more song, the melody was infatuating, with delightful lyrics. I was humming what I had never heard before, joining in on the simple chorus and clapping my hands, as was everyone else. Much to everyone's disappointment, after a failed effort for a curtain call it came to an end. If I was any judge *this* group was going places. I'd never heard of them: a new group from England. Most if not all of the crowd disappeared in a matter of minutes and the terrace was all but deserted. Invigorated by the music, but weary from the day's activities I collapsed into a chair at one of the empty tables.

At a nearby table (the only one occupied on the now-abandoned terrace) I spied the dark haired, well-dressed woman who had been next to us at lunch. I wasn't expecting it, but when she gave me a pleasant greeting, I shocked myself by voicing a response. *Uh Oh*, with a smile she motioned me to join her. Shocked at doing so I managed to hesitantly join her. A waiter came and we ordered drinks. I felt reasonably chic ordering a Ricard liqueur in a cute little ceramic pitcher (that I had seen someone do earlier in the day). She asked what I was doing in Cannes. Before I had a chance to think of some adventuresome tale to embellish my station in life, it was out—the plain truth. And a good thing too; we hadn't fooled anyone earlier in the day. She had known we were off the carrier, and in perfect English began an interesting conversation. She was not one of the kind we had ogled all afternoon.

She seemed pleased to be talking to an American. She was French by birth, had married an American, and was now divorced or widowed (never got that clear). Her last name was Kennedy. What's more, her first name was Jacqueline! She added she had met the real Jacqueline Kennedy at a New York Art Association benefit. And she herself owned an art gallery on Fifth Avenue, with an apartment above it, where she resided most of the year. She was still dressed in that high neck dress—its collar turned up nearly to her cheek bones. It was hard to guess her age since even now she was wearing tinted glasses. We talked and she made me feel very comfortable. We spoke about the JFK assassination and the controversial Warren Commission report. At last I was engaged in a less deceptive activity, and it was good not to feel guilty. Throughout, our repartee was respectable and without any innuendos.

Wilted there head down, I glanced at my watch and realized the last liberty boat had departed five minutes ago, while at the same time hearing her say: "Well, young man, shall we make our exit"? Even in the midst of the shock in hearing it, I was pretty sure I knew what she meant. I had not expected it and had no interest at all in ending up somewhere alone with her, (I hadn't for a second harbored the thought of any type of moving encounter with her.) Everything else happening today had been a game, and up to this point with her, just an innocent conversation between two strangers. I hadn't considered this outcome. I was not prepared to answer, but I did. It was almost as if there was no option, responding negatively would maybe even have been an effrontery. I weakly smiled and stammered the affirmative, in spite of a frightful awareness of what I was likely agreeing to. *Could I have just been so flattered by her proposal?* My confusion must have been apparent, but she appeared to take no notice of it, or to my lukewarm acceptance of what was likely an opportunity to be relished.

She rose, turned towards the entrance to the foyer and reached back for my hand. I took it. What was I doing? *Rog, what's happening here!?* During the journey Jacqueline continued to smile with sweet anticipation. My stomach was churning and I couldn't get Sara's face out of my mind's eye. At the door to her room. I watched as she entered and flicked the switch on a small, fringe-shaded table lamp. From what I could see; as externally grandiose as the hotels were, the rooms (at least this one) were not large or modern. Uneasy and uncertain, I scanned the dimly lit room. It was as if we were in her private dwelling. And I was almost right. "Yes Cheri, it's mine. Stays locked up all year. I only use it for my summer holidays." Not only was the room small, it was crowded with large personal furnishings, including a ceiling-height dark teak armoire, an old roll-top desk, a brass-strapped antique trunk, and low black marble table.

She sat down in the only chair in the room. I remained standing. How long would I have to stay and how would I be able to leave politely? I scanned the room for a small bar, some alcohol or glasses; make it a nightcap. I had no idea of what to say or do. I guessed if I were to play the part I'd allowed myself to audition for (and got), now was the time she would be expecting me to walk over and take her in my arms. No way I was going to do that. If I did there'd be no chance of changing the direction it is undoubtedly going. My thinking was disjointed and without answers.

She got up and started straight for me, pressing herself firmly against me—head to toe. She was now kissing me full mouth! A long kiss. Done, she stepped back, never taking her eyes off me, *and began undressing!* I had no intention of doing likewise. In the limited light I observed her nude body. She wasn't as tall as I had thought, and perhaps a little fuller than I had noticed. Her thickening waist and not-so-round buttocks gave away her years. She was older than I was, that was evident. Her skin was pure white; an apparently finely cared-for lady. She did not seem to take note that I was still dressed.

Completely naked, she turned, pulled down the spread, climbed onto the bed and beckoned me with both arms. Talk about one confused male. I was frozen. She looked directly at me and allowed her knees to spread, and again motioned me to join her. No alternate action came to mind and I reluctantly (frightfully) lowered myself to sit on the far edge of the bed. With both hands she reached over and pulled me down alongside her. Never mind I'm fully dressed (still wearing my shoes). It may have been the softest bed I'd ever been in, sinking terribly in the middle. I was becoming mired in a cloth sex pit. *I would have given anything to be back on the ship.*

The room seemed warmer by the minute. My plight was pretty much destined when I let her take my hand on the terrace. It was all my fault. On the terrace I could have said no—feigning sorrow, claiming some excuses—which I certainly had. First of course—me being married, and then if it were to come to it: me not being able to perform. She pulled me over on top of her, locked her arms over me and begin a kissing the likes of which I had never experienced (or seen). This must be occurring in that parallel universe. To avoid the certain outcome of this; to extricate myself now, would be impossible, though I continued to do nothing. I took no action to indicate a desire or intention to proceed with that which was surely expected. She was not dissuaded, sighing and saying—I guess, sweet things in French; every other word being *cheri.*

She had to be wondering why I hadn't leaped out of bed pulled off my shoes, shed my trousers, and climbed back in on top of her. She had to be questioning what the hell I was waiting for. She let her knees fall wide apart, the insides of her open thighs were wet and shining. She began tossing her head from side to side while exhorting me. But once again and as usual, I was not physically responding to her heated female efforts; not in the slightest. I'd like to say, strictly because of the weight of my guilt as a married man, but my thoughts were equally of my failure with Connie in Minnesota and with my wife on my wedding night and most usually thereafter. I felt no desire, no heat in my loins, not even the beginnings. I became more sweaty and more and more concerned. In spite of being full of reluctance, any healthy male would have risen to the task. But not me. There was no question she was ready, but I was not. (Perhaps a blessing in disguise.) Even were I desirous of doing so, presently I would not be able. I didn't know if I was more disheartened or relieved by the condition.

I knew I had to do something; couldn't disappoint her completely. In desperation I pressed my fully clothed pelvis against her mound and began a series of rhythmic upward motions, hoping that would cause her to lose focus on what she was waiting for that wasn't happening. Without reaching it myself, thankfully and surprisingly I felt her reach hers. She let out a long crying moan and locked her legs straight out. I was smothered in her arms, mercifully not asking me to explain why I had just done what I did. She confronted me with the fact that she knew I had not "taken my pleasure." She said she couldn't sleep, could not go on, until—in her words, she had "killed me" (evidently not realizing I was already mentally and physically dead).

I laid flat on my back, stunned, completely drained; all but overcome with deserved regret, and the familiar chagrin of my inability. Jacqueline positioned herself into a half sitting position against the headboard and pulled me upwards to join her there. Once there she took my head in her hands and guided it over onto her large and soft white breast. Holding it there, she stroked my head and whispered to me in French. I was more than tired. I was a wreck. My mental clutch was slipping. If I didn't sleep soon, I'd be hallucinating. I was able to pull out one of the too-thick pillows and inch her down until we were almost lying flat. In that position and after an extended time of deserved torment, I finally lapsed into a state of semi consciousness; dreams awash with undecipherable disjointed scenarios (other than a constant theme of distress). I didn't feel good about anything. I could not shake that I knew I was where I shouldn't be. Finally—mercifully, I slipped off into a deeper and less fitful slumber.

I woke up with a start, a headache and moderate nausea. Nightstand clock showed slightly after three. Jacqueline was breathing heavily and didn't stir. Though I felt very ungentlemanly about it, I slid from the bed and quietly stole out the door. I wanted to get as far from the scene as fast as I could. As if distance itself could erase my shameful activities. All I could think of was a long, hot shower, and a couple hours of real sleep. I went quietly down the deserted hallway, down two flights of steps, a quick trot to an emergency exit, around the side and onto the abandoned terrace. But still not feeling any better. Outside, I found the "exquisite lady" was now deserted. La Croisette was bathed in silence under the soft sodium light of the frond-muted streetlamps. Not a single thing moving. I jogged the half mile to the dock and asked the Shore Patrol guy to let me ride back to the ship on their next shift-change (the saving grace for those dragging themselves to the dock after midnight). Mercifully they let me onboard the next boat.

I was able to get into my stateroom without waking Jim. Left my soiled clothes in a damp pile on the floor. Back out and down the passageway to the "head" (the Navy word for the shower and toilets). I felt like I was the only thing moving on the ship. Scrubbed myself. Back to the room. Quiet. Didn't want to wake up Jim. No teeth-brushing, but one long mouthful of Lavoris. Into the rack. Tired and weary but unable to sleep, I lay there wondering what had I let happen? Could I convince myself this was something happening in a parallel universe? *Not* be a part of my real life; not be a blemish on me as a married man? Just a necessary experiment. Perhaps but not likely. Could spending that time with Ardith, and now having found myself in a strange woman's bed, mean this Mediterranean cruise—far away, alone and with no witnesses, be allowing me the opportunity to taste that other life, and search for that one woman with the right chemistry? *But if so, and I were to find it or her, what then?*

Back on Board

It was two remorseful days on the ship before I could muster the courage to think about going ashore. Everything there is to see and do in Cannes and I ended up in a tiny dark hotel room with an older woman. All those other activities (whatever they are), and I ended up like that. Do I even know how to just plain recreate? Or if I am going to end up with a female companion, why can't it be like the other guys, just an innocent afternoon or inconsequential peccadillo with some American college student. Between my nonsensical campaign in Rome and now this first night in Cannes, I was worried—*real* worried. I was pretty sure the night with Jacqueline was a one-and-done. Remembering my times with Ardith though, left me wondering.

Second day—0730 hours. Gotta get up. Jim was in a hurry to do something but had a project for me. Whatever it is I've got to be sure it's taken care of. I've got to perform. I've got to pay the piper. I've got to be worth my salt, especially in Jim's eyes. My day's project was engraving and installing twelve CAUTION placards in the cockpit, announcing the possible non-functioning of an over-speed protection circuit. This caused me to be seen round and about, which was good. Made it appear I was at least on the job. Had a good lunch and set about visiting the shops. I was able to review at least a dozen worksheets in each shop, edit the ones that needed editing (almost all of them) and therefore help my guys zero-in on the corrective action that would be needed. Also was able to help sort out personal problems several of the men were having with their pay or other issues. I was gratified to see how much it was appreciated.

A Squadron Mascot, One Big German Girl

The next morning I was on the flight deck squinting at the Cannes shoreline glinting in the morning sun, waiting for the next liberty boat. Almost the same group as the first day: Bob, Don, Nick, Mike, and I. (No Major Burnham this time.) First thing on the schedule, visit the local shops and purchase some souvenirs to mail home. Finished with that we strolled to the Miramar, and having brought our swimwear with us this time we actually went into the water (which it appeared the local sun-worshippers thought was a completely unnecessary beach activity). We played water polo and volleyball—were so darned All-American and clean cut, it was pitiful. We were able to act like we weren't all but overcome by the salacious vistas in every direction. Paid way too much for an hour on water skis at the famous Martinez Beach *Ski Nautique*, but it was worth the price—we met Erica!

Erica was one big (about 5ft 9), noticeably healthy (chesty) German girl. A good-looking flaming redhead, about 30 years old, with what I guess some people may have called large hips and thighs. Freckles everywhere and a smile that made you melt. (And unlike Jacqueline, she certainly held the potential of being that woman with the right chemistry!) She had just shown up at the ski boat ramp and started a cute teasing banter with the five of us. No timid soul this one I could see. She wore a modest bikini but had a body whose most eye appealing parts were not able to be masked. She rode in the back of the tow boat, laughing heartily each time one of us undertook a stunt and wiped-out. It was looking like we just might have found a great female companion for this in-port stay. At one time, two older European guys came by and spoke with her a few minutes; couldn't tell if one of them was a boyfriend. Didn't seem so. Surprisingly to all of us she accepted our invitation to join us for lunch.

At lunch, one of the guys posed the idea of us all going to the Palm Beach Casino that night and win big. And the surprising good news was that Erica wanted in. And I was afraid, from her enthusiastic response that she might have the gambling bug. Oops, too bad for Bob. Major Burnham spied us, came over and asked him if he would go back to the ship and check on travel arrangements for the major's skiing trip to Garmisch, in December. *"Now? This afternoon, you want me to do this right now?"* Bob certainly wasn't wild about it, but the Major didn't give him any choice. The Major (who used to live next door to Mike back in the states) then asked Mike about his wife and kids, and Mike shortly excused himself. Twenty minutes later, after the strawberries and cream (again), Don Goft (almost never seen without Bob) also left. Nick had separated earlier, having been personally invited onto the private yacht of some rich Greek over here. By chance, I was the lucky recipient of these developments. By default I had ended up alone with Erica. If I was ever going to look for that one woman, Erica certainly met the initial qualifications.

Sitting there in her company, to all outward appearances I was as qualified as the local studs, and was beginning to consider that I could actually become a bona fide part of the "scene," even though I had yet to be a final player. She continued to talk about trying the roulette wheel that night. In fact, I was beginning to think she meant *we* should try it— together. Thinking ahead to this eventuality, before they left I had managed to borrow thirty bucks from Bob, and twenty from Mike, besides what they left as their share of the tab for lunch. (And based on the tab it's a good thing we enjoyed it as much as we did.) Don had said he thought he had some extra cash in our recently acquired squadron hotel room.

Erica's sexy green eyes, wide mouth and big body had all my attention (and every guy's for six tables in every direction). I'm thinking she's got to be just wasting some time with me; certainly she has better things to do (which turned out to be half true). I didn't think she would stay with me much longer. She showed me some old photos in her wallet. She told me about an American baseball player she had met here last spring. It was a well-known major leaguer whose familiar name I won't mention. It was two-thirty. We'd had a lot of sun. I felt good, but didn't need more beach time, but had no idea for the next activity. Fortunately, Erica asks me if I would like to go meet her friend. "Sure, why not." Would you believe, I'm strolling down La Croisette with my own huge-titted European female.

Her friend was staying in a high rise a little further down La Croisette, and was one of the guys who had stopped by at the beach. He was playing cards with another guy on the balcony. He may have been a permanent resident or here on vacation. I think it was his place alone. Erica gave no indication of having a room there or any belongings on the premises. His name was Fritz and he was German that was for sure. His companion was French. While neither one looked real successful, they weren't acting like money was a problem either. I couldn't tell if Erica knew Fritz from Germany or met him here. I think from Germany. Both guys were in their forties and were of small stature. For once I wasn't the smallest guy in the room. They were both balding, wearing open-necked sport shirts, smoking (a lot), and nursing drinks. Erica introduced me. Fritz didn't appear at all jealous. (I had been worried about that aspect of things.) While at first he didn't look thrilled to see me, he shortly relaxed and was quite sociable. He told me to have Erica fix me a drink. Though I didn't feel like drinking, the process would at least give us something to do. Erica fixed me a red-colored drink in a tall glass. It had a strange taste—bitter, but good; hard to describe. It was my first Campari-soda.

Erica started reading a slick French fashion magazine while I did my imitation of a guy standing awkwardly in the middle of a room. She motioned to me to go talk to Fritz. *Great! I can see Fritz is waiting for that.* Both guys were leaning on the balcony railing and talking seriously in low tones. I felt like I had stumbled in on some kind of plot, like they should have been wearing shoulder holsters and poring over the floor plan of a bank. I knew I couldn't talk to the French guy, I'd have to speak to Fritz (who had spoken to Erica in English). I was so far out of my element, to have any credibility at all I would just have to admit my status and talk about the things I knew. A good decision. They had already guessed I was an American off the ship. Fritz wasn't a big fan of the US military and I had to downplay our role over here. They both looked preoccupied, and I suggested to Erica that we step out for a breath of air. She agreed.

I made the mistake in describing our upcoming jaunt, of indicating we could "do a little shopping." It was thirty minutes and 300 Francs later that I got her out of a neat little accessory shop. *Damn.* Had a feeling I was going to need that cash later. But the good news, evidently it's true that buying stuff for women *works.* There was a marked increase in our proximity after the belt and earrings were in the bag. We were now strolling hand in hand. And I had a *lot* in my hand I can tell you. We passed several guys from the ship, and they gave me some "Holy Shit" looks. (It was hard not to gloat.) A dinner date never got arranged. I think she intended that it wouldn't. But, are you ready for this: She made me promise to meet her at the Palm Beach Casino at nine! I told her she could count on it. In our squadron hotel room I met the "Goffer" and got almost thirty bucks worth of Francs from him. Jogged back to the boat dock and caught the first launch back to the ship. I had time to lie down for an hour and get a good meal. Had no idea how this evening with Erica would shape up.

The Palm Beach Casino

I was surprised and a little worried, out of the four bold guys at lunch, not one was ready to try the casino. Me, I had a date—had to go. It may not have been Monte Carlo, but for me it was more than enough. Just like in the James Bond movies; lots of tuxedos and floor length dresses. Me? I was wearing a hieroglyphic print Egyptian linen blazer that I had bought when I was stationed in Japan. It was either a powerful fashion statement or tacky as hell. (The guy who ordered it didn't have the nerve to pick up.) I climbed the fifty-foot wide, brass-edged marble steps, through the columns, past the guards, and to Reception to show my passport. Yeah, I did have my passport. Lucky for me, just as I was leaving the ship one of the guys told me that you needed your passport to get into the place.

One of the casino staff at the far side of the entrance gave me a wave of approval, which made me feel even better (knowing how little I deserved it). In fact it was almost a "Hi." Things *were* looking up. The money I had managed to collect was wadded in my pocket. I touched it to reassure myself, though I had the feeling it would not be there long. I was through the door and in! *So far so good folks.* Large carved oak archways, high ceilings, huge frescos and tapestries on the walls; lots of highly polished, lustrous woodwork and paneling; wall to wall oriental carpeting throughout. I was in what was just the first of several gambling areas. There appeared to be at least two large main rooms and some sort of recessed private gaming alcove, protected from prying eyes by an intricate mahogany latticework. (It kind of said the same thing to me as the Carlton had: *"Think carefully before venturing in."*) Considering that people were winning and losing thousands by the minute, it was pretty quiet. No moans, no cheers, no cussing, only hushed comments.

Spied Erica at the *Cachet d'Argent,* surrounded by at least six guys. How was I gonna get in there? I'd be surprised if they were speaking English, probably French or German. (Erica spoke perfect French.) What luck, she saw me, and what's more—right in front of my wondrous eyes she was excusing herself and coming my way. This was too good to be true. To contrast her rust colored hair she was wearing a Kelly green ankle length gown. She was a knock-out! Once again it was as if I had been assigned a part in a script. In no way was I capable of achieving this in reality. I was going to need a lot of luck this evening. I was in over my head, again (but maybe experiencing the beginning of that new and exciting life I was destined for).

Everything went great, though I wouldn't have been able to carry it off, had she not been on my arm almost constantly, and surprisingly giving me lots of attention. (A doorman once told me: "The best credentials in the world, is a beautiful woman on your arm. You'll get in anywhere.") Erica was my credentials in the Casino. Seeing her on my arm, no one screwed with us. Even the usually rude croupiers were passably respectful. I got bolder and bolder, which in turn caused her to fawn and coo all the more. *"Wow Ma, look at me now."*

The downside of all this was that we were in a gambling house and Erica was bound to want to try her luck, and likely with my money (more accurately—the whole squadron's money). But she was *not* inconsiderate. She was actually concerned about our losses; acted as if she knew I was there on a shoestring (but never voiced it). In fact she cashed a check of her own. *Checks!* I did have one with me but was already thinking how a cancelled check from a casino would look back home. Mostly she made small bets, which helped. But she made a lot of them. One time we had a minor streak going on the wheel. We were playing the 20's, the even and odd 20's—all *ten* of them, on *every* spin. We won about six times in a row—had a big pile of chips in front of us. In fact, more than I thought we had won. Good, I saw her pocket a couple of the largest denomination chips, probably for safe keeping (for the comeback we would likely have to stage after blowing our present winnings).

I had a drink in my hand the whole evening. Don't know how many I had. Never felt tipsy. Actually in this place I might have looked too young to drink. Erica smoked, which was hard to believe with her gleaming white teeth. Maybe she just smoked on these occasions. We slipped away from the activity, over to an eighteenth-century brocade loveseat. It was right next to that private alcove I had seen earlier. She waved at two men who were in there playing some weird game. One of them was Fritz. Erica explained the Baccarat game to me. Not for the meek. High stakes in there.

It was then that the 500-Franc chips came out of her purse. Four of them! She giggled. I had only seen her take two. We were in better shape than I thought. What's more, she gave me two of them—as a gift! A helluva gift considering they were worth about $100 apiece. Boy, would I like to hide one of these babies somewhere, and sneak it out at the end of the evening. If I can hang on to even one of these—nothing more, I'll at least be solvent in the morning. *Please God.* We tried other tables and other games. She was always by my side and kissed me often. I have *no* idea why. And she didn't care in front of who. *Keerist, what a night!* We were in and out of chips so much I never knew where we stood. Most the chips were in her bag most the time. Somehow, we got way ahead several times, and believe it or not (I was impressed) she went to the cashier and cashed out, twice! Usually gamblers don't do that. She stuffed a bunch of money in her purse both times. I'll bet she'll remember *this* evening. Maybe just maybe I'm bringing her good luck.

The gambling gods were with us is all I can say. And I *did* manage to stash away one of the big chips. I hadn't let Erica see me hide it. I would come back tomorrow and cash it in. Didn't want her to know I couldn't afford to lose. Erica was good to me. Real affectionate; going where I wanted to go; doing what I wanted to do; standing when I felt like standing, sitting when I felt like sitting. I had never in my life been the recipient of such respectful, let alone beautiful, sexy female company. We were a good couple and you couldn't miss us in there (at least *her*). You might well imagine I was unable not to frequently wince thinking of how my evening's activities would play back home.

A little while later, after checking her watch, Erica indicated the evening was over and we were on our way out. What's next? Where are we going? Maybe I should have gotten a hotel room. Don't know if she has one or is staying with Fritz. (I tried to coax it out of her several times during the evening, but never got an answer.) She knows I'm on the ship, and if I'm planning on spending the night on it, this might be the time to split. No way of knowing what's going to happen yet, but I can suppose (and just sit here and let it). The lingering guilt of my recent late-night incident here in Cannes was still haunting me; might as well start worrying right now, on both counts.

Couldn't believe how easily we got out of there and away from her two friends. They saw us leaving—came out of the Baccarat room, shook hands and asked how we did. Fritz was real friendly. Erica gave him two of the big chips she still had, a quick hug, and then they said good night. (He got the best of that deal!) Out the main entrance. Saw that guy again, the one who waved to me going in. Now I recognized him—it was the Frenchman from Fritz's apartment earlier in the afternoon. Erica didn't seem to notice him. Even away from the group she kept giving me kisses and squeezes. We were out, down the steps and into a limo in two shakes. But we hadn't yet established *where* we were going. We'd gone about 100 yards when the driver slides open the privacy glass, looks over his shoulder and asks me for directions. Unable not to reflect on my status as a married man, and my recent episode with Jacqueline and remembering what took place (or didn't take place) and how I felt afterwards, I had serious mixed emotions and faltered, uttering nothing in response to his question. Fortunately in the midst of my uncertainty Erica shouted something in French and we were off. At least she had a plan, and I was ill-prepared to object to anything.

A Place Not Frequented by Ordinary People

Five minutes later we were being dropped off in front of a small, ultra-modern but darkened, apparently private club, right across La Croisette from the *Palais des Festivals* (where each summer they hold that famous Cannes Film Festival). A bunch of SL's, Jags, unknown Italian sports cars and stretch limos were double-parked in front of the club. You might imagine I was getting worried. I'd pulled off the casino bit, but I was sure—here, I had a good chance of being exposed for what I was. We found a small unlit and unmarked door. Opened it and entered. Once through it I had even more reason to feel out of place. The door opened onto the center of a two-foot-high platform that spanned the entire front of the room—a makeshift stage apparently still set up from an earlier presentation. Two steps inside and *Bam!* fifty sets of eyeballs were on us. Likely, to come through those doors you were supposed to *be* somebody. *Two steps inside and there was no one in the place that wasn't looking at us.*

The dimensions of the club were unusual: quite deep front to back, but only about twenty feet wide. Just a few yards in front of the stage was the first row of a sea of at least thirty small round tables, wedged tightly together—with no aisle; no way to proceed further. *We were stuck.*

Floor to ceiling mirrors ran the length of both side walls and the rear wall, doubling the impact of all the formal jackets, shiny lapels, black ties, sequined dresses, high coiffures and sparkling jewelry. There were all kinds of international cinema memorabilia hanging about, but not a seat in the house! The place was jam-packed. We were stranded on the only free floor space there was, still under unanimous scrutiny.

But fortunately I had those best credentials: Erica on my arm. One glance at her and the waiters immediately began yanking tables around (practically pulling chairs out from under people), brushing crumbs, dumping ashtrays, and smoothing new table clothes. *Bingo!* We were seated. I knew that this kind of treatment required the maximum tip. The first thing my hand hit in my pocket was the 500 Franc chip I had saved. I don't know if I thought it would be cute, or if I didn't think at all. I'm not sure. I pressed the rectangular slab of plastic in his hand. We're talking a big tip—around one hundred U.S. dollars. We're talking stupidity! Erica had seen it and looked momentarily startled, then reached out, grabbed it back and pressed a couple fifty Franc notes in his hand. Everything was okay except I was a little embarrassed. Erica brushed it off, smiled invitingly, lit a cigarette, reached across the table and took my arm. I'm thinking, this can't last, *why me? What does she have in mind?* We had our laughs, coffee, a great dessert called Crème Brulée, a couple liqueurs, and at last (finally) after what seemed like twenty-four hours together it was time to call it a night.

And Now What

We were at the cutting edge. I knew *I* was the one who should make a suggestion, but I didn't. I was absent any motivation, knowing it was now I should begin making my excuses, while at the same time waiting to see what idea she might have. No, I don't believe it—we *were* going to spend the night together. In fact, from the way it was handled, she may have never considered otherwise. *Will I never learn?* With a few positive thoughts, but greater uncertainty, I was ending up with an outcome that just about anyone else would have predicted (and mightily appreciated)! And having gotten it, I'm *not* feeling good about myself—on two counts. While the eyes and body of this super-sexy Deutsch moll should leave no male with any doubt about a more than satisfactory response, if I had a repeat performance of almost all my previous failed trysts and my recent late night with Jacqueline; if I was forced to pull off another pseudo-screwing thing like I did then, Erica would certainly know the difference and why. And it'd be way more than humbling. She told me her hotel room number (and had me repeat it). My instructions were to wait 30 minutes and then come on up. But are you ready for this, *she's staying in the Carlton Hotel!*

Penetrating the Carlton

I circled the area for thirty minutes, in the throes of alternately deciding to make a break for the dock, and then shamefully turning towards the hotel again. One o'clock. Still a block west of the Carlton I felt it peering down on me (disapprovingly). Later as I closed in on it, I think it was grinning and shaking its head. *The joust was about to begin.* Without being registered you couldn't walk in past the staff. At this late hour there was very little activity, so it wasn't as intimidating (but no chance to slip in with the crowd either). From a safe distance I saw three clerks behind the desk. This was not going to be easy. I was shaking more than a little. However, now (without remembering making the final decision) my plan was to do it. *No matter what, get to Erica's room.*

I checked the rear and both sides of the hotel, but no unlocked entrance. Possibly another way: The main entrance was to the far left of the front of the building. To its right were several sets of sliding glass doors opening onto the now damp and deserted terrace. The furthest right ones were more than fifty feet from the main entrance. Peering (best I could in the dark) through the furthest right ones, they appeared to lead into a large, unlit— apparently no longer used dining area. If one of those doors were unlocked I could slip in through it, sneak across the darkened dining room, and get to the base of a wide stairway, without being seen. *Please God, let one of those doors be open.*

I made my way onto the patio. Not a soul in sight. Bent low like a stalking commando I snaked my way through the white metal tables, now topped with upside down chairs. Arrived at the wall of glass doors and crouched there under the awning, breathing heavily. Far to the left I could see the well-lit reception, but they'd have a hard time seeing me. I tried the furthest set of doors. Not open. Tried the next set. Great! Not locked. Slid it open and squeezed through. Here—for the moment, I was out of their line of sight (thanks to a row of columns inside the abandoned dining area). But to reach the marble staircase on the far wall, I would have to cross a wide area, completely open except for a couple statues and a glass display case. During the midpoint of the crossing I would be in full sight of anyone at the reception desk.

The three clerks were still talking among themselves. Probably not expecting any new guests and appeared to be disinterested in anything beyond their circle of light. *Here goes*, about to make my break for West Berlin—crossing the mine field before the wall. Checked my watch. I wasn't going to be early, that was for sure. Damn near an hour. *Shit*. I mustered all the courage I could. Deep breath. Now or never. *Go for it!* I'm on my way! Moving quickly but not running (yet). Halfway across I feel eyes and can't resist looking towards the lobby. *I'm nailed!* One guy who had been behind the desk had come out into the lobby. He was in plain view. So I was in plain view. He was looking right at me. I picked up my gait. He started walking towards me. I quickened my step. He was pointing his finger in my direction and yelling something to me. Now he's *running* towards me. *Shit!* No way to justify my presence. No chance of talking my way past him.

I burst ahead. Out of the blocks. I was moving! Preservation outweighed morality. Raced up the steps two at a time. The guy was at full speed now himself. I could hear the clatter of his heels on the polished floor. He was shouting at me and calling to the other guys. I heard more footsteps. The Carlton had been violated and it wasn't sitting still for it. *Shit, what now!?* What floor!? 304, 304! Should be the third floor! I already passed the first floor, and the second I think. Here then, get off now! Grabbed the banister, swung around. Almost tore my arm off. I was full speed down the wide carpeted hallway. Flying! Oh no! *How could that be?* The numbers going by were in the 200's! *I'm one floor too early.* When I turned my head to catch a glimpse of my pursuers I lost my balance and almost went sprawling.

The hotel guys had just rounded the corner at the top of the stairs. I had a good lead on them! But at the moment I was still in full view. End of the hall, round the corner, up the staircase again. On the right floor now—the 300's! This is it! If I can make it inside her room before they come round the corner at the top of this staircase, they won't know which room I went in. Made it! Into her room and the staff still on the way up the steps! *I did it!* Finger to my lips. *Shhhh.* About ten seconds later the footsteps went thudding by. I'd lost them. I was home free. I collapsed into a chair, my lungs were on fire. My legs were trembling. I was soaked. But I was there. Erica began laughing heartily, making me feel even better.

Perhaps because of the kaleidoscope of scarcely credible events, or because I was assigning it to that "parallel universe," I was surprised to find myself—even realizing the consequences, prepared to go through with what was undoubtedly coming; an experiment—an opportunity to maybe meet up with that right chemistry. She made us both a liqueur and we talked about our time together. Unlikely as it should have been, I felt manageable anxiety; almost able to portray a cavalier attitude (somehow having dismissed the fact that I may soon suffer another humiliating failure, and be always remorseful for having discredited my wife and our marriage).

Erica went to the bathroom and I heard the shower. A minute later she peeked around the curtain and motioned for me to join her. No good way to turn down that invitation. I joined her, though next to her I felt short, thin, and generally inadequate. Fortunately it was steamy and soapy, and she never seemed to be sizing me up. *Thank you God.* Out of the shower and dried off, she made straight for the bed, flung the cover to the floor, slapped the sheets and invited me to join her. I did. I should have been shaking as usual, but the love-making this time, assuming it would occur, might not be the main event of the day. I think Erica could have done it or not done it, and it wouldn't have made any difference to her. So much exciting had already happened, and I was already hoping the act would not be the measure of our time together. While we were joking and kissing I noticed the phone dangling by the cord off the night table. I pointed to it. Erica leaned over the edge of the bed and picked it up. Would you believe, after our talk, the shower, and ten minutes more in bed, a guy named Peter was still on the line! She talked to him about five minutes, and ended up saying: "But Peter, truth is love, love is truth. Good night."

The REAL story!

It seemed like Erica really liked and trusted me. For what reason I don't know. We could have been high school buddies. Maybe I felt less guilty and more confident this time because it wasn't a seduction with expectations to fulfill. It would just be how the evening ended. Other much more important things had happened today. Although true enough I was shutting some things out of my mind and praying that I wouldn't disappoint her. Suddenly she jumped out of bed and came back with one of the big 500 Franc chips, that she called a *plaque*. She must be growing those frigging things. I was secretly hoping it was going to be a gift. (She still had my other one from the private club.) She was giggling and squeezing my arm. "Look at this, isn't it beautiful?" I didn't know what she meant. She rolled over and got up on her hands and knees, held the chip out, and looked me straight in the eyes with the damnedest expression on her face. I focused on the chip in spite of the fact that just behind it two pendulous pink-nippled breasts hung almost to the mattress. The chip was like a hundred I'd already seen tonight, a quarter inch thick plastic—about two inches by four inches. I looked and said, "Yeah it's neat."

She was out of bed again and over to her closet, some ruffling around and back to me with another 500 Franc chip. "See this," she said, shoving this second rectangular slab under my nose. "This one is a real one! Go ahead. Compare them." Almost breathless and amidst gleeful laughter, the details of an incredible story unfolded. Fritz was her brother. He was a composite materials engineer with the Krups company in Germany, who had his own lab and R&D unit. He developed prototype molded plastic appliances. It all began a year ago when she met a cashier from the casino. He convinced Fritz it could be done, although it turned out to be no easy task. Even with access to all the Krups facilities it was a frustrating, long and expensive process developing the mold for just one chip—the 500 Franc chip of course.

"I don't believe it" I said, *"Counterfeit chips?"*

Erica rattled on with the details. A lot of trial and error before they got it right. It hadn't been so hard to get an exact mold for the precise size and weight. Finding the right combination of dyes took a while. The real complicated part was the conductors: thin ribbons of copper foil that went into each chip, from end to end. They had to be layered in during the molding. Every night the chips are counted and placed in slots—like cassette holders. These bins slide, like metal drawers, into a steel cabinet. One turn of a key and a voltage is applied to all the drawers, and each one has to pass an amperage continuity check. One bogus (or even cracked) chip, and the drawer won't pass inspection. What's more, but this wasn't as complicated, the engraved Casino logo was inlaid with a light-frequency sensitive material. Every time the chip went across the cashier's counter, with special glasses he was able to verify its authenticity.

"How in the hell did you learn all this? From that cashier guy?"

"Some of it yes, but mostly Fritz did it. We kept five chips after last summer's holiday. Didn't cash them in. Took them to Fritz' laboratory in Solingen and he went to work on them." Fritz had almost given up on the project several times, since at first it was costing them so much, and one of the other workers got wise to it. Without access to the high-tech equipment it would have cost more to make them than they were worth. I told Erica there was no way they were going to be able to continue getting away with this. (I hated to think about her getting caught.) How many chips did they start with? How many did they have now? What if someone saw a difference? She just laughed and slapped the bed. "We're not worried." We lay there holding hands and looking at the ceiling. I had to laugh at myself, and not seeing what was happening all evening. It all came clear to me now—how it always seemed we had chips we didn't win. Why she cashed out twice, and finally, why she grabbed back the 500 Franc chip I had tipped the club waiter with. And me, thinking she'd remember this night because of the luck I had brought her.

I worked at not dwelling on my coming infidelity, helped by the fact that Erica who had been kneeling above me, lowered herself and began moving her warm and damp most private part on my abdomen. *Please God, even if just this one time.* Unbelievably, it did not occur. Perhaps aware of my incapacity she took hold of me and positioned it against her opening. Limply nestled there she began to move it rapidly forward and back. Her utterances as she did so began to indicate it was causing her pleasure. In spite of this not being a result of my masculinity, I was greatly relieved, in fact overjoyed. *It happened!* She had the big "O"! I lay there comparing the extent of my regrets of this infidelity, to having been at least partially responsible for having pleasured a woman. I could just imagine the joy in being able to do so through actual penetration; *the gratification every other man knows and takes for granted.* Could there be a chance for me? If so, if ever, it's bound to happen on this cruise.

Chapter Fifteen

WHY ARE WE HERE IN THE MED?

Back on Board

We steamed out of Cannes—myself and many others I suspect, more than ready for the structure and normality we'd find within the confines of the ship, things familiar and things of order. Unfortunately, even if I chose to I knew I would find little solace in relating my escapades or confiding my concern to any of my squadron mates. My time ashore had been dishonorable, not defensible in intent. I did write a long and intended loving letter to Sara, although it was of course very difficult. Obviously I was doing a lot of second-thought thinking and should have. The other guys were laughing and reminiscing about stupid (but blameless) activities: somebody having a few too many beers, races in cabs, great meals, playing darts with some European guys, night club shows. What stories could I share without deserved embarrassment? As you might imagine, I was more than ready for this at-sea period. Turn-to on my job. Clean up my act. Get with the program.

With no flight operations scheduled the first day, I set out on my "visit-all-the-shops" tour. One hour each. I hit the Metal Shop, the Hydraulics Shop and the Electric Shop—all before lunch. Too many inflight discrepancies were taking multiple attempts to get it fixed. (This is not uncommon since many problems only occur in flight.) One malfunction in particular had been worked on three times. Interviewing the technicians who worked on it, I discovered the second and third guys were to a large extent repeating the same trouble-shooting procedures the first guy had done, checking, adjusting, and changing the same components (without success). I designed a new worksheet for aircraft discrepancies on which the first technician assigned to trouble-shoot the malfunction, would enter the discrepancy number, briefly list his conclusions as to the reason for the malfunction, and then a list of the systems or parts he had checked, adjusted, removed or replaced. If the same problem turned out not to have been fixed, the next guy to tackle it would know exactly what avenues had been explored the first time. It went on to become a form used fleet-wide (and Major Burnham got a lot of credit).

I also used this at-sea period to hit the weights. Spent a lot of time in my hideaway up on the forecastle, much of it trying to keep my benches from sliding and losing my balance. It was a neat and private place. No one ever came up there (except Dale, a Navy bodybuilder who brought up a pair of his own dumbbells). I began making two between-meals trips to the wardroom each day. Once in the morning and once in the afternoon— for a thick peanut butter sandwich, a glass of chocolate milk, and an orange. Don't know why since I became a teenager, I would have been so preoccupied with being bigger. (If I had spent as much time on anything as I spent worrying about my darned pecs, I would have earned a Ph.D. in it.)

One day a rumor ("scuttlebutt" in the Navy) began circulating that we might be being followed by some Soviet subs. The SONAR guys had said they had started picking up a strange kind of "ping" that they had never heard before. A whole new attitude began to permeate the ship. There were classified briefings, 24-hour watches, and lots of telex's. Even had a couple "General Quarters" (Emergency Station drills), and two "Pilot Alerts." But nothing was as exciting as when the "ping" was identified. *That* caused a lot of excitement on the ship. Up in the forecastle, one of Dale's dumbbells had been rolling back and forth, tapping an adjacent steel gunnel. That was the strange sound the SONAR guys were hearing. The Soviet Sub turned out to be a thirty pound dumbbell. Colonel Cunningham was *not* amused.

And Now, Our REAL Mission in the Med

You might imagine (now—at the peak of the cold war) that the US had a massive retaliatory plan in the event the "Evil Empire" initiated hostilities. That means should Russia launch even one missile westward (or should someone somewhere *think* they did)! Well you're right, we did have a plan, about a thousand Air Force planes, as many pre-destined rockets, and a dozen submarines with guided missiles, were waiting—24 hours a day, to do just that. Milling around here in the Mediterranean the Forrestal was well within striking distance of a bunch of strategic Russian targets in the Eastern Bloc countries; so the Forrestal was assigned its targets, VMA-331 had its targets, and *Roger Yahnke had his!* But what and where? Two days ago we were assigned our exact individual targets. I got mine—the one I would keep for the whole cruise, my very own thing to personally demolish: a Russian military installation in a small village in Romania.

And VMA-331 was not just your vanilla-flavored attack squadron, we would be attacking with *nuclear weapons*. Mushroom shaped clouds in the mid 60's! We were no longer designated just "Attack Pilots," but rather "Nuclear Weapons Delivery Pilots". The weapons were stored in a well-guarded area on a lower deck—twelve of them; four for each attack squadron. And the procedure for dropping an atomic bomb was a lot different than a regular bomb, because survival of the pilot was not guaranteed. The shock wave and radiation spread so quickly, it required a special release maneuver by the pilot, to avoid being killed in the blast.

How to Drop a "Nuke"

To maintain a safe distance from the impact point, the profile for dropping a nuclear weapon was referred to as a "Loft Maneuver." You sped in at exactly (and I mean *exactly*) 500 knots True Airspeed, as low to the ground as you could get, and that was supposed to be just 50 feet over the ground (to stay under the enemy radar) until you passed a point, exactly 24,000 feet (four nautical miles) short of your target. This point was known as the "Pull-up Point," and everything was math and physics from there on in; that's why you had to be exactly 500 knots.

Passing over the pull-up point landmark you hauled back on the stick—mightily, until you pulled four "G's". This would have your lips drooling, your belly over your belt, and all the blood pooling in your legs. As you continued upwards and went through a nose-up angle of exactly 45 degrees, there was a small "click" (the parameters were met) and the automatic release circuitry cut loose the weapon. It wasn't a matter of flying *over* the target, or even *seeing* it, because you never did. Inertia, centrifugal force and gravity, guided the weapon to the target in a high arcing trajectory. Meanwhile you didn't stop the backward pull, the aircraft continuing right past straight up, until the nose of the aircraft came back down to the horizon behind you—pointing back in the direction from which you had come (albeit, now you're upside down). This method of reversing course was the fastest and was supposed to keep you out of the injurious effects of the blast.

We practiced this maneuver hundreds of times, using small, twenty-five pound projectiles which had the same aerodynamics and flight trajectory as the actual nuclear weapon. The ship would act as our Pull-up Point, towing our target (a beat-up wooden sled) exactly 24,000 feet behind it. We would start about twenty miles away, and speed right at the ship at five-hundred knots. Passing over the ship, we'd yank back, and do our loft maneuver, tossing our dummy nuclear weapon towards the sled. A minute later radar would give us a "read" on where our projectile had impacted—how close we had come.

In addition to the necessity of maintaining exactly five-hundred knots, you had to hold a consistent pull-up force of exactly four "G's" throughout. These two elements were vital parts of the physics that determined the trajectory and final impact of the arcing projectile. Also, the release point had to be as the plane passed exactly forty-five degrees nose-up. If it released too soon, or too late, the impact area would be too short or too long. But the most difficult part was keeping the damn wings level during the pull up. That was real important. If one wing or the other was down even a little, you'd be in a slight turn and you'd loft your weapon perhaps the correct distance, but off to the left or right.

Finding these targets, getting from the Mediterranean (Agean) Sea to a town a couple hundred miles inland—flying a route you'd never seen, was not a sure thing. S2 (Intelligence) supplied us with the necessary detailed, large-scale maps of the Balkan states. The next day each of us spent most the day gluing a series of them together, to construct a mosaic stretching from our coastal "entry point" to our assigned Pull-up point. On these maps—using a selection of colored felt-tipped pens, we would trace our specific route, making navigational notes, and "tic" marks over key land features to later assist us in ascertaining we were on our assigned track.

The Pull-up Point

The finish line on these maps was not your target, it was your individual Pull-up Point. Hell with the target. First you had to find the Pull-up Point! Every pilot took pride in how accurate and detailed his strike map was. To maintain the necessary familiarity with our routes and the terrain features, we were supposed to spend an hour a day reviewing these maps. But even being able to arrive over your Pull-up Point, *would you be able to recognize it!* Approaching it at such a low altitude and going five-hundred knots, it would be real easy to be *past it* before you'd identified it. If so, the Loft Maneuver can't even be attempted. You couldn't complete your delivery. You're screwed. At tree-top level and scenery-blurring speed it would be real difficult to see and identify a ground level Pull-up Point, so they were always tall, man-made structures such as a tower or a crane yard or high bridge, with enough vertical height that they would be visible above the horizon as you approached them. To make us able to recognize our Pull-up Point we would each receive a U-2 photo of our individual Pull-up Point.

Everyone was excited about receiving the final (virtual) part of their sacred target folder. It would be a special computer-enhanced 8 X 10 glossy. The photo interp guys told us that the resolution of these prints was incredible. It was going to be just like being there. The photos were passed out and signed for. Each pilot scurried off to his own private spot to study his Pull-Up structure: the radio tower, tall crane, or suspension bridge. I snuck away to an unoccupied table to view mine—the photo of the Pull-up Point from which I would launch my morsel of death and destruction (which would vaporize about 10,000 people immediately, and cause another 60,000 deaths in the next 24 hours). I could see every detail, like I was up in a hot air balloon looking down. It *was* like being there. Except, my Pull-up Point was a church steeple! A frigging church. And the damned photo must have been taken on a Sunday, because worshippers were filing out. The steps were full of families. Old ladies and little kids. *Geez! There's a guy and his wife walking down the steps holding the hands of their two little girls.* I didn't include this in my letters home.

Chapter Sixteen
THE ISLAND OF RHODES

Winter and Gray

Mid November. Our next in-port was Rhodes, which the rest of the world calls *Rodos* (the island of the Cyclops in Ulysses' travels). 25 miles off the Turkish coast but owned by Greece. Not even half the size of Puerto Rico. Unlike Cannes with its luxurious white marinas and golden beaches, Rhodes looked bleak; monochromatic, nothing bright or festive. It was doubtful much would be awaiting us here. Not a soul visible in the dock area. Deserted. An *Out of Business* sign might be hanging on the city gates. Summer was over and a slight chill was in the air. I doubted there could be many tourists here this late in the season. Sadly for me and my quest, the attractions of the summer holidays were likely over. (Maybe for the better.)

My section wouldn't draw liberty until the second day in and I could easily wait. (Especially the way Rhodes was looking from here.) Since I'd been pressing my luck ashore, this lackluster in-port might give me an opportunity to spend more time on board and earn my keep. And this first day I did in fact get a lot done. I had a banner day stamping out a variety of small fires in the Maintenance department (and was seen by everyone.). Bob and Don who had liberty this first day popped back on board about 2230 (10:30 p.m.). According to them, the small downtown area held nothing and wasn't worth venturing into. And there was just one beach—a small gray pebbled beach; not even a quarter mile from where the liberty boats tied up. The few tourists appeared to be European senior citizens on a cheaper, off-season vacation. The beach was directly across the street from three wood-sided "so-so" hotels. However, some good news: They had seen two large tour groups: a British group led by an effeminate guy in brown suede shoes, and a German party led by a giant woman with wild hair.

"Yeah, so?"

They admitted they did meet a German girl—Ingrid; good looking but didn't speak hardly any English. Her group had been on the closest beach to our dock, right in front of one of the hotels. They obviously had not had a rousing time (and those two bachelors always found where things were happening). I got a good night's sleep, had a great breakfast, and made the 0930 liberty boat. Tried to balance myself in the middle of the boat to stay away from the spray and the crusted salt and grease on the gunnels. I was wearing a neat black cashmere sweater I'd purchased in Rome.

From the dock it would only be a short walk along a narrow curving road, to the small beach where Bob and Don had met Ingrid. The sidewalk was the top of the harbor's sea wall. Clumps of dried kelp hung off the edge attracting their share of flies. A worn smooth, skin-oil-glazed pipe rail— originally there for safety, now supported a half-dozen kids with fishing lines. Don't know about fish, but the water lapping just below contained its share of trash. Just like the guys had said, ahead of me to the left I saw a couple small, two-story wooden hotels. Each had a barely grassed front lawn in desperate need of watering and boasted not a single shrub or flower bed. While being unpretentious they were respectable appearing; probably catering to the same clientele each year. The street in front of the hotels separated them from the pebbled beach now commencing to my right. Other than an occasional small car crawling by, no traffic to be seen. I couldn't see a single restaurant. (The most economical vacation packages were the ones where you had to eat in your hotel.)

I was disappointed at how many elderly people were on the beach. They may have been from England or Germany, but they looked like they were off farms in the Ukraine; pale skin, bowed and bent, most overweight, varicose veins, gray hair. *Whew!* This was no Cote d'Azur! Men and women alike were doing full-clothing changes right on the beach (taking turns holding up large towels around their spouses during the critical steps). Compared to other Mediterranean beaches, this one was not at all picturesque. I strolled it as if I were just another vacationer enjoying the warm sun. Glancing out to sea I could understand how the beachgoers might wonder what that strange gray shape was on the horizon.

Found Her

It was noon before I stumbled on Ingrid. That's German I'm hearing, she's blond and like they said—in a skimpy black bikini. After two not-necessary trips to a concession stand (so as to pass by her blanket) I stopped and was able to convey I was a shipmate of Bob and Don. The guys were right.

143

Ingrid did not speak much English, but hopefully enough (considering I spoke no German). She did not seem to be "on the make." Our chat was a task and her girlfriend didn't speak *any* English, which made it even more awkward. I hoped to improve the conversation by feigning an interest in learning something about the German language. Ingrid nodded that she would be more than willing to help.

I decided to find out if in German, a noun had a different suffix depending on whether it was the subject or object of a sentence. To discover this, I would ask Ingrid two sentences in German: *The man kicks the dog*, and then *The dog bites the man*. With these two examples I would be able to listen carefully to the word *man* each time and listen if it was different when used as the subject than when it was used as the object. When I asked her the first sentence I received an understandably non-complimentary, quizzical expression. I then realized, without her knowing my grammar objective, this sentence must have sounded really dumb. With not much enthusiasm, and waning interest in me as a student of much potential, she responded, *"Der Mann tritt den Hund."*

I guess this was getting boring enough for her girlfriend who excused herself right there and then. Seeing this reaction to the first sentence, can you believe I still went ahead with the second sentence: *The dog bites the man*. Ingrid—now undoubtedly thinking she was in the throes of being picked up by a complete jerk, snapped back, *"Die Hund beisst den Mann."* I could see she had lost all interest in giving me any further German lessons. I rallied somewhat in the next hour, being as polite and friendly as possible. About three, she decided she had best join her travel companion. We bid a warmer than expected farewell, and I was able to arrange a dinner date for that evening.

A Most Appreciated Occurrence at Dinner

When I walked into her lobby, there she was! She looked happy to see me and took my hand almost immediately. *Could be a good sign.* We decided to eat in town and chose the most upscale hotel on the beach. The right side of its ground floor was an open terrace, set up as a first-class eating area. Diners could look out at the sea over a low stone wall holding a line of colorful potted plants. White-jacketed waiters were scurrying about, covering the round tables with peach-colored linens, setting the silver and putting out crystal. Classical music was coming from somewhere. (Glad I was wearing a coat and tie.) As soon as we entered, the maître d' rushed over, greeted me with more respect than I deserved and escorted us to a choice table. *Could it be (for once) one of those nights when things go right.* The ordering went smoothly. Asparagus soup and then the always acceptable avocados stuffed with baby shrimp. A chilled beer for me and a bottle of Tavel on order. More folks filing in. (Good thing we got here when we did.) We both decided to go with the plat du jour—veal marsala. The whole meal went great. The food was just fine and Ingrid seemed to be enjoying herself, and the waiters were refreshingly pleasant.

Halfway through the meal an incident occurred which could not have done more to bail me out after my morning's (apparently stupid) German language lesson. A scruffy dog had somehow gotten up onto the terrace. When the Maître d' spied it his first reaction was panic, but quickly regained his composure and attempted to conceal his distress from the diners. He began some urgent signaling to the closest waiters, but it was as if the mutt was intercepting these signals, managing to outmaneuver his pursuers. The staff tried to carry out their other duties as if there were not a ridiculous farce unfolding. The ones who passed close enough to the mutt to have some influence, either hissed or shook a foot in his direction.

Ingrid and I were doing our best to avoid breaking out laughing. Finally one waiter started straight for the mutt—who upon seeing this went partway under a table, only his butt remaining outside the low hanging table cloth. The waiter hauled back a leg and kicked him! I looked at Ingrid. She looked at me. I said, "Der Mann tritt den Hund!" The look on her face—it was worth a million! As a result of the kick the dog ran out the other side of the table, and took a chomp out of another waiter's leg. I looked again to Ingrid. She knew what was coming: "Die Hund beisst den Mann!"

The meal was a success, thanks in part to the dog incident. I felt relaxed and was not concerned about the evening's eventualities. This was fortunate, since while we were having a Cointreau in the hotel lounge, in comes her travel companion—beat after a group dinner at a monastery somewhere. The two of them had a short conversation, and Ingrid said they were going to call it a day. I interpreted a sweet "Good-Night" as *Don't worry, there will be another time for us.* Trying not to seem like I was rushing things, I suggested a dinner date for the following evening. (No way I could come in during the early part of the day; just have to hope Tripp will stay on board for the evening and swap duty with me.)

Another Dinner and the Crash
Thank you Lord: Tripp had no plans to go ashore in the evening. I caught the 1830 liberty boat and met Ingrid in her hotel lobby. She looked great

wearing an open-necked sequined black sweater. Found out that this was going to be her last night on Rhodes. So where to go tonight? She had an idea: there was a neat little Turkish restaurant about thirty kilometers out of town. I hadn't yet had a reason to check into the taxi situation but could see Ingrid was intent on going to this restaurant. In a few minutes we had our own chauffeured (not new) Mercedes. Five minutes outside the city our route deteriorated into a rutted, barely two-lane road, winding and difficult to navigate at dusk. I wasn't sold on our chauffeur, but was forced to ignore his lack of application, in order to concentrate on what Ingrid was trying to say. With the language barrier, even a simple conversation bogged down quickly.

The restaurant was quaint, but evidently word-of-mouth travels quickly, as half the tourists on the island were availing themselves of this supposedly unknown taberna. I made the best of the baked fish and downed my share of the wine. We finished eating and it was still early, only nine-forty-five. Outside I was at first unable to locate our chauffeur, then spied him up the road with a gaggle of the other drivers, engaged in animated story telling. I waved and yelled until I got his attention. He signaled with a beau geste wave that said *don't worry he'd make this his last story.* When finished he trotted over to where our limo was parked. We were in the car and on our way back to town, and maybe an extended evening.

Although I had already been unfaithful, it had occurred almost without design; this evening I could claim no innocence. I had to admit I was acting with intention. While sitting next to Ingrid, attempting to interpret her comments, I could not avoid hearing the road noise and became worried about our speed. I craned my neck to see the speedometer; only 120 kilometers an hour, but too fast for the winding road we were on (and us with no seat belts). I tapped the driver on the shoulder and pointed at the speedometer. He nodded *Yup, that was a speedometer.* Back to Ingrid. A couple minutes of translating was interrupted by a sudden stab of brakes and that awful screech you fear. In the split second before the impact I yanked my head up, to see emblazoned in the headlight glare—about six feet in front of the hood ornament, a gigantic silky brown *horse's ass!*

Thud! We hit it head on (ass-on)! The car snapped in a half-turn towards the center of the road. The amount of turn stayed to the left and the car began a sideways skid straight ahead, but threatening to tip and roll. I could feel it was going to happen. When that Mercedes did start rolling, I never did figure out which way was up or down, or have a moment's clue about which way to move to avoid injury, or do a single thing to save my life, except close my eyes and holler. Then all was quiet and dark, and smelled bad, like gas fumes, burnt rubber, and hot metal.

We were upside down! The wheels were spinning. Half the windows were out. I didn't hurt anywhere. (I think.) There was glass everywhere. Ingrid and I were wrapped up in a ball on the felt ceiling. She was clawing for upright and talking an undecipherable blue streak. My left foot was stuck between the driver's seat and the side post. It didn't hurt, but I couldn't retrieve it. *Fire, what about fire?* With a yank, my foot was out of the shoe. I couldn't get either of the back doors open. We exited through where the rear window should have been. Our chauffeur was inside yelling, and *his* door was wide open. Suddenly realizing he was free he clambered out on his hands and knees. He kept yelling. The engine was still running. It turned off with the key.

Standing there Ingrid says, "I think we are very happy." *Happy, my ass, my evening could be over!* (Later I found out that with her limited English she had meant to say "lucky," not "happy.") Now more confusion on this previously deserted country road: A third hysterically screaming guy appears out of nowhere to join us, near the dead horse, and our Mercedes on its roof. Don't know why but he's really frantic. The deranged newcomer has ahold of my sleeve and is tugging me to come with him. Without a clue I let him begin dragging me into the darkness. It's then I spy *another* car further back the road—also upside down. I didn't know there was another car involved. I had only seen the horse. What the hell had happened here?

Shit, there's a kid in that car! I could see a young boy in the back seat. A puddle of gas was burning on the ground right in front of the car. The crazy guy runs up and stomps on it, which does nothing. He runs back to me frantically pointing at the kid. I'm guessing he can't get the door open. But neither can I. I tried to rock the car. *Surprise!* It rocked easily (being almost perfectly balanced on the center of its roof). I holler at him to pull on the door while I do my impression of Superman, easily tilting this side of the car up. While amazed at my apparent strength, he yanks the door open, and the kid clambers out. The crazy guy, who I guessed was the driver, grabs the kid and runs about a hundred feet from the car. Keerist! I didn't need this. *How about my evening?* As the story was pieced together, the guy with the kid had been traveling some distance in front of us, and in trying to avoid the horse, lost control of his car. The horse stayed in the road until it got rammed by us.

I gave a hopeful "everything's okay" glance over to Ingrid. Fortunately, she was now looking reasonably calm and (please God) just might still be up to concluding the evening in the anticipated fashion. Tiny pieces of broken glass in her hair were reflecting the moonlight, as if she was wearing a squashed tiara. I barely paid any attention to the crazy guy with the kid. He was jabbering to me a-mile-a-minute. With the help of an English speaking local I was made to understand that the boy's father, who evidently was someone special here on the island, would want to thank me. I had to visit tomorrow—tomorrow for lunch. He shoved a card at me with a raised inscription that read *Konstantinos II*, and listed an address. I nodded okay, mostly to get rid of him. In spite of this mishap I was still ready to make the best out of what remained of the night. This meant— first, I had to secure us a ride back to town. I got one of people who had stopped by, to give us a ride back to town.

The Rest of the Evening

The ride into town was devoid of any romantic conversation (me being in the front seat and Ingrid in the back). I was wondering how this all would pan out. Now my left foot did hurt, and I had a bad cut on my right wrist. But still hoping. We strode into the hotel like survivors, fresh from the front. We were above menial conversation at this point, and without speaking she retrieved her key. Then took my hand and we were on our way *straight to her room.* No invitations, no explanations. I don't know if she had decided the excitement of the evening just called for finishing it up this way, or if she felt like she owed me something after my couple day investment, or if she had it planned from the beginning, or if it was just the way a young woman feels she deserves to end her summer vacation.

The room was small and wasn't air conditioned. The window just above the sidewalk was propped open. The one yellowed ceiling light was not mood setting, and the walls were pale green. Looked like a room in a Tijuana medical clinic. Not in there thirty seconds and her skirt is sliding down her legs to the floor and her sweater is coming off over her head. Saw her wince as she pulled it over her shoulders. There were still shards of glass in it. Looking at her there I could better admire her cute (but somewhat odd) figure. She was short-waisted—in fact almost *no* waist. And she would not have needed a bra for support; her breasts were not bulbous, just small pointy cones, unusually wide apart and facing even further to the sides. (Surprised I hadn't noticed this on the beach.) They were delightful and I could imagine fondling and kissing them. The gray nylon panties she was wearing were ordinary, but they were sumptuously packed—front and back. Even in the dim light, just below them I could see the soft, fine blond hair on her thighs.

Studying the silk undies, staring at that well-tanned little belly and the puffy mound of her most private part, I was thrilled to think I might be coming aroused. It may be that these German girls have some of that chemistry. We spent about ten minutes in the bathroom, Ingrid now naked and me in my hopefully beginning-to-fill undershorts. I tried to lightly swipe off the tiny glass particles stuck all over her but had to pick them out one by one. Got them out. Enough of that. She was into the bed and the ugly light was snapped out.

I could see it was going to be up to me. She was not an Erica. I started my contribution; the things I thought would be the most arousing to her (and equally importantly—to me). After a few minutes I was greatly relieved to feel myself firming up. She spread her legs in apparent anticipation. I kneeled over her, gave her a long kiss on the mouth, and then reached down to assist in an insertion, *and realized it was gone!* During the two-second kiss it had disappeared. I was completely de-armed. No threat. Sick.

I felt obliged to contribute to her reaching satisfaction, so began increasingly fast rhythmic manipulations with my hand. She welcomed it, and even without me inside her it appeared she was determined to take her pleasure this night. When she finally reached it (talk about no waist) her hips went right up under her armpits. For me, as you might imagine that while I was grateful for that, I was way more than a little discouraged by the same non-performance I had lived through many dozens of times since my wedding night. If did believe that someday I would succeed, and I did, it would not be with Ingrid. And there's no way she could represent an entry into that new and different life awaiting me. Again as usual, I laid there after the act, feeling as if I was in the wrong place. Like I should be somewhere else and the sooner I was there the better. Shamefully attempting to be unfaithful and again failing. Where is that woman with the "right" chemistry? Finally about two, still awake and a mental "basket-case" I got up, dressed, tip-toed out, and begged my way onto one of those liberty boats reserved for the shore patrol guys (who I was getting to know real well by now). I laid awake a long time. No excuses this time, I'd done it on purpose.

Lunch With a King

About 1100 the next morning, going through my trouser pockets I found the card from last night—the one the crazy guy had given me, with the kid's father's address on it. Even though I could get Tripp to standby for me, I wasn't sure I had it in me to venture ashore—especially just to meet some kid's father. But you never know, it might add more color to what has turned out to be a colorful-enough in-port stay. After mulling it over and reflecting on the driver's plea that I meet the boy's father, *Hell, I'm gonna go.*

I found a gaggle of taxi drivers and gave them the card with the father's address. Evidently it wasn't a trip they wanted. Either they weren't familiar with the area or some other problem. After several turned it down, one indicated he'd take me. Upon arriving, the residence was indeed someplace special, surrounded by a high white stucco wall, covered with ivy and fuchsia flowers. An amply built, stern-faced guard grilled my driver then swung open a steel gate, exposing a spacious estate, with a manicured lawn—sloping uphill at least 100 feet, to a large stone cottage. There appeared to be nothing behind the cottage, as if it were perched on a cliff. The driver pulled in halfway and stopped. I was out and he wasted no time in making his exit.

Scanning the expansive lawn I noticed a half dozen men lounging at various locations; more as if they were stationed there. Took a breath and started up the drive towards the house. None of the men approached me (although they watched my every step). There was a wide shaded porch with several pieces of summer furniture. I mounted the steps to the front door—which was wide open. In fact every door and window in the house appeared to be open, attesting to the wonderfully balmy day it was. The sun was brilliant and the air was skin temperature.

I rapped a couple times and waited in a foyer with an upright shelf filled with old stone and metal artifacts. The guy who met me was dressed like a butler. Fortunately he appeared to be expecting me, because I could see he wasn't a guy to be fooled with. I was invited in and guided past a step-down, to a long terra-cotta-paved hallway. Looking down it I was able to see the rear wall of the house, which was four sets of open glass-paned French double-doors, side by side. Through them I could see a terrace which appeared to span the whole width of the cottage. Beyond its railing lay a breath-taking view of the Mediterranean. I had arrived at a much higher elevation than the city. The cottage was on a cliff overlooking a hidden lagoon. (I could now see our first impression of Rhodes had been the result of a too-limited sampling.)

A family was on the terrace. Upon seeing me they stopped what they were doing, came quickly inside, and spent five minutes showering me with praise and thanks. Talk about nobility, aristocracy, status. They say when you see it you recognize it, and there was no question about it here. From their attire, mannerisms, and surroundings, I could see these were privileged people. Suddenly it dawned on me, remembering the name on the card: *Konstantinos II*! I was about to have lunch with the recently exiled King Constantine of Greece! I was on guard immediately, *way out of my league here*. But from them—for the next two hours, came no statement or question (or even a mild reprimand of the help) without a kind expression. They had no doubts or fears, you could see that. The father (who was really the kid's Godfather) was young—about 35 years of age, handsome with straight black hair. His wife was similarly attractive, also with straight (and long) black hair. Both spoke perfect English. You might imagine we went over the previous night several times. I was in for a wonderful, leisurely Mediterranean midday meal on their terrace. The wrought iron railing next to the table was fifty feet above the water below. Looking down, around, and at the host and hostess, for sure I had never been in such special surroundings. The meal started with (of course) a Greek salad, then a plate of sliced meats and a wide assortment of breads. Dessert was a fruit plate containing at least two fruits I didn't recognize. Throughout the meal they kept my glass full of a light Rosé Greek wine. *I was living that other life I had up till now only fantasized about.*

Finally it was time to excuse myself. I hated to see the afternoon end. I was in a different, uniquely polished world. I could feel it in the air wafting past my skin. I had been whisked high and away from the world I knew. My host and hostess had been so gracious, so well educated. They had spoken with such awareness about current world affairs (and *the arts*, again). I only hoped I'd held up my end of the conversations. While bidding farewell in the foyer, on that shelf of artifacts, there was a uniquely hammered silver bracelet (I'd seen coming in). The father noticing my attraction, reached down, picked it off, *and gave it to me!* A gift I would always treasure; found in a cave on the island over a hundred years ago (and being worn as I type this).

On the way down the hill my heart was pounding, my mind was racing, and my feet were flying. I was hardly touching the ground. Didn't ask for a cab to be called, or even think about the distance. I was still euphoric from my experience. Any future in-port adventures would have even more to measure up to now. Three months ago I had not dared to think my mediocrity would go unnoticed. After this day I was even more inclined to believe that maybe—just maybe, my life was *not* already a closed book. Something else, whatever it was, (whoever it was) may be awaiting me. Back on the ship, knowing what a blessing I had (my wonderful wife and two children) I would spend a deserved worrisome night—unable to sleep, reproaching and questioning myself, delving into my anima—trying to unwind, discount the actuality of another whole life awaiting me. I now surely doubted I would be able to refrain from continuing this search for my destiny. I did write a letter to Sara, but it wasn't easy.

Chapter Seventeen

A NOT-SO-GOOD AT-SEA PERIOD

Things Like This Happen

I previously mentioned the ship's elevator; that large square platform protruding out from the hangar deck, just ten feet above the racing water below it. It is used to bring aircraft up and down between the hangar deck and the flight deck. The second day out, prior to our first launch a Navy Crusader had been brought up on the elevator. Arriving at the Flight Deck a tug was attached to the aircraft and towed it to its pre-launch position. The elevator was lowered to the hangar deck to receive another aircraft ready to be raised to the flight deck. The driver returned and left his tug at the edge of the elevator opening where the raised plane would soon appear. Unfortunately he had not set the parking brake, the ship listed in a swell, and the tug rolled over the edge, falling about fifty feet, onto the lowered elevator, on top of a young sailor. Some 18-year-old, mother's son; perhaps some Iowa farmhand who had joined-up and was just doing his duties, was tragically lost.

Real Embarrassing

The following day our first launch was a four-plane division, bound for Sicily; there they would spend four days at a US Air Force base, using their target range. The crew was excited, checked their aircraft and through an exterior door in the nose of the aircraft, packed their extra flight suits, clothes and toiletries in an unused radio compartment. They launched and at about 5,000 feet while they were joining in formation, the number four man starts hollering about the plane he was following, being on fire. *"Fastfleet Three you're on fire! Fastfleet Three, you got flames coming out of your aircraft!"* (And anybody that thinks a fire at sea is the worst thing that can happen, has never had a fire in flight!) The airplane may only stay together a matter of seconds, so an immediate ejection is the only recourse. It's standard policy throughout the military.

The wingman kept yelling and the division leader ordered his number three man to "Get outta there!" The canopy flew off, the ejection seat hurtled out, and an unmanned plane sliced down into the sea and was gone with a gulp. Only one problem: just after the pilot ejected, the number four plane got close enough to ascertain that the "flames" coming out of the nose section, was really one pants leg of a day-glow-orange flight suit that the pilot had packed in that nose compartment. It had gotten sucked out through the hinge and was flailing and shredding in the wind stream—*looking* like flames! The pilot was rescued okay, but the Navy was out about three and a half million dollars.

Meeting the Navy Pilots

During our times ashore we would often run into the Navy pilots. We'd adopted one guy in particular—Norm Lundquist, a Crusader pilot from Navy fighter squadron VF 103. Nick and Earl had met him a couple in-ports ago and he had started to run with us, especially Earl. Tall, blonde and crew cut, Norm's standard wardrobe ashore was gray flannels, maroon V-neck sweaters, and white tennis shoes. (He could have been one of those kids from the Heights.) If ever there was an All-American boy it was Norm. A little naive and with a ready smile, he was from Sioux City, Iowa. One time having a beer with Bob Harmon (actually Norm was having an orange juice and club soda), Bob suggested he do like he and Don were going to do; order a Jaguar XKE over here and have it shipped back home. Norm said, "Hey Bob, it was almost a scandal when I left Iowa to go to *Florida*—to be a *jet* pilot! If I came home with a foreign sports car, that'd do it!" We all laughed and secretly admired the small-town life of a guy like Norm.

Another Night Launch

It was just at sunset that I felt the big craft in a slow turn, which I knew would be putting us directly into the prevailing wind for the launch. After a couple minor heading adjustments, the ship's speaker announced the "corpen" (the ship's course for launch) and called for all flight deck personnel. About thirty minutes later over the P.A. came the call: "Pilots man your aircraft. First launch pilots man your aircraft." Our four guys, Jim, Doug, Tripp, and Earl— one by one struggled upright from the various locations where they'd been uneasily lounging since completing their briefing. They stretched, shook out the wrinkles and began gathering up their helmets, kneeboards and other paraphernalia. We gave them a thumbs-up as they paraded by us wearing a look of obedient resignation.

They filed out of the Ready Room like the gladiators of old going through the hatches to the floor of the Coliseum.

Not Scheduled? Watch It

Observing launches or recoveries is no dull pastime. It's a high-speed kaleidoscope of huge hurtling objects. It takes exactly six minutes to launch twelve planes. Then, exactly one minute after the last one has been shot off, the first plane from the previous launch slams into the deck; and eleven minutes later the last one is down (Twelve minutes to recover twelve aircraft.) You've never seen an operation this big be this precisely timed. There's so much being done by so many people, and it's all "life or death" stuff. Launch personnel are continually ducking under 1000-degree jet blasts and jumping over limb-severing cables. Even in heavy conditions of rising and falling decks and in near gale force winds, it appears to be unfolding with the orchestration of a philharmonic. The ship's company flight deck crew is at high risk, constantly only yards from death or dismemberment. It's a miracle there aren't serious accidents every launch. Pilots not scheduled frequently sought out safe locations to watch these launches.

Myself, Bob, and Ernie decided to watch this launch. After two flights of stairs (ladders) inside the superstructure, we ventured out onto a small, balcony (referred to as the "Vulture's Nest"). High and protected it was a popular vantage point to observe the action. The prevailing wind was about fifteen knots, and the carrier was underway at about fifteen, so the combined wind across the deck was at least thirty knots. Even up in our protected area the buffeting wind was making our eyes water, chapping our lips, and smothering our conversations. Bob rubbed the outside of his arms and complained about not having worn his flight jacket.

The now hot cats were steaming and oiled, ready to do their thing. There go the test runs. Nowhere on the ship could you miss hearing the horrendous slamming and hissing of the wenches and pistons. Even up here high above the din, it shook us. But not like the guys walking on the deck, the screaming and thudding was just inches beneath their feet. Inspectors were now running the lengths of the shining wet tracks, kicking lumps of grease back in the slots. The pilots were in the cockpit and the plane captains (remember? mine was Sgt Baldwin) had removed the last pin in the ejection seat and were now removing the ladders. The canopies were coming down. Although the launch looked as if it were being accomplished in a frenzied manner, to the ship's company personnel it was not the confusing operation it appeared to be. They had done it hundreds of times. Every man knew exactly what he was supposed to do, and how and when—to the last detail. The launch personnel (cat crews, wire crews, crash crews, ordnance crews, taxi directors, etc.) could be well proud of themselves. Once again, each group wearing their bright and uniquely colored vests to identify their flight deck functions.

All the crews were in their aircrafts. The engines were running. The deck was clear. Things were about to happen. As usual we would use four cats. The two forward-aligned cats (shooting you straight off the forward bow) and the two angle-deck cats (that shot you off the off the port side). Taxi directors were running this way and that, hailing planes left and right, urgently signaling them forward, jockeying them into sequential positions to be hooked to a tug and hauled onto the next vacant cat. *No delays!* You didn't know which cat you'd be launched from until the last minute. Sitting there, all strapped in and straddling a screaming jet engine you'd be nervous as hell, looking in every direction for your signalman. Then there he'd be—suddenly right in front of you, frantically signaling you forward, commanding an immediate response, without a second's delay. "Now! You"!

The chief in charge gave the signal for the first aircraft to be hauled onto the number one cat; our A-4 Skyhawk piloted by Jim. Two guys were on their hands and knees underneath it. They're at the nose gear now. They've got the halter attached (the hook that connects the aircraft to the catapult). The blast fence right behind the aircraft started up. (Just behind each launching plane a blast fence raises up to deflect the powerful jet blasts from a horizontal rearward vector to a harmless, vertical, straight upward direction.) There's the run-up signal. The helmeted and goggled Cat Officer was leaning into the thirty-knot wind, his yellow sweater billowing and trouser legs flailing. He raised his hand and gave that familiar, high energy, almost frantic circular motion that meant *Power Up!* We watched in anticipation, half holding our breath, knowing so well the feeling and what was coming next.

Seeing the signal, Jim jammed the throttle full forward, and a roaring yellow flame torched out of the plane's exhaust pipe, hit the raised blast fence and was deflected to an upward vector of roiling black smoke. Under full power the nose dropped down as the front strut was compressed under eight thousand pounds of thrust, now trying to tear the aircraft loose from the still attached harness. The salute, and *Ka-frigging-bang!* There she goes. The aircraft was propelled out of its own image, streaking forward and off the bow, on its own. As always: first a scary-looking sink, until the thrust takes over and it begins to climb. Doug was next. He's off. Nick now at full power. There he goes. Number four—Earl, was next on Cat three.

A Navy Crusader was being directed to the number four cat (the outside cat on the port side), crossing just behind Earl on cat three. Bob wasn't happy with where the Crusader was taxiing. "Geez Rog, that's dangerous. That Crusader's gonna pass right through Earl's jet blast."

"No worry Bob, Earl's just at idle power. The blast fence will raise up before he gets the signal to come to full power." Right while I was answering, the launch officer started the full power run-up signal for Earl (who had no way to see behind him). Earl went to full power *but the blast fence hadn't come up.* It was like watching a glass of milk tip and not being able to reach it or do anything. Just paralyzed. The swept wing Crusader, passing through Earl's jet blast, at first almost in slow motion, its right wing raised up, its right wheel lifting up off the deck. It tilted further left, and began a skid on the left main gear towards the edge of the flight deck. In front of God and country it went over the edge and was gone!

In these over-the-side incidents, as the aircraft is rolling inverted, ejecting even a half second late would be suicide, propelling you *downward* into the sea. But this time, before the right wing went through vertical, thank God, the pilot pulled the ejection seat handle. He did it! He got out in time. We watched the ejection seat hurtling away with a trajectory above horizontal. (We all wondered if—thinking we *might* be going over the side, would we have the presence of mind to pull the ejection seat handle before our aircraft rolled upside down.) This guy had done it. He had the nerve and reflexes to do it! We watched the hurtling object—half-man, half-metal, arc out and away from his aircraft. We all were watching for the next thing—an *important* thing! We were watching for "seat separation," when an air bladder in the cockpit seat automatically inflates and pushes the pilot out of the seat. This separation also triggers the mechanism to deploy the pilot's parachute, decelerating the human projectile. No seat separation, no parachute!

But the pilot remained in the seat! Speechless we watched the guy and the seat come down together at a high velocity and hit the surface. There was a huge spray and he ricocheted into the air again. This time he and the seat fell back with only a small splash—not a hundred yards off the port. By now the crash alarm was going full blast and the ship was already heeling hard in a turn. The inaction and lack of animation that occurred when the plane was going over the side was short-lived. The deck was electrified now; accelerated activity everywhere. People were running and pointing and shouting. Binoculars were out. Commands were booming over the loud speakers. A light skiff and three rubber rafts were put over the side. The rescue helicopter was launched. The crash alarm continued howling.

The ship circled for almost an hour, while the boats and chopper frantically crisscrossed the impact area, apparently without success. The chopper repeatedly dipped down to within five feet of the water, but was unable to sight the pilot. Divers went in two or three times, also with no luck. The edge of the flight deck was lined with observers. In a couple minutes I could no longer be sure I was looking at the right spot. But even when I had the spot I never saw him come back up to the surface. Never saw him after the second hit. Not a good sign. We waited topside till the search ended. The carrier had to abort the search, to turn into the wind to recover our four aircraft. Geez. Makes you feel sick. I was pretty sure I'd seen a man die. He had ejected in time, but *why the hell didn't he separate from the seat?* He was in the air for at least three seconds and should have separated from the seat, and then the parachute would have deployed. Something didn't function right. I felt a little ill. *Shit!* Decided to go down to the wardroom. When I got there several other guys were already there and looked as if they felt as bad as I did. I sat down next to Nick, who looked like he was taking it bad. "Did you see it Nick? Bob and I were up in the nest. We saw the whole damn thing from the flight deck."

"No. I was in my stateroom. One of the guys from VF103 phoned me up. That's how I learned it was Norm."

"Lundquist?!"

"Yeah."

Earl was sick, knowing it was his jet blast that blew his new Navy friend Norm over the side. Of course it wasn't his fault, the blast fence activator had malfunctioned. Norm's body was recovered the next morning.

Why Did He Stay in the Seat?

When they recovered Norm he was still strapped in the seat. This being the case, an investigation was ordered, to find out why he had not been pushed out from the seat. Too late for Norm, but a critical oversight was discovered. There is a Handbook of Maintenance Instructions for every type of aircraft. It covers the removal and replacement of every piece of equipment on the aircraft. When periodic safety inspections are performed on the ejection seat (every 100 flights) the maintenance technicians use this manual as a step-by-step guide, carefully performing each listed sequential step." Nothing is done from memory. Everything must be done "by the numbers."

In the section on the ejection seat, the pages for the disassembly of the seat listed each step, but the pages laying out the steps for the reassembly, *left out one step!* While the disassembly instructions showed a piece being removed for cleaning and inspection, it failed to list that part's replacement during the reassembly process. If the guy who put the seat back together was not the same guy who took it apart, he would not know about the missing piece. The piece in question here, was a small brass bushing that guides the steel arrow that puncture the nitrogen bottle, whose escaping gases inflate the bladder—pushing the pilot out of the seat *and deploying his parachute.* This bushing was not around the arrow in Norm's seat. Without it the arrow had jammed in its track and never punctured the nitrogen bottle. Therefore the bottle never released its pressure to inflate the bladder, so Norm was never pushed free of the seat and no parachute deployment! What's worse, after checking all the other Crusader HMI's on the ship, it was discovered that the omission was in every one of the manuals. In time, this bushing could have been left out of more seats. All the Crusaders in the fleet were grounded until all the seats were inspected to make sure the bushing was there, and a reprint was published to that page in the HMI. Not in the best of spirits we limped into our next port. My letter to Sara was more serious than the others.

Chapter Eighteen
ISTANBUL AND BELKIS

TeaTime at the Hilton and Meeting Belkis

As usual we moored about a mile out, and also as usual, when the anchor hit the water most of us were topside checking out another new skyline. Squinting through a bright haze we saw an expansive landscape of gleaming rose tile roofs, glinting gold domes, and a hundred minarets poking skyward; a large city that seemed to stretch from horizon to horizon. Built on high rolling terrain it was divided by two large rivers. Looked like it would be easy to get lost in Istanbul. First-timers like me had doubts about what conduct would be acceptable in this strange city. Turkey is a Muslim country and although it tolerates an Orthodox church, it still had strange civil laws on the books—drawn directly from the Quran. I'm surprised the Navy didn't schedule some "appropriate behavior" briefings for us before letting us go ashore.

The second day was my day off and although I had considered staying on board (and in so doing pay back Tripp for at least one day he lent me), I weakened and ventured ashore. Downtown it didn't look that different. Most women on the street weren't wearing veils or in that long black garb. It wasn't difficult getting a drink and some sidewalks advertised "shows upstairs." I say it didn't look different, but Bob said that last night he saw guys with ugly looking automatic weapons on several corners. I came upon the Hilton and decided to investigate. Evidently every Sunday afternoon was "Teatime" and I had picked a good time to be there. Lots of Turkish, but western-looking, frosted haired, large ear-ringed, middle-aged woman with darkly painted lips, catching up on the latest gossip (and doing some serious men-watching). The carpeting was maroon and the tables were black; a nightclub atmosphere at two in the afternoon. As usual I was alone. To facilitate my search I didn't need a half-dozen hangers-on.

Through a comedy of errors and miscalculations, I was graced to meet an attractive, petite, and older woman; and no average one I can tell you! Her hair was blonde or silver and she was wearing a sequined black sweater, large chandelier earrings, and was strikingly made up with a *Roaring Twenties* black beauty mark on her cheek. She spoke perfect English and being so blonde (if it were) I was surprised to find out she was 100 percent Turk: Belkis Soylemengoza, *the daughter of the Turkish Minister of War*. But not enamored with politics. She'd been married to a politician once—the Mayor of Istanbul. She told me that she'd never get involved with a man in government again. Her husband had not been voted out, he had been shot out!

For once I had not picked a 5'9" 38D female. Belkis was tiny. From close quarters I noted a considerable age difference. I sensed that she was not going to be *that* woman or be part of a new life for me, but it would be interesting to hear what she would have to say. She looked like a thin Mae West and acted and sounded like Zsa Zsa Gabor. Every other word was "Dahling," and it was perfectly natural for her—she could get away with it. It seemed like everyone that came in the hotel knew her. Our conversations were frequently interrupted by demonstrative waves, kisses, and hellos. She could flash a smile in a heartbeat, and instantly come back to her story as if the greeting had never occurred. During our repartee she asked me "Have you been to England darling?" Embarrassedly I admitted that I'd only been at Heathrow, and then just a couple hours."

And then the story began, one that had me captivated for at least an hour. Here's the short version: It occurred when she was 18 and attending a private school in England. They took their meals in the pub beneath their quarters. One night at dinner she noticed a dashing young Englishman eating just several tables away. Belkis said he made her heart flutter and she couldn't help stealing glances at him—which he returned. Her nanny (Aunt Eda) later asked her if she had seen that man at dinner. Belkis relayed to me that "Not being daft dahling, of course I said no." Aunt Eda said that was good because *he's the biggest playboy in all of England*. In the morning when she awoke, her bedspread was covered with roses, which was a great mystery to Aunt Eda (but not to Belkis). A few nights later— just as she finished her dinner, he stood, walked briskly to her table, and right in front of Aunt Eda, scooped her up, and carried her out the door. In the cold damp air outside he plopped her down in his open Mercedes and without saying a word, sped two hours north to his grand manor. There for several weeks he wooed her until she became the willing recipient of his ultimate advances. The man was Adrian Conan Doyle, *the son of the author of Sherlock Holmes!* Four months later his wife returned from a curhaus in Germany, and late one night visited Belkis's room. She said she knew Belkis could have any man she wanted, and to please give her peace and leave her home. Belkis did.

It was much more detailed than my recap, and it wasn't the only story, but the time came to say goodbye. She made me promise to meet her in two days—Saturday night, and that we'd have a grand time.

A Night to Remember

Turns out she had a "double-date" planned. Though I had assumed we'd meet the other couple at the restaurant or a hotel, we drove into an upscale part of town—to the residence of the German Ambassador. At the gate we were met and grilled by two sturdy men, who I'm sure were more than domestic staff. We were ushered through a grand entrance and into a marble floored foyer, where we walked across a spectacularly inlaid black, yellow and red coat of arms, and under a giant chandelier. You might imagine I was impressed (and nervous) but Belkis was in her element, beginning an animated conversation with a well-dressed gentleman who could have been the ambassador himself. I heard voices and footsteps descending a white circular staircase. Basked in the brilliance of the foyer light, I spied our companions for the evening. Belkis was hugged and kissed, and all sorts of niceties were exchanged (in English and French. No Turkish). The gentleman was in a gray-striped business suit. (I vowed to buy some sharper looking clothes.) He was about forty and she I think—a little younger. She was stunning—in fact, regal, in a long white gown, hair piled high, with a tiara. *Wow, what friends Belkis had!* I knew that I had seen these faces before. They were familiar—famously familiar. But where? In the newspapers? In the movies? In another minute I would know: He was Maxmillan Schell, the German movie star. And the lady? *Whoa...* Princess Soraya—the ex-wife of the Shah of Iran!

Belkis introduced me with her usual editorial flourish. My ancestry and life's work, while somewhat vague, left one with the idea of good blood, status and noteworthy accomplishments. The next couple hours there was never a moment that I wasn't afraid of making some giant faux pas. I think we went to the best restaurant in Istanbul, where we were shown to a prominently located table (Belkis being greeted about six times getting to it). Observing the décor and clientele, I was worried about what the check would look like. Here—alone with us, our guests were amiable and informal, and the chosen topics were not what I would have expected. He was concerned about uncared-for pets in Germany—dogs and cats without homes. She asked lots of questions about suburban life in the USA—particularly about women working. I even managed to get into the causerie, relaying a couple of what I hoped were interesting anecdotes. But the real surprise of the evening was yet to come.

Overnight in the Hoosegow!

Leaving the restaurant we hailed a cab. I was in the front seat. Belkis, Maxmillan, and Princess Soraya were in the back seat. Although Maximillian was the perfect gentleman, the driver took an instant dislike to him. Halfway to the German Embassy, he gave Princess Soraya a light peck on the cheek. The driver saw this and went ape shit. Maxmillan—a Christian (which translates to "infidel") was with a Muslim woman. That alone was unthinkable, and unheard of, but infinitely worse, he kissed her! A giant "No No." The driver turned around every 30 seconds to berate Maximillian, before stopping in front of a building with green globes. The driver was out, up the steps, and inside. Not two minutes later he emerged with a uniformed police officer and began pointing at Maximillian. I knew the beef was the kiss. At first I thought Belkis was mad, but I could see her muffling a laugh. The three of us were ushered up the steps and into the station. While we were being booked, Belkis plopped herself on a corner of the chief's desk. The cab driver was acting satisfied, like he'd won and was just waiting to see us led to a cell, which we were. Through the bars I paid him a bunch of Lira for the ride and he left.

The way Belkis and the fat chief were talking, I thought it was being done just to appease the driver. What I thought was supposed to be just a momentary appeasement of a local Muslim cab driver, turned out to be an overnight stay in the Istanbul jail! I'm sure Belkis could have made one phone call and had us out of there in a minute, but to her it was a grand opportunity for "theater" and she was playing it for all it was worth. About three in the morning (I guess Belkis was responsible) our meal came: a large flat piece of bread, several types of cheese, and a bowl of a light green, creamy herb dip. And to top it off, a delicious cake made out of dates and brown sugar. (We even got some homemade wine from the jailer.) We played cards—a strange game with cards having only symbols (no numbers).

I couldn't believe where I was and what I was doing. An ordinary (not even ordinary) A4 pilot, here—with *these* people! Belkis and the princess hardly stopped talking the whole night. (I'm sure circumstances had brought them together when younger.) It was a helluva night, I couldn't believe it. Once again, no one who knew me, knew where I was. *Me in jail in Istanbul with Maxmillan Schell and Princess Soraya!* Who's gonna believe it? Talk about an in-port visit. We were out in the morning. I was off for the dock, but not before Belkis told me to save Friday and Saturday as she had another real surprise for me.

A Trip to the Black Sea in the Off-Season

Belkis's surprise was not going to be for three days, and I used them onboard—every minute of every day, to earn my keep. Made whatever improvements I could in our aircraft maintenance procedures and had good talks with the guys that worked in the shop; even got off an overdue letter to Sara. On the day of the big surprise I made the trip ashore and hailed a cab to Belkis's apartment. She ushered it away, having arranged for one of her own. Her driver appeared to know her and be overjoyed to have her as his fare. Without a word about our destination we were on our way. I was being whisked away like a prisoner across nighttime Istanbul; first through gaudy downtown, then an abandoned industrial area, then past some tiny markets on the outskirts of the city, then through a barren farming community. The mystique of an unknown destination was exhilarating—I was someone in the midst of something sinister. We drove for about an hour. Belkis didn't say a word. In silence we continued into a remote and completely uninhabited area. No towns, no lights, no other cars. No activity. There was no moon and the starlight was dim; an especially dark night—which added to the suspense (and my feeling of again being at a location not known to anyone).

Finally we were "someplace." We rounded a bend and were in front of a large, unlit building. I could see no signs out front. The entrance was completely dark; only one or two upstairs rooms emitting light. It looked like a resort hotel at the height of the off-season, maybe even closed—housing only a skeleton staff. The driver couldn't get out of the cab fast enough, committed to assisting Belkis in every way. When he was sure there was absolutely nothing else he could do, he accepted a big hug and was on his way. A member of the hotel staff collected our luggage—mostly Belkis's. I only had one piece, closely resembling a gym bag. (I vowed—as soon as I could I was going to get one of those neat Italian calf-skin bags with lots of straps.) Up the steps and into the reception area, which did little to change my mind about the status of the establishment. Belkis approached the counter with her usual disarming manner, flashing her smile and inquiring about our reservations. Needless to say, I was a follower here.

The concierge acknowledged that both the rooms were ready. *Both? Two rooms?* Evidently this was what she had reserved. But ah-ha, as I listened further I learned the two rooms were *communicado*. Adjoining rooms. He then said—eyeing Belkis with an intimidating look, "And Madame, I'm sure you won't be wanting the key for the door between them."

Oh, that son of a bitch putting her on the spot like that. What can she say now? Belkis looked him dead in the eye, smiled and replied unashamedly, "More than anything in my life." *Holy Shit! Did she tell him or what.* I had never even imagined a woman so boldly express a desire for me—even in private, let alone to announce it like that! I was now sure tonight was going to be the night. The hotel *was* empty. In the lobby and all the way to the room we didn't pass or even *see* another person.

Inside the room was a row of vertical windows that extended from waist height to the ten-foot ceiling—wide open. A damp wind was blustering in, billowing the sheer curtains upwards to the ceiling. Leaning on the wet sill probing the blackness, the wind bringing tears to my eyes, I couldn't make out a thing. But I could hear and feel the crashing of waves against the hotel's stone foundation, straight down beneath our window! *The sea!* Open water below! Where *were* we? Belkis said we were on the Bosporus; the turbulent passageway through which the Black Sea escapes towards the Sea of Marmara and then the Mediterranean. To me, the dark sky, the gusting wind, and the force of the sea, suggested a rebellious wildness. Belkis was in and out between the rooms, trying on several outfits. I still didn't know what our plans were. We each had a glass of Turkish wine before making our exit.

A Dinner Out Like None Other

Finally dressed she indicated it was time to be going. Departing, it was obvious the previously stung concierge had learned who he could fool with. Only a movement of Belkis' finger had him obediently off to get us our transportation. Waiting outside the stars were the closest things I could see. The cab arrived and we were on our way. From inside our speeding metal capsule I could see nothing except the headlights reflecting on the road ahead. After about fifteen minutes we made a turn and slowed down. *Wow, what's this?* From what I could make out (which was damned little) we had arrived in what appeared to be an old and long abandoned village; a completely unlit ghost town with small deserted wooden structures. Not a solitary light in the town. Not a single car or person in sight. Not a sound or movement.

From Belkis's utterances I gathered she was telling the driver to go slower (though we were already at a crawl). She was straining to locate some landmark. A little further and she let out a yell. The driver stopped. We were out and he was gone. We were forsaken, abandoned in a dark and desolate night space, just standing there alone on the narrow wooden sidewalk. Still not a sound or movement. Belkis went a few steps in one direction, then turned and a few steps back past me in the other direction. Finally, apparently discovering something she began stomping her foot. Beneath her I heard the sound of rusted hinges and creaking wood. A large door swung up from the walk. A flood of soft light, voices, smells, and ambiance escaped upward towards us. The night was suddenly aglow. Silhouetted in the reflected light was a stocky figure bounding up the steps towards us; a mustachioed dynamo of energy upon whose hairy torso hung a sweaty undershirt and leather apron. He took Belkis in his arms and swung her around. An exchange of salutations and repeated hugs, and then my introduction, of which I understood nothing since it was all in Turkish. (Even if in English, I probably would have been hard pressed to know who she was describing.) He shook my hand and wrapped me in his huge bare arms, and I think gave testimony to his privilege in meeting me. He led us down the stone steps, into an empty but warm and inviting fire-lit space; just one cement-floored room; a very large, heavily beamed, low-ceilinged room, with crudely plastered walls.

Oddly, it stretched uncluttered from wall to wall; not a single stick of furniture. *Not a table or chair in the place.* The only seating was a line of crude wooden booths on each of the two side walls. An open hearth was aflame in a far corner. Spanning the room's rear wall were two long glass display cases filled with all manner of fish, fowl, and meats. The space between the inner ends of the two cases was centered on an open arch through which the help (the owner's wife and daughter) entered and left the kitchen. Behind us—on the wall we'd just come through, was nothing. Midway across the room, several gnarled posts supported warped and dust-covered joists, from which were hanging earthenware jugs, pots, egg baskets, and other farmhouse paraphernalia. The flickering light illuminated shocks of straw and mud sticking out from the mortar above the joists. In Turkey the patrons are supposed to inspect the kitchen. We complied. There were meats, vegetables, soups and sauces, and juicy-looking entrees in various stages of preparation. (Enough to get my appetite going.) Several huge iron skillets with long handles, as well as other brass and copper cookware.

The next few minutes were "theater" to me, but actually happening. There were five of the high-backed wooden booths on each side of the room. Each was identical, with hard unpadded bench seats. (All equally uncomfortable.) Belkis began checking them out, sampling their perspective and mood-setting location and seeing how she fit. Like a housecat testing the cushions, she would settle herself down on a selected bench, squirm a moment or two, evaluate, then shake her head disapprovingly and move on to another. After several tries, finally: "Ah yes darling, this one will do."

We were paid touching visits by the owner's wife and daughter. The only other two diners in the place gestured respectfully to Belkis. I still had not heard a word of English. I just sat there reveling in the atmosphere and sipping what Belkis told me was the best farm wine in all of Turkey. The owner had brought out a bottle specially for us—actually a small clay jug with no opening at the top. With a knife he whacked the neck of it, shattering away the top inch and we were ready to pour. While waiting for our meal, which we let the owner choose for us, I noticed the graffiti scratched in the soot-stained plaster wall alongside our booth. Some in English, some in French, there's Italian, and of course, what I guess was Turkish. I'll admit I may be overly sentimental, but I read a commemoration which I have never forgotten, and have often reflected upon; visualizing a young, dark-eyed girl, with stars in her eyes, who knew exactly what she wanted, and scrawled these words:

> ### Tonight I am more happy than
> ### I have ever been, because
> ### I am with the one I truly love.

To be *able* to love—that's it. Not to *be* loved, but to love. To be one of those few people who have that gift and can know that happiness. So far—sadly, I have not proved to be one of those people. Whoever scrawled this had that capability (and I hoped the referred-to relationship would be forever). I imagined a young woman in love. Nothing more beautiful, nothing more prized. However, based on my behavior there could soon be a short supply of this kind of loving woman. The evening was a wonderful experience. In addition to a savory home cooked meal of roast duck, eggplant casserole, and baked apple with fresh cream, there was incredible conversation (and I mean *incredible*). I was engaged in a deep and prolonged colloquy with the owner, who spoke no English. I don't know if our seeming success was the result of intense effort or much more likely— two of those ceramic pitchers of wine. Neither the owner nor I considered for a moment that we weren't conversing flawlessly; our gazes locked, nodding, interrupting each other, and then agreeing wholeheartedly.

Finally, time to go. No idea how much the bill was; in Lira it was about half of what I had. The owner visited our table and whispered something to Belkis. Lots of good-byes, more hugs and kisses and we were on our way up the steps to the bizarre soundless world above. It was as windy and black as before. I surfaced on the walkway behind Belkis. As my eyes adjusted to the darkness I was aware of large shapes, heard noises, and then was able to make out *a two-horse drawn carriage in the street in front of us.* I recognized the smell of heated animals and the treated leather of the carriage compartment. The owner helped Belkis in and I stepped up behind her. *Who's gonna believe this!?* A couple shouts, a crack of the whip, and the carriage jerked forward, the hoofs pounding the packed dirt. The trip back to the hotel was taken at a good clip, maybe even too fast. The horses were moving out, on a narrow, rock-strewn road carved out of the cliffs above the crashing waves below. Peering down out of the fringed windows, I had a view similar to the one out of our hotel room. Of course it was my first time in such a carriage and I was captive to the creaking, rocking, and the smell of leather.

Tonight?

Back at the hotel I assumed this would be the night she'd grant me intimacy. But after everything that had happened this evening, making love (if I could) might be less exciting than the earlier part of the evening. But this woman was going to do it right. My room was lit only by well-placed candles. Two snifters of brandy awaited our taking on the small table at the foot of the bed. After what I guess was a reasonable time to make a gentleman wait, Belkis appeared and tarried (in an alluring and provocative way) at the adjoining door. She was wearing only a see-through long black lace gown and high heels. I suppose now is as good a time as any to make a confession. When I first spied her in the Hilton and described her as probably being in her late *forties?* Seeing her now I'd have to say fifties (or even sixties)! Whatever her age she acted the perfect seductress with all the right moves. I was sitting on the end of the bed, next to the small table, brandy in hand, waiting, wondering (and worrying like hell). After a minute or two of leaning like Marlene Dietrich against the side of the doorway, she walked straight over to me, and stopped—her smooth white abdomen not fifteen inches in front of my face. There, she pulled her shoulders back, put her hands on her hips, and put one foot up on the coffee table—now my face not a foot from the inside of her white thigh.

My expectations in having initiated (and now continuing) this relationship with Belkis, were a mystery to me. From day one I knew she would never be that one woman I was praying existed, nor could she possibly represent the key to that new and exciting life I felt was waiting for me. Soon enough we were in bed and I was taken back. For such a strong-willed and commanding person otherwise, holding her now—there was nothing to her. She was tiny, her legs and arms were thin and soft. Her skin was warm and smooth, but loose. Her hair seemed dry and stiff. Her perfume was strong. Being the recipient of all this theater made me even less confident in carrying out my role in her plan. But I felt like I owed her something and I *did* want things to play out the way she must be envisioning them. I didn't want to disappoint her, especially after the evening's magnificent buildup.

I'd never been in bed with a woman this old, but commenced the expected foreplay, and even more daring exploration. Her opening felt spacious—yawning, and as such, with the help of my hand I ultimately managed to stuff part of me inside her. Certainly it could not have been what she was expecting to feel. I was shocked at how easy what little of me there was made it in. With my scant rigidity, I wasn't exerting adequate pressure anywhere, and to avoid an accidental extraction I had to exclude worthy thrusting movements. While she had to have felt my insufficiency, perhaps at her age, her satisfaction lay in just knowing she had a man inside her. Myself, I was not at all proud of myself.

We had a fresh (windy) breakfast on what would have been a picturesque terrace in another season. The ride back to Istanbul was picturesque. Inside the city we stopped at the Political Club and then the Hilton lounge for tea. At the Political Club she introduced me to the Poet Laureate of Turkey, whose last name sounded like mine. Big joke there. (I got an autographed copy of his award-winning book of his poems.) Belkis was showing me off again, which I have to admit was damn flattering. I'd never been shown off before (and deservedly so). It was late afternoon and the crowd began thinning. I was tired and I could see that recent activities had taken a toll on Belkis as well. Although we gave a lot of lip service to "next times," *and her visiting me in the states!* I think we both knew there was no chance of it. I was quite sure when we said good-bye, that I would not see Belkis again.

Back on the ship and reflecting on my time in bed with Belkis, besides the deserving recriminations, I remembered some advice I had once received. *Don't start sleeping with older women, it'll destroy you!* I wasn't sure exactly what that "destroy" thing meant, but I had an idea, and in view of my existing problem I sure didn't need to do anything that would make things worse. If I was at all concerned about one day validating myself in the rack (and you and God know—I was) it was not going to be with the likes of Jacqueline (that first night ashore in Cannes) or now Belkis. These women were not of the age and personality I would need. Early on I had sorrowfully discovered it wasn't Connie from Minnesota, or even more discouraging—tragically, my wife Sara. I had no alternative except to cling to the belief that I would, somewhere, and perhaps on this cruise—find that one magical woman!

Chapter Nineteen
A WORLD FAMOUS ARMS DEALER!

Meeting Leo

On a previous in-port stay I had been fortunate to meet a most accomplished man: Leo Lippe; the very first director of Paramount Pictures, the first president of the American Society of Cinematographers, the head of the OSS in Europe during WWII, and now the CEO of a large and well-known stateside gun company. Since the production was accomplished in Italy, Leo had a permanent residence in Milan. I had been in the liberty boat about to leave the dock when I observed him (in an expensive camel-hair topcoat) asking the Shore Patrol guy, if he and his wife could get a tour of the carrier. The Shore Patrol guy answered they couldn't do it without a sponsor. Overhearing this from the boat, I volunteered to be their sponsor.

On the way out to the ship, Leo told me about his company that made replica firearms for collectors. (And leading me to believe, much more.) The tour of the carrier couldn't have gone better. The Skipper even told me to bring them to our formal squadron dinner that night. In spite of being hugely successful, Leo acted sincerely impressed with everything he saw, as if he was truly humbled to be part of our military pomp and circumstance. (Oddly his 4'8" wife Winona did not speak a word during the whole visit.) I was pleased that my squadron mates treated them with such respect. In this short visit Leo and I seemed to become unusually close. Later that night taking the boat back to the dock he said if we ever put into Genoa I could hop a train to Milan and visit them. I told him we would be there the eleventh of February. He reflected a moment, and seemed pleased, hinting I might be able to accompany him on something that could be real exciting.

And it was about to happen because here we were in Genoa. I got the first liberty boat, jogged to the train station, and boarded one of those *Rapidos* to Milan. I arrived in the Milan train station, purchased the required tokens and found a phone with a tone. Got through to Leo.

He picked me up and said everything was a go for tomorrow. His tiny wife Winona acted thrilled to see me, as if we were dear friends meeting after a prolonged absence. Only in their apartment five minutes she runs to another room and returns with a black leather hat box and a hugely proud smile. I was about to meet "Flipper," a ceramic seal Winona had picked up in the islands somewhere, and was—to judge by her fawning attention and stroking—*their child!* Leo never said as much but I had to conclude Winona was not "playing with a full deck." In spite of this he treated her as lovingly as any husband I ever saw. (When he was with Paramount Pictures he had met her on the set of an old black and white western when she was playing the Indian maiden.)

It was almost noon, but Leo had the makings for an omelet strewn across the kitchen counter (piles of diced onions, mushrooms, ham, and cheese). During the ceremonious preparation I grilled Leo as to the details of our trip, about which—up to this point, he had only hinted. "Yeah," he said matter-of-factly, "tomorrow we're going to Sofia!" Which I knew was the capital of communist Bulgaria; the "black hole" behind the iron curtain. *The last place in the world for a USMC Captain to be!*

"And tell me again Leo, what's the deal? Why exactly are you making this trip?"

"A long story Roger. I may buy some guns, in fact a hundred thousand of them." He continued, gesturing with an onion in one hand, the knife in the other; pausing only occasionally to nibble a piece of ham. "During World War II—in 1943, the Italian 10th Army and the German *Afrika Corp* led by General Rommell—the "Desert Fox," were hard at it in North Africa and needed weapons. The Nazis, out of the North Sea port of Bremerhaven—launched an innocent appearing commercial tanker with a hold full of guns—a hundred thousand of them. It made it safely past the Netherlands and Belgium, through the Strait of Dover, and then down the French coast. So far so good. But off the coast of Portugal an old Royal Navy frigate manned by a bunch of English naval cadets, challenged the tanker. The damned kids fired across the bow. The tanker tried to make a run for it but steamed right into two British Navy battleships. Of course *these* guys knew what they were doing; corralled it and ran it into Lisbon. Everyone knows that the ship was moored in Lisbon. And it's a matter of record that the guns got unloaded. But for twenty-plus years, nobody has been able to find them. They never turned up anywhere; just disappeared off the face of the earth.

There was a small delay again as Leo checked two different containers of cream, shook one, rejected it, poured the other into the mélange, whipped it a minute or two, and dumped it all in the fry pan. "Now, and here's the catch! These weren't just *any* guns. They were the Mauser Karabiner 98k—the most accurate and easily maintained firearm ever designed. You can't get enough mud into that breech to stop it working; only nine pieces, three pins, and two springs!" Almost reverently he said, "I would love to have met that Paul Mauser. In fact our famous Springfield rifle was almost an exact copy of one of Mauser's first bolt action rifles. It will always be the best. A classic—like a 47 Ford. And all the tooling to maintain them was on board the ship as well. A goddam bonanza! Well six months ago they turn up in Bulgaria.

While all this was very interesting, I pondered the reasons Intercontinental Arms (Leo's replica gun company) would want *these* guns. Perhaps Leo was working for the CIA (with his arms business cover) to buy these guns and get them off the open market. After brunch Leo took a look at my passport, checked my suitcase and chuckled at all the clothes I had crammed in it. Later in the day he tossed a canvas bag into the guest room and said, "Fill it up, that's all you'll be carrying. We won't be checking any luggage. May not even stay the night." *May not stay the night?* The way I'd figured, we wouldn't even get there until late in the day. We had a pleasant rest of the day and evening, mostly me answering questions from Leo about operations aboard "one of those flat-tops." I was impressed when—though I was feeling like it was bedtime, Leo insisted on staying up until midnight, so he could listen to the Voice of America radio station sign off with the *Star Spangled Banner.*

The Trip!

Leo poked his head in about seven. I was hungry and pleased when he asked if I wanted another one of his omelets. I did and it was great. If I would have been less nervous it would have tasted even better. A few minutes in the doorway double-checking, a big hug and some last-minute instructions for Winona, and we were on our way. "Like I said Roger, we'll catch a ten-fifteen flight from Milano to Belgrade—about an hour on the ground there, and then a short flight to Sofia." *Wow, two flights, two countries— three counting Italy, all in one day!* Into his modest black Fiat, out of the parking garage and onto the crowded street. Crisp morning. Clear. No one in the world except Leo knew where I was. None of my friends—no one. I was far away and about to get a lot further. God was I lucky to meet Leo that day. How many other people are there in the world like him? Found myself shaking my head, wondering could I ever return to a nine-to-five life after getting an idea of the intriguing people and places and situations out there?

About an hour in the departure lounge and the flight was called. We taxied promptly (and to me—too fast) and were in the air. No turning back now. Leo jotted some things down using that same personalized pocket notebook (and miniature gold pen) he had used the last time I saw him. He jotted down a few things and then stuck the pad back in the inside pocket of that same great looking camel hair topcoat. (So help me, someday I'm going to get one like that.) It wasn't a great aircraft; not new and small, but it would not be a long flight to Belgrade. A couple times Leo made a flirtatious comment to a passing stewardess, which knowing him I recognized were completely harmless.

On the ground, Belgrade looked like what I'd imagined an Eastern Bloc city was supposed to look like. No longer was it clear and sunny; now at one-fifteen (in keeping with the mood) it was gray and windy. The airport was just another airport. Things were organized, but not a lot of color, not many people smiling. A hard-working bunch, Lots of apparently barely-making-it people doing mundane tasks: sweeping stacking, cleaning, hauling stuff—doing crummy work. We filed down a narrow, bare-bulbed corridor towards the immigration desk. If I wasn't with Leo I would have been a wreck. Shouldn't be a problem, the Alitalia guy in Milan had checked my passport and handed it back to me. Leo was walking without any hesitation. Grabbed my ticket once, checked something, then handed it back. I was a follower today—that was for sure. Going through immigration and customs was no sweat; maybe because we weren't going to stay in Yugoslavia (Serbia now). In fact we only stayed about forty-five minutes and never left the international lounge. Evidently Leo heard our flight being cancelled and was noticeably irritated. "The sonuvabitches don't think they have enough passengers to make money, so they're gonna save us to fill up the next flight. Jesus Christ! Over here they can get away with that." The cancellation was overruled and our flight went, only twenty minutes late. Enough time for one more nervous pee.

If the Alitalia aircraft was less than new, the *Jat* flight was even worse. A smaller size jet, but then as best I could count—only fourteen passengers. The upholstery featured elephants and giraffes; probably bought from some African airline going broke. No female flight attendants either; all guys and not the friendly type you're used to seeing. As the flight progressed I sensed Leo was becoming more business-like. He read and reread some old correspondence.

"Roger, no one is going to ask you anything. So don't worry. Only a couple of the big shots speak English. If anybody does ask anything, don't answer at first. In fact don't answer at all. Put out your hand with a half-smile and nod. If you have to speak, tell them you're my nephew." Then he began to mumble, "If all goes well, let's see... three o'clock now, should be on the ground shortly after four; ought to make it on time. Yeah, Roger, we might be able to get the 9 p.m. return flight out of Sofia." Geez, this guy's planning what I know is a very important deal, *and only allotting suppertime to it.* Personally I would have liked to stay all night—see more; get the feel of things.

We're There!

Four o'clock. A bad touchdown, but we were on the ground—safe and sound (for the moment) in *Bulgaria!* The afternoon light was fading fast, could be dark in another hour. If this was the capital it must be a small country, or the airport's a long way from town. Couldn't see a city skyline. There were fields with scrub pine on both sides. We walked on wet and crumbling tarmac—about fifty paces to the terminal building; a two-story wood building painted a pale yellow. Sofia, Leo had said—just like the girl's name, but the sign on the front of the terminal had an extra letter. Leo told me that U.S. citizens were allowed to enter Bulgaria. I knew if he said it, it must be so, but it was definitely on the "banned" list posted on the ship, I knew that. Blind faith, that's what I needed now.

Sometimes a person can become so bogged down with their own affairs, on the job they're just concerned about getting through the day; that's the mood I felt was prevalent among the immigration officials here—half of them women; large, apparently well-fed, but with bad teeth and chapped skin. They had concerns enough of their own—you could just see that. Causing any trouble for us would have necessarily caused them trouble. If we got through, they got to go home. If we weren't an obvious problem, they weren't going to create a problem they might have to solve. Leo told me that entering most European countries, foreigners get a stamp in their passport—authorizing their stay. However, this indelible record of entry could have serious consequences (like a fine, or even imprisonment) for a U.S. citizen who had visited a communist country. The Bulgarian Ministry of Commerce, needing the hard currency of U.S. and Western European businessmen, had an arrival procedure that would keep track of visitors without discouraging the desired travelers. When Leo and I got to the desk, without even one question; in fact barely a glance, the agent spying our U.S. passports, reached for a special pad. Instead of stamping a page in our passports, he gave us each a small form to insert in the passport. If we got stopped by any authorities during our visit, we just showed them the piece of paper. Upon departure we'd turn the paper in and have a "clean" passport. No way to know we'd been to Bulgaria. *Cool.*

We were through and out onto the wet concrete walk in ten minutes. (No bags to claim.) It was still one of my least favorite gray and windy, low-hanging clouds days. Leo hesitated under a galvanized metal awning (struggling against the wind to remain attached to its pipe framing). Not sure why. Didn't know if we needed a cab, but I hoped not since there wasn't one in sight; in fact not a single car loading or unloading passengers. We could have easily been the only passengers on the day's only flight. If I didn't feel it before, which I had since Belgrade, there was no doubt I was standing on a street in a different world. Europe had already been so impressive, and now this. I had a whole new baseline to judge and upset my life. A year ago I had never heard of St. Tropez, or Chateau Neuf du Pape, or the Via Veneto, or dreamed of going on a double-date with Maxmillan Schell, and now *a trip to Bulgaria!*

We didn't waste any time. Leo now ahead of me strode briskly across a puddled street (where a passing car soaked my left trouser leg). Next, straight through an almost empty parking lot; only a handful of cars, all of them black and splattered with mud. Once out the other side of the lot Leo slowed to a normal gait—in fact now sort of casual, on a path that cut across a weeded lot. I was at Leo's side, *going I had no idea where.* It had been just misting, but now it was a full-fledged drizzle. Don't know what prompted it but Leo waxed philosophically: "Certain rules you can live by, no matter what you're doing in life. Doesn't even matter what you're doing. Lord knows I've done more than my share. How far to go? Who knows. What's right? By whose standards? You know what I say Roger?" I didn't answer. He continued. "It doesn't matter all that much where you draw the line in life, but once you've drawn it, can you stick to it? *That's* the real issue." I would have occasion to reflect on this more than once in the years to come (not to mention these past months)!

In five minutes—only a few hundred yards away from the airport, you would have never guessed there was an airport anywhere in the area. Empty wooded lots in all directions. Not a sound. Noticed my teeth were clenched. Had a slight chill. Trudging along here now behind Leo, made me think about the quote: "the troops would follow that general straight through the gates of hell." That was me following Leo. He was motioning ahead to a spot beyond a line of trees. Coming into view around a curve in the road I saw what could be our destination: an old three-story wood-sided hotel. One that might have been popular in days gone by but was now showing the consequences of years of inattention. "They'll be there; at least a driver. Should be. We're right on time.

The Meeting

The sign said Hotel Bryuksel. We crossed the street and started up a narrow concrete walkway that led to the entrance. It was a long uphill trek; the hotel being situated atop a baren bluff. There was a terrace in front—or at least a cold and wet, twenty-foot by twenty-foot bare concrete slab. (No Cannes beach hotel here! But you had the feeling they knew it.) A peeling white wood railing bordered the long-abandoned terrace, which looked all the more out of place in view of the gray skies and now pelting rain. We started across it. The once brightly paneled red Campari umbrellas now a faded pinkish-gray, tied closed for obvious lack of use. Couldn't make it straight to the entrance since some sections of the route were under water. *Talk about an off-season resort.* No one in sight in front of the hotel or in the entrance. Almost dusk. Some hard artificial illumination was spilling out from one lone chandelier just inside the foyer. We entered.

Inside the unheated hotel there was a modest reception desk on the left, a few pieces of old furniture, and an open archway to the right. Leo turned towards it. I followed him into a sparsely furnished sitting room. There were two men standing against an empty fireplace on the far wall. They could not have looked more like they just popped out of a James Bond movie (indoors but still wearing low-brimmed hats and heavy coats). *Whew.* Even if they did not know Leo, there could be no mistaking it, he was "the guy to be met." They put down their teas (or vodka) or whatever they were sipping in small ceramic cups, and came forward to meet Leo. The small one I'm betting is the driver, held back just a bit behind the taller and younger guy, who I then noticed had a thick cane that he didn't seem to need. He spoke first. "Mr. Lippe I believe." (So far none of them speaking English wasn't panning out. This guy spoke perfect English.)

"Yes, in person." I was anticipating a longer response by Leo. But that was it. Leo was right about the part of them not caring or asking about me. They didn't even look at me. Out of the corner of my eye, I could see the hotel employees standing in front of the reception desk, heads lowered but eyebrows were raised. They were watching our every move. There were no hotel guests in sight. There was no bar or restaurant that I could see. No music. No sounds. The place was deserted. (Which considering the decor I'd observed so far, is exactly what the management should have expected.) The short guy, who was carrying a satchel in one hand, gestured with the other, to start with him towards the far side of the room. Leo did, and I with him, out a side door into a gravel parking lot.

Now Where?

There it was—the "getaway" car; an Al Capone, curtained, old black sedan. Since the two men appeared to be heading towards the front of the car, Leo and I steered towards the back. (I was right, the short guy was the driver.) Safely inside, Leo looked over, smiled, and clamped my leg. (A gesture well appreciated about now.) The vehicle accelerated forward, then heeled left in a hard turn out of the lot. It was almost dark when we came out of the hotel, difficult to see well, and now from inside the car, with the tinted glass and curtained windows, I would have no idea whatsoever of the passing countryside. Tried to imagine wooded areas streaking by, bridges or overpasses; strained to hear horns, or brakes, or other traffic. *Nothing.* In addition to being well sealed off visually, the muffled silence led me to believe we were in a sound-proofed vehicle. No one spoke. Only two, maybe three stops. Suddenly there was a marked deceleration, a turn, the gas applied, and I could feel us starting up an incline. A few seconds of this and it was all over. We were stopped. Engine off. Doors opening. Heart pounding.

As dark as it was when I climbed out of the car, it appeared almost bright in comparison to the last thirty minutes in the back seat. I stepped out onto a graveled surface, glancing quickly across the roof to see Leo's direction. *That's good, he's coming around to my side.* We were in a private drive; a curving, tree-hidden drive in front of an old house—a big, gaunt, empty-looking house with a large barren porch. No curtains or shades on any of the windows. Inside, harsh incandescent light was hitting hard on bare plaster walls. To the steps, up and onto the porch, then in through the wide-open front doors. The house appeared to be abandoned, certainly not presently lived in. Inside there was a room to our right, without a stick of furniture. Scarred wood floors. Old fashioned fixtures. Exposed wiring and electric sockets like I'd never seen. And I was beginning to notice, no heat again.

All I Can Say is Wow, You Shoulda Been There

Leo paused and I almost walked up his back. The two men in front of us had turned left into a ground floor room and indicated to Leo to wait in the hallway. I could hear them talking inside. No idea what language they were speaking. One guy leaned out the doorway and motioned us in. I followed Leo. The room was about twenty feet square with a yellowed ceiling light. No shades on the windows, nothing on the walls. Leo was led to a straight back wooden chair, dead center in the room, and motioned to take a seat. His chair faced a long table in front of a wall with two big windows through which I could look out onto the porch we had just come up on. Besides Leo's chair and the table, there was not another stick of furniture in the room. Two men were standing behind the table. I could only see their torsos. A large metal-shaded lamp hung from the ceiling, shielding their faces from view. Two other guys were standing against one side wall, and two more on each side of me. I don't know that I had ever been more apprehensive—more in doubt and less in control than right now.

It was not comfortable peering into the darkness outside, knowing that anyone outside could easily see into this well-lit room. If there were any spectators outside (and you guessed there were) we were on display. *Easy targets.* The guy behind the table offered Leo a cigarette. He waved it off politely, crossed his legs and adjusted that great camel hair topcoat. One of the guys against the side wall moved to the table and laid a folder on it, in front of what I guessed was the main guy. He never looked down at the folder just started speaking to Leo, without any small talk. (No *How's the wife and kids?* or *How was the flight over?*) He got right down to business. "Mr. Lippe, we have dealt with you before. As you know, we have something of considerable value. We are sure you will be satisfied. We have made a count you can rely on. We have inspected everything. It is exactly as we represented. There is no problem with delivery to Brindisi. We can seal this transfer without delay."

Leo spoke: "I believe you. I have no reason from our past association to expect any deviations. But Mikael, your price is way off base; no way I can do that." There was an awkward pause after Leo finished (though I think they were familiar with Leo and were expecting he wouldn't just roll over with the first deal). Even so, expressions of indignation were exchanged, a couple 'harumphs' and some paper shuffling. Leo continued before they had a chance to speak. "Now I know what the market for these are. You know what they might bring, *if* you can find someone to take the whole batch. I can and will, but at nine dollars a gun—nine greenbacks Mikael, and that's fair." The look on Mikael's face, which I could now see, convinced me he was not so sure. He did not seem at all pleased with this offer. I had no idea what price he had conveyed to Leo earlier, or any idea of what would constitute a fair price.

"Mr. Lippe you are not our first choice. We are only just making life easy for ourselves. The Chinese will give us twelve dollars a gun, and the North Vietnamese over ten. And we have two other potential customers as well. We are not in trouble here, believe me as well."

With this—and I will never forget it, while I was pressing my back into the far wall, wide-eyed, teeth clenched, I watched and listened, as Leo from his isolated "hot seat" in the middle of the room, responded: "Listen, would I be sitting here, 65 years old, with enough money in the bank, to write you guys a check for $900,000—that you know is good, if I spent my whole life believing shit like that?"

Kheerist! In a matter of seconds Leo had switched the mood from one of strained tolerance, to one of antagonism. One that I didn't think we were well-placed to be involved in, let alone initiate. Leo, ten feet from anyone or anything, seated in the center of the uncarpeted, dusty wood-floored room, was a voice from an island. They had him positioned like a suspect being grilled down at the precinct. He had taken the disadvantageous seat all right, but he was not playing the part of any captive; that was for sure. Mikael pointed down at the stack of papers in front of him and said that it would please them perfectly to accept the other offers.

At this, Leo further prejudiced our well-being by replying in the most nonchalant manner: "Mikael, why don't you go down the hall, have a smoke, wash your face, change your shirt, put on a new tie, and come back down here. And I'll make believe you never said that. Nine dollars, take it or leave it. I don't need them either."

It's Over

A conference ensued behind the table. From my vantage point I could not see their faces due to the hanging lamp. Another guy strode in the room from out of nowhere. This had to be the really head guy. The new entry paused just a second as he went past Leo's chair—I thought maybe to extend a greeting. If that was his original intent, he must have thought better of it, and continued to the table. After fifteen minutes of subdued conversations behind the table, they motioned Leo to the table where he affixed his signature to some form, and the deal was closed at nine dollars a gun. There were no handshakes. There was no obvious lessening of the tension. But it was over. No ceremony. Nothing. In two minutes we were back in the car. (Actually not the same car and only a driver this time.) We were on our way. This car had a ceiling light. It was on and no switch to turn it off. It stayed on the whole time to the airport. Leo just looked straight ahead.

A Regret That Never Leaves You

The flights back, the airports, the drive to 16 Piscale Brescia—all were uneventful. In order to catch the last train back to Genoa I could only spend about an hour at their apartment. Just before I left he said he had a surprise for me, and what a surprise! He gave me one of his products—a brand new 41 caliber, 7-inch barreled, blued "Super Dakota" (a replica of the old western six-shooter called "The Peacemaker"). Heartfelt intimacies were exchanged and a silent bond was understood. For reasons not understood, Leo had taken a serious liking to me and it was possible there could be something else coming; me joining him in the arms business, or another venture (Didn't mention it but Leo had accidentally dug up about a ton of sheet metal smelted in the 16th century, and got some wild idea about fabricating counterfeit suits of armor out of it; in fact gave me four books on it to study.) It was as if—in spite of all the obstacles, Leo and I would someday be a team; that at last this could be the beginning of that other life I felt I was destined for. While I often admitted to myself that such a conviction was just a default in my character, I was now ready to believe that another life for me may well exist! In the meantime I'd have the Super Dakota to take out and fondle from time to time, the memories of my trip to Bulgaria, and live to tell his story a thousand times. *But I'd never see Leo again.*

Chapter Twenty

THE LEONARDO DA VINCI

A Short Visit to a Cruise Ship

One more thing (a *big* thing) while in-port in Genoa. I was just finishing an evening snack on our last night in-port (the ship would be pulling out at noon tomorrow) when Mike Ballard came bursting into the wardroom. "Hey Rog, there's an American cruise ship two piers up the wharf, loaded with tourists. Might not hurt to go up there and meet some stateside people."

Even though I was enervated and satisfied after my adventure with Leo, I said "Okay, why not?" It was already after eight, but it would only be for an hour or two and we would easily be back before the last liberty boat at midnight.

Approaching the cruise ship, treading on wet concrete, winding our way around coils of old rope and stepping over assorted piles of trash, I read its name: *Leonardo Da Vinci*. I told Mike that didn't look like an American name to me, and we didn't look like the other passengers going up the gang plank. Bold Mike just grabbed my arm and we went up the steps with the others. As expected by me, onboard there were just a few Americans. Didn't hear much English. Finally we got a good steer: Second deck on the bow, there was some sort of festivity—a buffet or dance, or something like that going on. We struck out for it and could soon hear music and laughter.

We found it! On an exposed open bow deck, replete with twinkling lights and banners, a band banging away on a portable stage, and a long buffet table holding punch bowls and baskets of fruit. About fifty well-dressed multinational passengers were dancing, singing or just watching with glasses raised on high. We navigated to a far gunwale, leaned back against a cold wood railing and began screening the crowd. There were a few single young women and Mike said we maybe should just ask one to dance. To get closer we ventured up to the buffet table. By chance I found myself next to an eligible-appearing young woman—about my age, who for sure was not American. As you no doubt have noticed I had an attraction for the features and mannerisms of these European females. There was both strength and sensitivity about this one, maybe even a sadness. When I finally spoke, it was an embarrassingly weak "Good Evening." She didn't answer at first, then exactly what had I expected: While those lips did form English words, they certainly were not her first language.

Her name was Paulette Bonfils. She appeared happy and sad at the same time, returning to France after working as a nanny for a French family on Long Island. She seemed glad to be talking to me. We danced, and Uh-oh, don't tell me it's happening again, we molded together as one. Some women just fit against men. It's their gift (and curse as well, since fitting so well against *all* men, leads to complications). Without conversing we continued to dance. Each time I looked into her eyes she smiled back warmly. Gotta be careful here; I'm falling into the same scenario as other in-port stays.

After his second dance Mike signaled he was calling it a night and left. And it was late—almost eleven o'clock. I took the same stroll I'd taken earlier—over to the same wet railing, but this time accompanied by this thin honey-haired French woman. We looked up past the awning to the black Italian sky, which now seemed to have more than its share of stars. Next thing I knew we were kissing, and right afterwards I felt her arms slide around my waist. Not too many minutes later we were walking through the hatch to the interior of the ship, and undoubtedly her stateroom. *I was fully aware of what would likely occur there.* I was at the same time fearing that it would, and yet excited at the possibility that it might. What else did I expect? Up to this point I had not indicated I was averse to culminating the evening in such a manner, when in fact I was scared to death that it might. On the one hand I knew what a pleasure it would be to lie next to this woman, touch her bare skin and attempt to share her secrets. On the other hand, in so doing I would not only be attempting another infidelity but risking yet another humiliating non-performance. I was thinking about a lot of things—important things, and one practical thing: *I'd already missed the midnight boat.* (Now I'd absolutely have to get on the Shore Patrol's 6 a.m. shift-change boat.)

It was a tiny stateroom. You could barely turn around in it. No windows. All stainless steel and Formica. Knowing I was at least going to sleep there, I located a small alarm clock on the dresser and set it for

5 a.m. There was just one chair in the stateroom, and I collapsed into it. She sat on my lap, gave me a long kiss on the lips, and began taking me through a photo album. I wasn't sure if I was relieved or aggravated at this delaying activity. I was fast succumbing to the day's activities; in fact was dozing when she snapped off the light. She sat down on the edge of the bed, pulled me down beside her, began pulling off her outer garments, and motioned to me to do likewise. We laid on top of the covers still wearing our underclothing. She had made the decision. *We were going to call it an evening without the normally expected event.* She put a leg and an arm over me and nestled her head into my neck and soon was breathing heavily.

When the alarm went off at five, I clawed my way out of a deep sleep, feeling good about myself—even though my celibacy wasn't a result of proper decisions on my part. Dressing wasn't easy. The room was dark and I had trouble standing on one leg, trousers, then shoes, socks in my pockets. Paulette reached out and grasped one of my hands, which didn't make my dressing any easier. I kissed her good-bye and was out the door. I'm guessing she thought I was a passenger from another deck (not knowing I was going to leap off the ship and run a half mile down the waterfront to catch a greasy boat out to the carrier).

We often hear "My heart jumped out of my throat" or "I was scared to death." I now believe either could happen. When I emerged onto an exterior deck, where I was able to see off the ship. What I could see was water—water everywhere, left, right, front and behind. Only then did I feel the hum in the soles of my feet and realize *the ship was underway. It had pulled out some time in the early morning hours. We were at sea!* I was a prisoner, or worse—a stowaway! Suffice it to say I was in big—very big trouble. I explained my predicament to the Da Vinci's radio operator. He couldn't contact the Genoa U.S. Shore Patrol station, but he got ahold of the Genoa Marina, who would deliver a message to the Shore Patrol office for them to get to the Commanding Officer of VMA 331.

Miraculously, for the only time during the entire cruise, the carrier had only a one-day at-sea period this time—just repositioning to Marseilles, with no flight operations scheduled. And the Leonardo da Vinci was also on a one-day trip—to Nice, *only a hundred miles up the coast from Marseilles!* (The Da Vinci could just as well have been embarking on a six-day cruise to Tunisia!) With a two-hour cab ride from Nice to Marseille, I'd be able to hook up with the ship by eight or nine tonight!

When we hit Nice I was down the gangplank as soon as the lines were tied. Caught a cab and was pulling onto the Marseilles dock an hour and forty-five later. I was the first one in the liberty boat, and ten minutes later was climbing the aft ladder to the flight deck. The Colonel met me at the top, along with most my squadron mates. As you might imagine I received a stern talking-to from the Colonel and was docked one day's leave (and certainly deserved to). Finally in the rack I felt relieved, half safe (born again). Let sleep take over, refresh and renew me. I knew that tomorrow by the time I awoke, we would be one-hundred miles to sea—starting another at-sea period, with who knows what shipboard adventures awaiting.

Chapter Twenty-One
A WINTER RECOVERY AND A REAL SCARE

A Freezing Cold, Bad Weather Launch

Did you ever build a sundeck in July, perfecting your tan, watching a Yankee game and having your girlfriend bring you a cold Budweiser. But try the same thing in January, ears stinging in the wind, fingertips so numb you can't get the nails out of the pouch (and nobody willing to stand outside and watch). Well now, winter was upon us. The ship was plowing through rough gray seas, and we would be making landings through blowing sleet, and onto a slush covered deck. No fun. Tonight I was scheduled as a four-plane Division Leader for the midnight launch.

An Orderly Comeback for Landing

To guarantee the quickest most efficient recovery, pilots are given several time-critical, crucial check points and times for their return and landing. The recovery process for sequencing three flights of four aircraft has to be designed down to the second. It has to be this precise because time is of the essence. You left on a one-and-a-half-hour flight, with only two hours and ten minutes of fuel! Can you imagine getting back to the ship with minimum fuel and then having a gaggle over the ship while twelve planes try to sort out who's next? No fuel for that. So the recovery has to be the ultimate in efficiency. To make it so, there is a set-in-stone procedure for the recovery. Before launch Air Ops gives a time check over the radio. And it is not just a "to-the-minute" time hack, it's a "to-the-second" time-hack—meaning on the call you moved the second hand to exactly the twelve o'clock position. Each pilot was assigned his sequence in landing, and assigned a precise time to start his landing approach.

The Critical Nature of Every Recovery

Oscar—just a point in space, exactly three miles behind the ship was the assigned spot from which to start the landing approach to the ship. Certainly all twelve aircraft couldn't be over Oscar at any old altitude; that'd be a recipe for a sure midair collision. So each pilot, depending on his landing sequence, is assigned an "Oscar Entry Altitude." The first plane to land would be at the bottom of the stack, entering and orbiting at 2,000 feet above mean sea level (the water). I would be the ninth plane to land, so I was assigned an Oscar Entry Altitude of 10,000 feet (and know there were eight guys beneath me). The remaining three guys in my flight would be above me—at 11,000, 12,000, and 13,000 feet. Grinding around in the sky, we'd all listen—*not* talk, on a common radio channel, on which the ship continually broadcast the exact time. ...*In ten seconds it will be Four-Seven.* ...*...five, four, three, two, one. Time: Four-Seven.* If your clock wasn't already precisely correct, you'd adjust it to the exact time. And I mean to the *second!*

I already knew the number one guy (at 2,000 feet) had a "start final approach time: of 0130. Since I was ninth, my assigned "leave Oscar" time was 0138 (the first guy's time plus a minute for each of the guys under me). All this was predicated on everything going without a hitch. And the whole thing was only a second or two away from a real emergency. Each pilot would spend the whole time at Oscar, hoping like hell that no one below him would crash on the deck, or break a wire, or do something that would delay their scheduled time. The worst thing you could do was make a bum approach and end up getting "waved-off" (denied a landing by the LSO). Then you'd have to "go around," pour the coal to it, make a turn to a visual downwind—keeping the carrier in sight, and try it again from close in (without going back out to Oscar.) This meant that instead of using a minute, you used three or four. And each of the guys waiting—above you in the stack, are measuring their fuel in minutes. Delaying your buddy can mean the end of a long friendship. Each minute, when the bottom guy (orbiting at 2,000 feet) departed Oscar and started descending towards the ship, everyone else in the stack would be able to descend 1,000 feet. So each minute I had descended another thousand feet lower. I was now at three thousand feet, and as soon as the guy below me started his approach, I'd descend to 2,000 feet, *and be the next one to depart Oscar (at 0138).*

First the Landing

While orbiting and descending I remembered at launch time the sleet was just starting; just hope it was brief and not happening now. Sure, there's a non-skid surface on the flight deck, but it was a couple degrees below freezing, and the wet deck could be turning to ice. In fact before my cat shot, I had seen flight deck personnel taking runs and then purposefully sliding fifteen feet through the slush. I knew that this deck condition wouldn't affect the approach or the actual landing, but, *after landing*—trying to taxi forward, that'd be another thing! At night, with no visual reference and the ship heaving and listing, a slippery deck could easily spell a skid and disaster—*over the edge!* You knew that after landing they were going to make you taxi right up to within a few feet of the edge to park. In my A-4 Skyhawk I was eleven feet in the air, atop two, long, spindly main gear struts, and an even longer nose gear strut. And to make things worse, airplane tires are small. They have the same failing as motorcycle tires—the area in contact with the ground is about the size of a poker chip. Not much surface to grip, and there would be a poor coefficient of friction tonight. Real easy to slip and slide. One minute had passed. The second hand was at the top; 0138. I'm leaving Oscar, starting my approach.

This is it, *I'm on my way in.* Gear coming down. Flaps going to full. Adding some power. Trimmed up pretty good, almost "hands-off." Airspeed stabilized, and the angle of attack is right on. 600 feet per minute descent. *So far, so good.* At least I'm in good shape at this point. But it was not too hard to think you were in good shape this far out, with nothing to go by. (Not crucial yet.) God willing, this rate of descent will have me at the right altitude a mile out, to pick up the "meat-ball"—that three-colored, mirror-reflected light that would tell me if I was above, on, or below the ideal glidepath. I should be able to see it when I get closer in. If it was yellow, it would mean that I was too high. If it was red, it would mean I was too low (definitely *not* a good place to be). Orange is what you wanted: meaning you were on the proper glidepath! When the pilot first sights these lights he hollers "Meatball," so the Landing Signal Officer knows the pilot now has a reference to make the corrections necessary for a proper descending trajectory.

At two and a half miles I couldn't see the ship—not a hint of it! But that was normal. During night operations every white light on the ship is extinguished and the few dim red lights are there just to mark the overheads and hatches so the sailors don't hit their head or trip.

Two miles out and I thought I could make out a faint pinpoint of colored light that would hopefully soon turn out to be the meatball. Now, it was just a small rust-colored glow. Can't tell whether I'm high or low yet, but know for this distance, mathematically I should be 1,200 feet above the water. And the radio altimeter showed 1,190. Within ten feet. Great.

A mile and a half now, *and it is the meatball, and I'm on it!* Time to make a transmission: "FastFleet 504, Meatball!" Now the LSO will know

I'm on it. (He'd know even if I didn't call it.) That's his job. Might make a good one this time. Everything holding up so far. Must've got the power right the first time. Airspeed is holding right on. Still 600 feet per minute down. Looking good. *Things are computing.* Closer in, getting tense now.

A mile out, about twenty seconds out. Meatball looks orange—is orange. *Isn't orange!* Going to yellow. Shit. *Now it's white!* I'm high! Off with a couple percent power, drop the nose a hair, . Wait. Yeah, it's turning yellower, going towards orange. Coming down. It's orange again. I'm on the glidepath (number three wire height). So far so good. Fifteen seconds out. *Shit!* Turning deeper orange, on the way to red. Took off too much power. Now I'm going low. Add some power and a little back pressure, nose up a hair, a hair more. There it is—Orange! I'm on it, a hundred yards out. Five seconds. Still on it. Five knots fast. Squeak off a hair of power. Just a hair! Good. Hold it, hold it. Staying orange, flashing by me. *Kee-friggin-crash!* On the deck! In a wire! Stopped!

And Then, Something Just as Fearful: Taxiing Forward to Parking

As hard as it was to make the landing, the next thing I was going to have to do—taxi forward to park, was equally dangerous. After having been yanked to a shoulder-dislocating stop, I now had about five seconds allotted to me to let the arresting cable pull me back until the slack in it would let the tail-hook drop free. Soon as it did I'd shove the throttle up and shoot forward. (You had to vacate the touchdown area immediately so the next guy—right behind you, could land.) I'm out of the wire and moving ahead—frantically squinting through my smeared windscreen, into a black abyss, searching for the first (of two) taxi directors who would guide me to my parking spot up on the bow. I think I saw him—well not *him,* just two tiny dancing *pinpoints of light* which would be the Lucite wands he was holding aloft. The taxi director himself was not discernable at all; not as a shape or silhouette. Invisible! Those two specks of light at an indeterminate distance would be him.

I wiped a clear spot in the condensation on my windshield and peered through it at the tiny specks that had now become thin white circles. The invisible ghost was frantically waving his arms—meaning for me to quickly move forward, the next guy is slamming into the deck right behind me. *Get up here! Hurry up!* Easy for him to say. He's not moving, he's just standing there with gum-soled shoes, and has been out there for thirty minutes. His eyes are accustomed to the dark. And *he* knows where he is.

All this was being done on a heaving and falling surface while listening to the unnerving sound of my engine and the screaming of the turbine-driven wenches rewinding the wires. And as I had said, guiding you forward was not a *person*—at least not to you. You never saw a man, no form, not even an outline (for that matter, no deck, or even a horizon), *just two bouncing white specks*—the wands he was holding up. I strove to react properly to his directional signals, to guide me to the second signalman who would continue directing me. Solely guiding on these lights frequently brought on a disarming siege of vertigo, since besides them there was nothing, absolutely nothing visible to compare them to. You would add power, waiting for it to take hold and the aircraft to start moving. Even when it did, inside the cockpit, to you, *it was if you were stationary and it was the flashlights that were moving!* But you knew they couldn't be. The rule was: *the taxi directors never moved.* It was well known how this would disorient the pilot—if the director walked one way, *to you it would appear you that you were moving the other way.* They were forbidden to alter their position. Following these guys was mainly an act of blind faith.

Only five or ten seconds with this first guy and I saw the lights signaling a new sideways pointing motion. He was passing me to the second guy, who would motion me over towards the edge of the deck; *the scary part!* (Right on the edge of the deck and hopefully not over the side!) If the ship listed and a plane started did start over the side, the only hope was a six-inch high scupper drain would catch the wheel of the aircraft, and save you from a sixty-five foot plummet to the water below and almost certain death. In every case where an aircraft had gone over the side of a carrier, it had made a one-half roll and smacked the water exactly upside down. The speed and impact of this would implode the canopy, crushing and suffocating the pilot in a deluge of icy gray water. Not a pretty picture. And here's the life or death part: (Remember Norm Lundquist?) If a pilot felt his aircraft starting to go over the side, then—*before it tipped more than halfway*, he had to eject! If the pilot was a half second late in making the decision to eject, the angle of the aircraft would be too far over and the ejection seat would be propelled downward, causing the pilot to hit the water head first, still strapped in his seat, breaking every bone in his body and be dead before he had a chance to drown.

This second guy would be standing at the very forward edge of the flight deck, leaning back against a half-inch vinyl rope, strung through

36-inch-high stanchions. He was only three or four feet from his own sixty-five-foot plunge. And after he hit the water—not that it would matter, he'd be run over and churned up by the carrier plowing right over him. There's the hand-off signal. I'm over to the final guy. What's he signaling? *You want me to go still more to the right?* Shit. Getting nervous now. Gotta be real close to the starboard edge of the deck! *What the hell is this!?* The two lights were moving to the right! If I was moving to the right, the lights should appear to be moving to the left! I knew that. That just happened with the first guy. Maybe I'm sliding, could be turning. *Shit!* Could I be slipping? Could he be walking to his left (my right)? No way, *they know they're not supposed to move!*

The Dreaded Skid

Stabilized now, still coming ahead. I felt the ship list heavy to the starboard (the right) side. Now the lights were moving to the left! Oh no! *I think it's happening.* I *am* sliding. To the right. Brakes locked! *Oh shit!* I could be going over the side! *Eject?!* In a micro second—conflicting thoughts: If I eject I could end up drowning or never being found. Definitely don't want to eject unnecessarily! Stop! *Please God.* The lights were still drifting further to my left. He was either walking to his right now, or I was sliding right. Couldn't tell. Get ready! If I'm going to go over the side, I have to eject before it continues to tip further. Can't wait till it's gone all the way over. You're going to have to do it. It may be now or never. And then *it started over!* The right wing started downward. *Do it now! Can't wait!* But struggling with indecisive fear *I was frozen in what could be fatal inaction.* A second after it started over—at the same moment I knew I'd missed my chance (not ejected) and was a "goner," there was a hard lurch and no more motion. *I was saved.* The aircraft was hung up on something.

Before I knew it there were ten pairs of lights coming at me. There was noise on the airplane. Flight deck personnel were clambering up the left side of the fuselage and I could hear cables and hooks banging against the main gear. A woosh, and the canopy was gone. I was in the wet wind and sweet-smelling cold air. Hands were all over me and buckles were unsnapping. Straps were flying. Strong, gloved hands were under my armpits, hauling me up and out. Everyone was shouting. Things were happening. I don't know how the hell they got me down the side of that plane so fast. Never felt anything. Like a football fan being passed down the stadium crowd. What a crew. What action. I was aware of being slapped on the back while still shaking my head. Meanwhile, the aft end of the ship was alive and well with the last few remaining aircraft making their landings; none of them the least bit aware of my near disaster up here.

With the soles of my feet on the solid metal of the flight deck, and then my butt on the padded seat of the tug, I was overcome by a wonderful, warm and tingling feeling of sheer relief. Peering through the darkness towards my plane, I could see the left wing pointing to the sky, the right one hidden over the side. The aircraft was perched precariously on the edge, the left main gear caught on something on the edge of the deck, the right one completely over the side. I'd made it. But *not* through my own skill or decisiveness, that was for sure. As far as I was concerned, me—for my part, I had failed miserably, potentially fatally. I should have ejected. For the first one or two seconds, I *did* believe I was going over the edge, and I had "choked." I didn't do a damn thing! Had the aircraft not gotten hung up I would have been in the cockpit when it hit the water (upside down).

This lack of action on my part, exposed to me again (and believe me other times are coming) that while—after the Corps, I would go on to seek high risk employment (for sad reasons and to prove what perhaps cannot be proven) that may not have been the road I was meant to take. In the future I would put myself in harm's way repeatedly; suggesting an aptitude and ability to come up with what it would take. Deep inside I feared I might only be acting; able to sound and look the part, while likely lacking the born mental and physical mettle. In the years to come I would appear to be hanging right in there with the best of them, but secretly believing if push came to shove, I really wasn't one of them. (Jim Stremlow was definitely one of "them.") I don't think as long as it ran, anyone ever guessed I wasn't.

Oh, regarding this incident on the night deck: In my defense, the taxi director signaling me when I slid was relieved of duties and sent back for more training. He *had* started walking with his lights still on (the big "No-No"—almost guaranteed to disorient the pilot—causing him to think *he's* the one moving, when it was the signalman), which had undoubtedly caused me to hit my rudder pedals and tap a brake, starting the slide.

Chapter Twenty-Two

VALENCIA AND JUNE

A Plaintive Summary

Another week at sea completed accident-free, during which time—aware of my growing preoccupation with my times ashore, I had doubled my efforts on board, now as the *Officer-in-Charge* of Maintenance. (Forgot to tell you, my boss Major Burnham broke his leg skiing in Garmisch and was sent back to the states, and I was promoted.) The anchor had made its now familiar plunge. Another in-port and wondering what adventures might await me. I strove to consider my activities ashore as being carried out by someone other than my real self—that "parallel universe" thing. How and why was I letting myself get into these fantasy situations? The thought of my wife or kids, or my mother (or anyone) being aware of my conduct caused me to grimace. But I feared it was not in me to abort the quest, although I wasn't counting on some miracle happening; in which case I would regard this cruise as just a desperate "last-ditch" search that didn't pan out; a series of detached foreign dream-like occurrences that would eventually fade and not affect my marriage. *At least that's what I thought up until Valencia.*

I can't remember much about the city—a Spanish seaside town in the dead of winter, gray and deserted. I must have always been ashore at night since my only recollections of it are during the hours of darkness. Valencia in November was like Philadelphia—windy and cold. My Navy friend Dale and I had forty-five minutes before we had to be back on the dock to catch the midnight boat back to the ship. Enough time to grab a quick snack. Four times ashore and nothing special to report. (And it's true what they say about Spanish girls: *you meet em at church or not at all.*)

A Fortuitous Chance Meeting

But that was before we walked into *this* restaurant; a tiny, five-table neighborhood "hole in the wall." Things were about to change. It was too well lit and harsh looking, with pea green walls and a dirty white tile floor—no ambiance at all. But a few steps inside we got a real jolt. In the back of the restaurant, at two tables pulled together, were about ten heavily made-up, wild-looking girls, laughing, clowning, chowing down like mad, and *speaking the King's English!* All of them talking at the same time, arms waving, fingers pointing. Saltshakers, pitchers, food samples, magazines and 45 RPM records were crisscrossing the table at a quick pace.

We sat quickly at the nearest table. As striking as they were in their striped bell-bottoms and high heels (and raincoats hiding bare midriffs), as much of an audience as they must know they would attract, they appeared oblivious to the other patrons, totally engrossed in their own conversations—not trying to put on a show. They seemed much too comfortable in this strange eatery. Their animated cockney dialogue and spontaneous gesturing were a joy to hear and observe. Were these Brit girls having fun or what? Talk about carefree. Talk about being on top of the world. Talk about not being bored! Long legs were sticking out everywhere. Vermilion red hair. False eyelashes. There must be a theater somewhere nearby. These girls must be some kind of show girls, and lucky for us—speaking English!

I encouraged Dale (who was really good looking and could flash a great smile) to go over and try to strike up a conversation. He did, and surprisingly I was shortly being waved at to join him. I was not very confident, having some real doubts about how much of an impression a couple of square Americans would make on these girls. For sure they had been chased and courted by the best and the worst. While I'll admit they didn't fall all over themselves when we walked up, they were at least going to give us a chance. Most of them stopped talking as Dale gave them out names.

One of them responded, "American chaps are you? Off the ship I'll wager." We owned up to that, couldn't deny it (although I would have rather been a secret agent who had just flown in from Zurich). *We'll start with the truth and exaggerate when we get the chance.* I think they spent the first few minutes deciding whether we were worth talking to, and then began making room for us to join them at their table. They were dancers *not* show girls. Big difference I would learn. Don't ever call a dancer a show girl. They were part of a twelve-girl troupe from the London-based Stafford Ballet. (Not really a *ballet* ballet; they did physically demanding very athletic choreography routines between the acts of vaudeville-type shows.) They were contracted to the touring *Tony Le Blanc Show,* presently doing a stint here in a theater just down the street. (Tony Le Blanc was the Red Skelton of the Spanish stage.) In Spain nighttime entertainment and particularly burlesque-type theater was well received. Sellout crowds every night, and long runs. The girls had two performances a night—between acts. They had just finished their first one. Tony's second act was on right now, and they had to be back soon for their next routine.

The girls were a breath of fresh air. (A *gust* of fresh air.) Listening to their tête-a-têtes I was taken aback at the honesty and caring I was hearing. They would "ooh" and "aah" at each other's family stories, then lean forward with lowered head and finger extended, to offer motherly advice. Their sincere and down-to-earth behavior did not go with their bawdry appearance. They loved Spain and said Valencia was okay, but not as *sympatico* as Madrid or Barcelona (where they'd already done a stint). In Spain under Generalissimo Franco the streets were clean and safe, the people were honest, and living was cheap.

I knew we had to be back on the dock in just ten minutes to catch the Cinderella boat, but I knew another thing too: in the couple more liberty days I had, I was going to make every effort to get to know these girls better; one in particular—June. She was the ballet captain for the troupe (which translates to a cross between a mother hen and a drill instructor). Heavily dyed long dark red hair contrasted a knowing face with an honest smile. Her eyes shone with optimism and innocence, yet at the same time I could see she was someone not to be fooled with. I had a feeling this troupe captain could size up any situation, come to a fair conclusion and mete out firm justice. I was anxious to know more about her. Running out of time I decided to go for broke—try to schedule a date for tomorrow night. We volunteered to attend the performance and then invite them all to dinner. *They went for it!* This accomplished and reeling from our success, we excused ourselves for a speed run to the dock. I was still excited as I lay in the rack, thinking about the Stafford Ballet and June Rice.

The Stafford Ballet in Action

The next evening Dale and I were in town by six o'clock—a couple hours early. The same restaurant as last night, but a different crowd this time. Late last night, besides the girls, there were just a couple second-shift workers wolfing down a plate of beans. At this hour it was full of families; what appeared to be three generations: the gray-haired grandparents, their son the mustachioed hard-working husband, his dutiful wife, and their dark-eyed kids in shorts. About 7:30 I went to the theater and bought a pair of tickets. Think I got reasonable seats though I still don't understand those damn seat sections: *Stalls, Lodges, Orchestra, Dress Circle?* Plus I had to interpret a seating diagram viewed upside down through a window.

At eight-fifteen the doors opened and we were the first ones through. The theater was lavish and huge. Sparkling chandeliers hung from a high-domed ceiling ornately carved with gilded cherubs. Large tapestries and twenty-foot-high murals adorned both sides. A live orchestra was tuning in the pit. I had never been in a theater like this (of course I had only been to one other stage play in my life). The stage must have been seventy-five feet across, maybe more. I had a not-good feeling about a half-filled theater; about a show going broke and dancers returning to England. But five minutes before show-time, in they poured; all well-dressed—every man wearing a coat and tie; lots of older people, in their fifties and sixties. I was impressed. At nine hardly a vacant seat in the house.

Even without understanding a word, the show was great. Bawdy and burlesque, but certainly not X-rated. It appeared Tony Le Blanc was the country's favorite standup comic. It was a three-act comedy with lots of slapstick. Tony's leading lady was a six-foot bleach blonde, with huge bazooms (and this had not been overlooked in the writing of the script). The crowd loved the repartee and sexual innuendos. They were glued to the stage, bright-eyed and totally engrossed, laughing heartily on cue. I watched in nervous anticipation. I knew the girls danced between acts and so was anxious for the first act to finish. When it did—to the swell of applause from the crowd, I was on the edge of my seat waiting for the girls' routine to start (and happy for them that almost no one left for the foyer). A rhythmic prelude rose from the orchestra pit. It increased, the lights dimmed, a pause, and then a primitive drumbeat.

When the curtains parted, I laid eyes on a set that I don't know how anyone could have gotten onto that stage in just five minutes: a foliated jungle panorama with a real waterfall, and rock cliffs going up into the catwalks. The set was adorned by twelve, luscious, gold-dust covered Amazon women—*who would be our dates for the evening!* The bright klieg lights shone off their glistening bodies and sparkling costumes. Three stood tall and proud at the front edge of the stage, towering above us with their spears held overhead. Three or four were high atop a rock ledge, a couple sitting in vines, and one on a huge throne. What a set! I searched but could not be sure which one was June. They all looked the same, with their shining hair pulled back and sequined, heavy makeup, huge lashes, glitter on their eyelids, and the same large bright-red lip-sticked mouth. It could have been one girl on a stage full of mirrors. No way to find June.

When the show began I was shocked at the strenuous moves, split-second timing, and muscularity displayed by these food-munching girls of last night. The amount of energy they were expending was amazing. I was embarrassed at how I had undervalued their skills and commitment. They would explode into each new challenging feat, suddenly demanding their strong legs and backs to arch and spring and thrust them across the stage. Sitting this close I could see the clenched teeth and hear the gasps and grunts as they put forth maximum efforts. It was obvious they were as dedicated to their profession as I was to mine. (Can't believe I said that. *More* dedicated I'm sure.) The crowd loved it and I felt pride and excitement that I knew these girls and that I might get to know them better. I was having a hard time believing that these tempting sorceresses were the same sprawling famished girls I'd met the night before. Boy, could they be proud of what they were doing. The final two acts of the play were as funny as the first, and the girls' second performance was as fabulous as their first.

I was nervous in the theater, but no more than now, waiting in the restaurant at one-thirty in the morning. From the minute this evening was planned I knew the midnight boat was out of the question. I had Tripp standing by for me until noon tomorrow in case it would be an overnighter. If not it would have to be a desperate plea with the Shore Patrol for one of their early morning shift change boats. The restaurant had the same too bright interior. No romantic mood going to be set here. But these girls didn't need any mood-setting after their stage presence. I would learn that they were interested in simple things, real people, recipes, their cats, their "mums." Who would have ever guessed?

I wasn't disappointed, but it was a bit of a shock. Three of the girls were almost to the table before I recognized them as the previously spectacularly beautiful creatures we had seen gliding and leaping across the slanted boards of Teatro Principal. Instead of tall, glistening, statuesque figures, a frolicking gaggle of almost adolescent girls in old sweaters, faded jeans and army surplus jackets bounded through the door. Instead of cascading platinum and burgundy locks, there was straight, thin, straw-colored hair, and scrubbed faces with no makeup. Up close, some bad teeth, a few bruises and a skin rash. Entirely human.

A Dinner Date

Their liveliness, their joy, their shining eyes, and truths as they saw them, captured us again. Snatching chairs, joking, poking, laughing and consoling, it was them again: June, Laurie, Wendy, Claire, the rich girl from Manchester, the real redhead from Ireland, the twins originally from Argentina, and more. I wanted to take them someplace special that would impress them, but June insisted this place would be just fine. If she said so, although I wanted to impress them for June. Straightaway a couple girls gave Dale and I a big "thank you" for the invitation, saying they had to leave. I was a little sorry—would have liked to have treated the "whole catch." Dale had chosen Wendy and they were sitting together at the next table, heads close. As far as eating here, maybe these girls were no dummies. They weren't about to jump in a cab and go somewhere with a couple guys they knew nothing about (clean-cut Americans or not). No problem, we'll eat here and enjoy it. *Por favor Senor, traiganos las cartas.* (The girls spoke Spanish.)

Boy did these girls enjoy eating or what. It was a pastime they had perfected—especially June. She gave me a mischievous smile and snatched up the menu. After studying it just a minute, with a look of satisfaction she slapped it down on the table convincingly. With an impish grin, hunching up her shoulders, smacking her lips and rubbing her stomach, she signaled her anticipation of the treat in store. The rest of the girls were acting just like June—joyously animated and clearly unafraid to show their inclinations. It was obvious they were in the habit of making the most of the moment at hand. Enjoy it, whatever it was, wherever it was. (*Boy, would I like to be able to think and live like them.*) Surprisingly and gratifyingly June appeared to be perfectly content to be here with me. Nothing to indicate she had any regrets or second thoughts. Even in this dinky little restaurant with a new American friend, she was going to enjoy herself. She radiated happiness. I wondered if she was like this with every guy, or if just maybe she thought I was going to be something special.

She cocked her head to one side, closed one eye and squinted at me through the other, daring me to guess what she had selected. Whatever it was, I was sure it was going to be great; or if not she was going to devour it anyway. I suspected no one ever had more fun or enjoyed herself like this Brit lass. I told her about life on the carrier. Not much else I could say. (Don't know if she noticed how many areas I *wasn't* getting into.) I wanted to paint an attractive picture, perhaps shamefully—even one of eligibility, but I didn't want to outright lie. Already that didn't seem right. Of course I didn't mention I was married. Embarrassedly I'll admit I hadn't been starting any conversations with European women by saying I had a wife (and kids)! And certainly it wasn't because I didn't have a family I could be well proud of (or that anyone would not be proud of). It was just that with my well described shortcoming, and the mindset that I had too-soon closed the book on my life's story, I couldn't help dreaming of—imagining another scenario; a successful scenario. Things I was now being exposed to were enhancing the daring thought that there just might be another chapter in my life.

I tried to let June do the talking, although unless she was encouraged to do so she was very content to listen. And what a listener. From the way her eyes stayed on me I couldn't believe that she wasn't seeing right through me. When she did speak, for a change I listened. "You bet. Born in Birmingham; a couple hours northwest of London by motorcar. Everyone from there is called a "Brommy." Birmingham is what you yanks would call a blue-collar city, with lots of factories, trucks and smokestacks. In the early 1900's Birmingham was the destination of all the Irish immigrants. Now the Pakistanis and Indians are joining them. In fact Roger, and it's cute—because of this crazy ethnic cross section, an expression has arisen: *A typical Brommy with a shamrock in his turban.*"

June was one of two sisters; the daughter of a Scottish shoemaker—who from her description was a cross between Jimmy Durante and George Burns. She had wanted to be a dancer since she was a little girl doing soft-shoe routines at his side. She quit school in the tenth grade and enrolled in the only dance school she could afford; one run by a 60-year-old Czech woman and located on the unheated third floor of the old Birmingham train station. She sprang to the clanging of the cars hitching, and did her pirouettes to the circling of the locomotives in the roundhouse below. With the sniffles, cold ankles and chapped hands, she spun and leaped, and peered through soot-stained windows, picturing new and strange places, and imagining audiences all over Europe someday cheering her on.

Concerning this troupe, June had been hired first and tasked to recruit the other girls. All of them were seasoned troopers with at least one tour under their belt, except for Claire—she was only 17 years old and it was her very first tour. Looking past two tables at her young face and wide eyes, I wondered how in the hell her parents ever let her leave England. June had been concerned also and had told the owner that Claire was too young—to give her another year. He agreed, but just before they left one girl cancelled out and they had to call up Claire. The girls had danced in many countries but liked Spain the best. The theater company here lived up to its agreements, the girls were able to rent comfortable flats within their budgets, and the food in the markets (or the restaurants) was good and not too expensive, and it was safe.

June got an omelet and some kind of pork sausage. I ordered a steak. June made me get a plate of *Espinaca a la Crema* to go along with it. A few girls had split to different tables with their boyfriends. I was concerned that having invited them to dinner, I would not be able to track down the checks, and that the girls would buy their own dinners. Some did buy their own and still thanked me profusely. The girls—all of them, were great, but certainly weren't out to be impressed. They asked us lots of questions about the USA. Dale told them all about New Orleans and the Mardi Gras celebration. With no special effort on our part, the girls seemed to be having a perfectly good time, right here in this dingy restaurant. I had spent so much time of recent, envying the European men for their appearance and worldliness, and now all of a sudden I find that these girls are not only interested in America, but in average American guys.

The girls adored June. A half dozen times one or two of them came bounding up to our table, gave June a big hug or a kiss, and excitedly related this or that about herself, or her boyfriend, or her family in Liverpool or Manchester. It was obvious that as their leader, she was someone the girls looked to for advice. And I was sure it wasn't because she had just been *handed* the title of Ballet Captain. It was because of her experience, earning their respect many times over. At twenty-seven June was a veteran on the dance tour. She had been here before. (She'd been everywhere before.) I felt—and I think for the first time in my life, that June was a woman I could easily respect and admire, *and be faithful to.* Already I found myself hoping for good things in her life (with or without me); that she would get what she deserved, that things would turn out all right for her, that there wouldn't be tough times for her, or even mediocre times. I really did feel this way.

What Next

Wrapping up dinner and paying the checks—*at three-thirty.* Whew, was I going to be exhausted tomorrow! As much as I wanted to spend more time with June I felt myself slipping; dozing off in the middle of my own sentences. Need to rest, need to charge up. But I also knew tomorrow was the last night the carrier would be in port. If not tonight, it would have to be tomorrow night. So in spite of what duty problems it might incur, Dale and I laid on another date for tomorrow night. Maybe we could try going dancing—just the four of us. (No longer a need to impress the rest of the girls.) And the good news, June and Wendy went for it!

We were able to talk our way onto the first Shore Patrol boat (which wasn't until almost five o'clock). Entering my stateroom at 0600 I passed Jim on his way out. He gave me some mildly disapproving looks. Not a good thing, but he doesn't understand. With what he has going for him he'd never need to get involved in the type of thing I was mired in. Hopefully my reckless activity, coming and going (mostly going) had not become too apparent to my squadron mates. I'll work on that later. Have to sleep now—at least a couple hours. Then I'll get up and tear the place apart. Fell asleep like a dead man. The alarm went off at 0800. Showered, shaved, dressed, and to the shops; in fact the shops and half the ship, making sure I was seen and seen doing good things. It may be my shipmates were oblivious to the decline and fall of Roger Yahnke. I was gratified at how much the other pilots and the men in the shops *didn't* know about me. *Thanks again God.* And guess what? Today is my own liberty day. I don't have to swap with Tripp.

The Strangest Place I'd Ever Been

That night—same restaurant, one-thirty in the morning. Girls should be here any minute. I was nervous. Don't think Dale was ever nervous. (And he shouldn't be. He looked like an Italian movie star and could bench press 250 pounds.) There they were! I saw June. She was first, followed by Wendy, and Laurie—*a third girl.* We helped them get seated. Laurie was concerned her tagging along might be a monkey wrench in Dale and my plans, and the dating gods were with us: "No June, you and Wendy go dancing. I'm out on my feet and have some letters to write." Now Dale and I had to come up with the late-night plan. We weren't sure what our options were. We asked June and Wendy if they knew some after-hours club where there might be live music at two-thirty in the morning. Wendy responded. "Junie, how about the place out on the beach, in the middle of that big parking lot?"

"Don't know Wendy, haven't heard much about it. Think it's open now?"

"Yeah June, t'is. Claire's been there and said it had a good band.

"Claire's been there?" I could see that June was not at all happy that the too young and innocent Claire had been there. While she was still shaking her head and before Wendy could answer, Dale and I decided to jump on the idea. We hailed a cab and were on our way; long unlit stretches; empty crossroads; deserted neighborhoods in a winter ghost town. A few minutes later, a huge and completely empty parking lot, with one unmarked, unlit building standing alone in the center—to all outward appearances, locked up; abandoned. No outside lights. No signs. The few windows there were, were shuttered. After circling the building we found one unmarked door that we decided must be the entrance. And it was.

We entered one of the strangest, least explicable public places I'd ever ventured into. Once inside we were in a black abyss. The interior of the building was just one, large, unfurnished, cement-floored room. We stood rooted to the spot. No bar or tables. Not a single staff member—if there even were any, approached us. In fact I couldn't make out a moving shape (employee or patron). In the center, front to back across the emptiness was a floor-to-ceiling lattice work divider, separating the space into two rooms. In the space to the right—not a thing; not a stick of furniture— nothing. In the space to the left, an empty floor, seemingly for dancing. It was illuminated by only one recessed, dim ceiling light in both far corners (which did little more than mark its own location). In the farthest corner— in the dark, a band was playing. But not a soul on the floor. Against the whole other side of the lattice divider and the far side wall, were lines of straight back chairs; all occupied by hunched over motionless beings— guys and girls, but not speaking to one another. Hands clasped in their laps they were staring straight ahead. No sounds of laughter; not even a snicker. No bar or any place selling drinks (one of which would have come in real handy at this point). Our eyes searched for something that would make sense. Could it be this building is the bus terminal during the day, and they just move all the benches and counters somewhere at night? *What in the hell kind of place was this?* As far as I could see, no one was having a good time. Dale and the girls appeared to be as cool to this place as I was. June looked at me and drew the corners of her mouth way back and rolled her eyes. Dale shrugged his shoulders and Wendy (thank God) said "Oh well, as long as we're out here, let's go for a walk on the beach." *Best idea I'd heard yet.*

A Scary Bedtime with June

Five minutes from the club we found ourselves on an uneven sidewalk, making our way through a rundown, almost abandoned, seaside area. No new or modern buildings, only some small, derelict cottages on the beach, most in a state of bad repair. Weed clumps were blowing across the street. A dismantled car up on the curb. Other than the bare-bulbed street lamps above us, there didn't appear to be a single source of light anywhere. We were now stepping over foot-deep drifts of sand across the sidewalk, which fronted a row of old single story wooden hotels (that maybe came to life during the summer). Dale and Wendy—about a hundred feet ahead of us were stopped in front of one of them. Uh-oh, I was guessing Dale's intentions and was suddenly uncomfortable. I didn't know if June was sensing a turn of events here. We hadn't discussed anything along these lines; still just innocently holding hands.

A hushed conversation ensued between Dale and Wendy that would either end up with the four of us mounting the rickety stairs to this clapboard hotel, or an awkward outcome that would involve a "U" turn back to the parking lot to search for a cab. My suspicions were confirmed: Dale had done it. He'd sweet-talked Wendy into agreeing that at this late hour, they'd best not try to make it back to the city. The way my legs felt and as tired as I was, from a physical standpoint hitting the rack (alone) did sound pretty good. But *this* hitting the rack would result in a serious involvement, and I had no course of action other than to go along with it. Don't know how I mushed it by June, or how enthusiastic she was about it. I said we could just hang around in our room while Dale and Wendy did what they wanted in their room. We would just waste some time, or doze, or watch TV, or something. *Yuk.*

Dale was up the steps and into the hotel. About three minutes of uncomfortable silence and he was back out, flashing a big smile and waving us up. Inside—just one old guy. I took care of some semblance of registering. The place smelled like mildew. Creaking floors. Worn carpeting. Dim hallways. Cracked glass in the pictures. Onto the second floor and into our respective rooms; me with measurable discomfort. Once again, here I was on the threshold of a tryst, and feeling a lot more worried than lustful.

The one large grimy window in our room fronted the street we had just come in from, had no curtains or shade, and was letting in altogether too much light (from one of those bare-bulbed streetlamps). This harsh illumination did nothing to flatter the blank plaster walls and old furniture. There was a bathroom. One bed—a small single bed. June followed me in. Maybe too close, because when I stopped and turned, she walked right into me. The first things to touch me were the fronts of her huge well-muscled thighs. I was a little nervous as it was, and this sudden hard pressure from her big lower body didn't help.

I was halfway there, so I put my arms around her. Also gave her a light, almost friendly kiss. Her hair smelled good and her firm waist was enticing. I think she may have been prepared to see it through if necessary. I think she knew I was caught up in an unplanned event. Were it going to occur, she probably had envisioned it another way; maybe after a couple dates; maybe in her apartment on a lazy afternoon; maybe a nice hotel room after a night of romantic dancing. Still in my arms, June reached around and gave me a good whack on my backside—a mock spanking, and shook her index finger at me while sporting a tension-relieving look that said, *You're a real bad boy Roger.* Her levity at this time made me feel a little better. "No plan June. Just happened. Believe me."

"Don't worry, look here." She flipped on the TV. "BBC, we watch it about now almost every night, wind down with some news from home. And today they're supposed to have a special with Cilla Black. You should hear her." June eyed an overstuffed loveseat against the wall, strode over to it, hoisted one end like it weighed nothing, and drug it across the room; in fact, ran backwards with it—to a spot right in front of the TV. The illumination from the TV did nothing to soften our hardened confines. I'd never heard of Cilla Black before, but she was great. She sang her number one hit in the UK, "You're My World" ("...every breath I take, every move I make"). It was a serious love song, and June and I were very quiet during it. The show over, June was up. No hesitancy, no fudging.

She marched over to the bureau and matter-of-factly began undressing *in full view of me.* (I was feeling awkward enough for the both of us.) But it was quick and functional, as if she was in the dressing room with a bunch of girls. It definitely was not done in a manner to arouse me. It was the furthest thing from a seductive disrobing. She braced herself against the wall with one hand, reached down with the other and pulled off her scuffed shoes. After inspecting the soles, she shook her head disapprovingly and flipped them over her shoulder (as if into a trash bin). She whipped her sweater off over her head like a track athlete lightening up for an event, took aim and tossed it across the room where it draped over a straight-back chair.

I watched in amazement at her nonchalant behavior. She undid the zipper on her hip-huggers and started tugging them down, only to find they would not make it past her knees. Thumbs hooked in the material just above her hobbled knees, she hopped like someone in a sack race, over to the bed. Arriving there she twisted around, flopped over on her back, swung her legs overhead and yanked the trousers off. She popped back up and stomped around to the foot of the bed. There (in her bra and panties) she assumed a not flattering pose. Legs planted wide apart, flat footed, and hands clasped behind her back, she mimicked a Marine guarding some monument, and gave me a salute. She was clowning.

For some reason June was making this thing the least erotic as possible, perhaps for both of us. Certainly she wasn't ashamed of her body, but she wasn't displaying it as any prize either. I guessed as far as June was concerned, it was just there. No better, no worse—hers, the one she was stuck with. And thank God, it worked. It leaped and spun and danced for her—well enough that she wasn't dependent on her parents or anybody else, paying her own way through life. Next thing I knew she had turned on a heel and was marching (now imitating a drum majorette) knees exaggeratingly high, arms swinging, straight towards the bathroom. Before going through the door she did some little stage maneuver, leaning backward and blowing me a kiss. *God what a girl!* Evidently she wasn't bashful, not bothering to close the door. And no matter there was no hot water, she took a cold bath, in an old, chipped tub, under an unshaded hanging bulb. I peeked. Her white skin was a great contrast to her dark red hair, which was now wetly stuck across her shoulders. Out of the tub and standing there, her legs appeared much too long and large for her torso. Her glistening buttocks were strong and beautifully rounded, and her muscular thighs were well-shaped (and hard I already knew). But June was not big on top. Her arms and shoulders were thin, and her breasts were small. This was of no matter to me, my escalating interest in her (including both respect and affection) was not in the least effected by any physical shaping.

She strutted out of the bathroom, wrapped in a faded towel, and leaped onto the bed. A giant yank and a flap and she was under the covers. I wasn't sure if her natural boldness was making me more or less nervous. *Goddamit, this time it would be serious*, and as usual I wasn't feeling inclined—not by a long shot. And worse, I had no reason to feel optimistic about any changes for the better. I made a quick trip to the bathroom. The cold water discouraged me from taking a bath; just a thorough wipe down. Came out shaking—don't know if it was the cold water, the chill in the room, or my nerves. Into the rack. Our bodies smelled half of the cheap soap and half of perspiration. Thank God the sheets felt as if they might be clean.

Didn't know where to start but did feel as if some petting was in order. June was quiet and patient. She wasn't smothering me with hard wet kisses, or any kisses at all. I don't think it was a plan, but she just lay there passively, giving me time (which I sorely needed). She wasn't throwing her legs apart or grinding her hips, *thank God*. She was quiet. I kissed and caressed her, for some time. This big physical girl—so demonstrative in every other way was lying perfectly still. Still not ready and delaying as usual, I moved my face lower, past her smooth stomach, to begin kissing the sweet mound where her big legs joined her groin. My face there, I was surprised by a clean, sweet smell, like the fragrance of a recently bathed and powdered baby. It wasn't perfume and I hadn't seen her use any lotion. Maybe it was just that soap smell, but June's mons seemed to have an innocence, a purity, that I'd never had reason to consider.

In spite of all this, as I was fearing, nothing great happened. In fact nothing *at all* happened. Like I had no blood flow. As if my groin was anesthetized. I tried and waited and tried. Mentally shaking my head at myself, my body, my hormones, my historied fate! To say I was woefully lacking would be accurate. *If only we could have avoided entering this hotel in the first place.* I was disappointed and harmfully embarrassed. She never commented one way or the other. God what a letdown I must have been (again). I slid my arm under her head. She kissed me on the forehead, gave me a big, 'little-girl' smile (just like at dinner the other night), rolled half over, made a project of slapping a hollow into her pillow, and flopped her head into it. She was calling it a night. She may have intentionally been making it easy on me. I felt an obligation to her; to her consideration of me. Can't remember when or how I managed to fall asleep.

The Next Morning

When Dale pounded on the door about seven, I was in no shape to rise and shine. Felt terrible. Plagued once again by the previous night. Not ready to in any way make verbal reference to it. The good news: June didn't act like there was anything wrong. She held my hand, patted me on the back and kissed me on the cheek. The four of us straggled out of the hotel. The area looked a little better in the daylight. Started searching for a cab. Finally got one, and with the girl's good directions arrived downtown in just fifteen minutes. We stopped in front of our destination—the Cafe Andalusia, a neat little place and the Stafford Ballet's favorite breakfast haunt. (They normally ate breakfast about noon.) Inside, we ordered up two liters of fresh orange juice and four huge omelets with everything. Thankfully the girls didn't appear to hold any grudges. The girls made an event out of the meal, just like the night before (and as I would see again).

Unfortunately, the whole troupe had an appointment with some Spanish TV station at one o'clock; so this was going to be our last few minutes together in Valencia. This was going to be it. Neither of us was anxious to part (of course after last night, I don't know why June would have regretted seeing the last of me). We walked the few blocks to the *Edificio De Periodicos* for the TV interview. There, stalling outside the stone entrance, while Dale and Wendy did their talking, June and I did some next-time planning.

They'd soon be leaving Valencia for a stint in Barcelona, *where we were scheduled to anchor the middle of next month!* With serious intent June gave me what information she had to help me locate her in Barcelona. She pressed the piece of paper into my hand, folding my fingers around it; then pressed the tip of her index finger square against my nose and said, "Now Rogey, you be there, I'll be waiting for you!" I was justifiably surprised. I couldn't imagine our time together would be very high on her list, but she *did* seem a little sad at our parting. Not that June could ever be described as looking sad; from what I'd seen so far, she was one determined, resilient person, always ready for the obstacles and disappointments that she knew were out there. I was pretty sure that nothing could be devastating to June. Already, I sensed a feeling for June, like none I'd had before: a deep respect and wholesome affection. Yet crucially, she had proved not to be that one woman who would awaken me.

Chapter Twenty-Three
AIR AMERICA

The CIA in Southeast Asia

Back on board and in the S2 (Intelligence) office we were pretending to review our target folders (some time ago having decided we weren't going to be bombing anybody). Don Goft found an intelligence report about a Navy pilot who was shot down near the North Vietnam border and crashed in Laos. *In Laos?* What the heck were we doing over there? (I'd never heard of the now discredited "Gulf of Tonkin" incident that gave us an excuse to go to war against North Vietnam.) The report stated that a navy aircraft bombing the Ho Chi Minh trail (*Ho Chi Minh Trail?*) had been hit by ground fire. The pilot ejected and was in a densely wooded area. Even knowing there was no US military within 150 miles he was still using his handheld radio to try to get rescued before the North Vietnamese soldiers could get to him. About five minutes later an unmarked gray helicopter arrives out of nowhere. He knew it couldn't be from his carrier or our base at Danang. His narrative made for interesting reading:

> *"...The helicopter pilot must have had balls of steel. The ground-fire was horrendous and I knew he was taking hits. The canopy overhead was so thick he couldn't get the rescue sling down through it. I was afraid my chances for a pick-up were nil. But he climbed back up a hundred feet, pulled the power back and fell to within twenty feet of the treetops. Then just as he was about to hit them, he pulled full pitch with max power. The powerful rotor wash tore through the canopy, shredding leaves and snapping branches. He did this a couple times until he'd made a hole big enough to get the hoist through (all the while taking hits). I was on it and being lifted out! As I neared the chopper I almost leaped off the sling. There was an Asian on the skid, all dressed in*

*black and wielding a Russian AK47. He hauled me in. I fell
to the floor straining to see the pilot. In the cockpit was a
cigar smoking guy in a red Ohio State tee shirt, who offered
me half of his tuna sandwich. This was my first introduction
to Air America."*

We asked ourselves, *who the hell is Air America?* The sergeant in
S2, before being assigned to our squadron, had been stationed in Saigon.
Observing us he chimed in. "That's a secret CIA aviation operation
over there in Southeast Asia, doing all kinds of crazy stuff. And not
just flying helicopters; they have lots of weird single-engine aircraft; all
civilian pilots—living in Saigon and keeping their families in Bangkok or
Singapore. If any of you guys are thinking of getting out and want to make
big bucks, that's the place you want to go." Well as you might imagine, I'm
thinking, *Could this be what I'm looking for?* Mercifully avoid an official
legal separation from Sara, but still live apart! (And earn enough money
to take great care of the family.) *But was I really considering getting out
of the Corps?* The thought of telling my fellow officers I was resigning
my commission, was something I could not imagine doing. And I knew
nothing about being a civilian—went right from college to flight training.
A little scary thinking about civilian life now, after the unmatched security
of being in the military; especially as a commissioned officer. Later in
the day I spoke with the sergeant. He didn't have an exact address for Air
America, but assured me if I sent a letter addressed to them—in care of the
US Embassy in Saigon, they'd get it.

Chapter Twenty-Four
BARCELONA

Talk About Being Impressed with a City

With less than two months to go we pulled into Barcelona. For me this would be the coup de grace, finally proof there was a place—a city in which I would be perfectly satisfied. Making my way down its wide boulevards and mingling with its elegant citizenry I was sure I was observing an elevated society; captured by its ambiance; never tiring of viewing its expansive, wrought iron-fenced parks, slate and copper-roofed buildings, and magnificent avenues lined with shops of distinction. And in no city—not even Rome, had I seen so many handsome and well-dressed men and women. It was the most sophisticated city I had ever visited. I sensed a patriarchal atmosphere, an untainted reputation, a status which humbled me. (Comparing this perfection to my shallow activities and questionable motives caused me justifiable concern.) *If the Riviera was my baptism by fire, Barcelona would seal it in blood.* We'd dropped anchor at 0800 and I'd been tingling with anticipation ever since. And why? I was going to see June and the Stafford Ballet girls again! In Valencia June had given me the name of the theater they'd be in here—the theater just a block from the Puerta del Sol.

During the day I made my rounds like always; hit all the shops and spoke with the men. All twelve birds were up and ready for flight, which made lots of points with the Colonel (since the Navy A-4 squadrons only had eleven up most mornings). Put off shaving till noon knowing it would have to last till after midnight; was in the liberty boat at 1800 hours. Seemed I'd done this a hundred times now—each time anticipating a new and exciting adventure (and amazingly usually not being disappointed). The Navy enlistment posters say, *"It's not a job, it's an adventure!"* and for me that has turned out to be all too true. Once ashore I'd have at least two hours to find the theater. Up on the dock I surveyed the cityscape to get some clue as to a likely route to the city center. Squinting into the sunset over a rising skyline of treetops, I spied the upper reaches of a cluster of tall buildings about a mile away, which I guessed marked the heart of the city.

Now find Puerta del Sol. I decided to just walk—save my Pesetas. In selecting a route to the city center I chose a narrow, initially uncrowded, slightly uphill street. Two blocks in the activity began picking up: lots of tiny delivery trucks, and strange three-wheeled vehicles with canvas tops and browning acrylic windshields. And it paid to be alert as these vehicles thought nothing of popping up on the sidewalk. Bordering the sidewalk—not six feet back, were the fronts of an attached row of wall-to-wall tiny houses. Each patch of front yard was full of crude wooden shelving, overflowing with meat and foul and fish. Men and women in aprons, with brooms and mops and scoops and baskets of food, were hustling in and out of these places (dodging rosy-cheeked kids running in and out of the same doorways). I was now traversing the shellfish section. Every yard was cluttered with baskets of clams and shrimp. Every doorway had an occupant propping it up, and two feet away the front window supported a pair of elbows and another blank face. Everyone was dressed in combinations of white, gray, and black; checkered or plaid or striped, but no colors. White shirts, gray vests, black rubber aprons and boots.

While the street was fascinating, looking down a side street I saw a possibly better route paralleling mine. And I was right. But it wasn't really a street, it was a wide brick promenade, beautifully lined with huge elms—just for pedestrians. By accident (my usual way) I had stumbled upon the world famous "Las Ramblas"—the public walk that inclines from the port all the way up to the city center. I eagerly joined the crowd of well-dressed city dwellers and not so well-dressed tourists. Amidst them and energized by my new surroundings I again began making my way towards the city. The branches of the trees on either side met overhead, forming a large tunnel. The density of this canopy blocked out most of the daylight. Las Ramblas was already being illuminated by lamps atop sculpted posts, and colored lanterns dangling in the branches. Brightly decorated kiosks were selling everything from newspapers to tropical fish in plastic bags. Every now and then I'd come upon a juggler or some young hippy-type guy playing a guitar or harmonica for donations. It was a unique and pleasurable experience. The people seemed to have few worries. Even I here among them was gratefully aware of perhaps the beginning of a strange new feeling of well-being.

211

Finally at the top—emerging from Las Ramblas, I was certainly not let down by the sights that befronted me. I was at the edge of a large and bustling plaza, impressively ringed with statues and grand old *edificios*. In the center—with shiny black cars racing around it, was a huge circular fountain (shades of Piazza Republica in Rome). The sidewalks were jammed with crowds of especially smartly attired men and women returning to their neighborhoods at the end of the business day. I felt very much the newcomer but was hopeful of getting to know this city better (and having it perhaps accept me as an equal). The signposts announced it as Plaza Catalunya, and I had in fact stumbled into the city center. I remembered that June had said her theater was located near the Plaza del Sol. Now, find *that* Plaza!

While debating how, I was in front of a small but elegant store. It could have been a jewelry store or a place that sold precision instruments—a really classy establishment. I stepped closer and peered inside. The two side walls were lined with bronze framed glass display cases. The entire rear wall was comprised of perhaps twenty, side-by-side columns of small, porcelain-knobbed polished mahogany drawers, *that rose from the floor to the ceiling;* a multitude of three-inch by eight-inch lustrous repositories, obviously containing some unknown valuable items. Mounted on the ceiling above this cabinetry was a long metal rod that spanned the entire wall. Attached to it was a brass ladder with wheels at its base, so that it could be slid back and forth—the whole length of the wall. (A necessity to reach the upper drawers.) Inside, was a thin, balding, bespectacled gentleman. With one finger to his lips he was sizing up an equally statured customer. Then he made a quick turn to that rear wall of a hundred drawers. His hand traced a line up a column of drawers, slid over to the next, down two, and evidently the sought-after drawer. He opened it and extracted the treasure. A skillful flourish momentarily suspended it in air before it dropped over the back of his hand for a privileged viewing. Only a second or two there, then with equally artful movements he fashioned a "Windsor." *This was a Barcelona necktie store!* To me, all of Barcelona would be similarly refined.

Finding the Teatro del Sol

I pilfered a free map from a nearby hotel and was able to locate the Plaza del Sol. Good! (If *Puerta* and *Plaza* mean the same thing.) The humanity I was threading through—with their heads down, hat brims into the wind, and moving at a brisk pace, were to me—each and every one, an established individual. Reflecting on my own scant accomplishments and recent selfish objectives, I felt embarrassed and envious; all these honest people with jobs, families, and real destinations, moving with purpose. And then me—without credentials or defensible intentions, thinking only of myself; having plans that spanned barely a week into the future. I was an impostor—just temporarily on the scene. I hadn't earned the right to use these streets and sample what this city had to offer.

Evidently the map was printed by the Dry Sac sherry company, since their logo appeared several places on the map, including over their location in Plaza del Sol. On top of a building about five blocks ahead I saw a huge electronic sign: **Dry Sac Jerez**. *I'll bet that's it.* And sure enough, another five blocks and I was there—Plaza del Sol. Again, a large fountain in the middle, and ringed with all kinds of neat-looking shops and cafes. Checked the map once more to get my final bearings. Let's see, gotta be here—on this corner. So take that street on the other side of the plaza, just two corners up, then a left, and I should be in front of June's theater.

It worked. I found it, but still locked up and not a soul on the premises. There was a chill in the air and the wind was picking up. Only seven. The girls probably wouldn't arrive until eight-thirty. Strolled back down to the plaza. Wasted twenty minutes there. Dark now and the crowds from an hour ago had thinned out. Made my way back to the theater. Seven-thirty. Another hour. But I had an idea to use up that time. I'd arrange to have a big bouquet delivered backstage during the performance. Started looking for a flower shop but changed my mind in favor of a perhaps better idea. Back to the theater. Ticket window just opening. At the window (with no diagram to point at) I had a hell of a time conveying my wishes to the lady inside. Finally did. *I got three seats together, almost dead center in the fourth row.* I would sit in the middle seat and have an empty seat on each side of me. June would be sure to spot me this way. But two thousand one-hundred Pesetas! This neat idea was going to set me back about 35 bucks. I fingered the thinness of my Peseta wad and had second thoughts about the three-seat purchase. Slipped into the theater a couple minutes before nine. Another magnificent theater, even bigger than the one in Valencia. The foyer was decorated like the lobby of a five-star hotel, with uniformed attendants, thick red carpeting, gilded furniture, and expensive-looking wall hangings. It was packed. The only empty seats may end up being the one on each side of me.

The Performance

The orchestra began and the colored lights playing on the curtains began to dim. I didn't have much I could brag about. I knew I wasn't special, but right now—sitting here in this theater, I *felt* special—connected; part of something big and different and exciting. And soon I'd be with June. A woman who had won my admiration, and for whom I thought I might be experiencing—not what I had been searching for, but at least the beginnings of (for me, for once) a new and unselfish caring. I was relieved to sense that I could even *have* honorable feelings. The show was still the traveling *Tony Le Blanc Comedia*, with Tony and that same huge-bazoomed, bleached blonde. Even without knowing what they were saying, the show was an enjoyable slapstick performance. The first act ended and I was on the edge of my seat awaiting the Stafford Ballet. Wow! It was a completely different routine and new costumes. Even more gold and glitter than I'd seen in Valencia. This time it was a Roman street scene. The backdrop was the familiar near wall of the Coliseum. Right there on the stage, huge stone blocks (or what appeared to be stone) were stacked up to the cat walks. Groups of extras in white togas were crisscrossing the set. Real donkeys were pulling wooden carts. And now, what I was waiting for. Here come the girls! Leaping and twirling and cartwheeling, they exploded onto the stage, announcing the arrival of the legion. Wow, centurions on horseback! *Real* horses. *Kheerist* what a show. I strained to find June. Once again they all looked the same; huge, strong creatures strutting this way and that. Bright colored hair pulled back tight, feathered headdresses, sequined eyes, sparkles on their skin, wide-smiling red mouths, curvaceous lithe bodies. Almost had to pinch myself.

She spied me—saw her give an elbow to the girl next to her and whip a quick point in my direction. A moment later when she swept across the footlights, she winked and flashed one of her crazy grins. Seeing it my heart took flight. It was so exciting to have this all come together. I was afraid to speculate on the rest of the evening. To a robustly appreciative round of applause they finished their routine. I was a little impatient during the second act, waiting to see the girls again. But finally—another display of difficult, energy-sapping movements. The girls did a four-high pyramid. I was so close I could see the veins protruding in their necks, and their knees shaking. A max effort, but it held. June was on the bottom (which with those legs I could understand why). Being this close, I was more aware of the relentless tempo and sheer physical output involved.

In particular, I wondered how their feet and ankles ever stood up to it. Pounding, sliding, stamping, pushing off, skidding, jamming into the floor. You'd imagine their feet would be a mass of blisters and calluses. (I would find out later, they were.) Hairline fractures, that's what the girls dreaded. Lose a month's pay or *worse*—get handed a ticket back to England. Soon enough the intermission was over and the last act began. Thought about leaving early. No, not in good taste, I'll stay.

Meeting June After the Show

Standing just outside the artists' entrance I was only a few yards from the guard booth, manned by an elderly woman doing needlepoint. Caught her eye and gave a friendly nod. Was taken aback when she smiled and beckoned me closer. She didn't speak any English, but I knew from Valencia that the Spaniards referred to the girls as the *Inglesas*. I tried it and it worked. Again—surprisingly, she motioned me to enter and go on down the hall. I smiled appreciatively and nodded my thanks. *Boy, not much security around here.* Didn't think it would be this easy. Came to a flight of steps descending into what looked like a factory basement. A little eerie. Just a short way down the deserted concrete-floored passageway below, I began to hear the girls' laughter. Boy were they having a good time!

I continued towards the source of all this mirth. Their dressing room was a temporary cubicle whose walls were propped-up plywood partitions (that could have easily been pushed over by one person). They didn't go all the way to the ceiling, and over them I could just see the tops of the girls' headdresses, as they moved about inside. Two or three light fixtures (bare bulbs) were hanging from bent nails in the ceiling. Tops of clothes-trees, piled with all manner of attire protruded above the partition. From time to time, some piece of apparel would fly up and drape on one. Twelve of them were jammed in this small area, but from the sounds of things, no one was complaining. They were letting the good times roll.

The partition used as a door was ajar, but I wasn't about to barge in. On the wall alongside it was that famous WWII poster of Uncle Sam in his top hat, pointing right at you, except instead of saying "*I want YOU!*" it said, "*Did you take your PILL?*" Got my nerve and announced myself. "June I'm here." Tried to make it sound casual. I was sure they'd been plagued by "stage door Johnnies" and I wasn't eager to look like another one. *Though what else was I?* June came bounding out, almost carrying the rickety door off its hinges. I was smothered in a giant bear hug that squeezed the air out of my lungs. (Thought for a moment she was going to pick me up.) *Was this girl glad to see me or what!*

"Rogey, you made it did you! Oh look at you!"

A great big kiss on the mouth, and then one on each cheek. The same kind of kiss—not sexy or passionate; rather a hard kiss full of strength and meaning. I had never been kissed like this before (including by my wife). It was a kiss that made me feel ten feet tall. In a matter of seconds half the troupe had collected in the doorway, giggling and clapping and shaking their fingers at June. They were happy for her—rooting for her (or me, or us). In no way did I deserve this appreciation. I don't think I'd ever felt more important.

June described a nearby café where she would meet me in about fifteen minutes, and sent me off with a slap to my backside. Back out the artists' entrance and into the night air. Found the place easily, picked a clean table and ordered a Dry Sac sherry. Quarter to one—early in comparison to other nights. In twenty minutes in they came: June, Laurie, Wendy, and young Claire, followed by a half dozen others. Wendy wanted to know, where was Dale? I told her he had the duty and couldn't come ashore, but he'd be here tomorrow evening. All those who had met me in Valencia came over to our table. Two girls had fallen by the wayside. Two new ones added. They all took their turns giving me kisses on the cheek. Lots of questions, *How I'd been? Did I miss June? How long could I stay?* Each one took her turn. Claire dropped to one knee alongside my chair. "Roger. No Wendy, let me! Roger, will you take June to visit the states? Oh, I know not now, but after these *espanoles* have had their full of us?" While June was truly extra protective of her youngest and newest dancer, with this she grabbed Claire's throat and feigned strangling her. Receiving so much attention, I felt like a celebrity and was beginning to think I rightly owed June something; something I was hoping I might someday be able to deliver on.

A Second Dinner Date

Time to come up with a plan for our late night (early morning) meal. She put it to the girls for a vote. Le Drugstore won hands down; a new place that had just opened. A couple of the girls thanked me but bowed out for one reason or another. I would have liked to have brought them all along. Two cabs full did it. June on my lap (and not light). We were on our way to Le Drugstore. I was buried in the back seat with about four of them, being smothered and pressed by all manner of firm thighs and round buttocks. By now I loved the sound of their accented voices as they chattered non-stop. They smelled good, and their hair was brushing across my face. Now *this* is what a sailor calls "a real night ashore!"

We were there in ten minutes though I hadn't seen anything since we left—my nose having been buried in the middle of June's back the whole way. The girls piled out of the cab, and evidently Le Drugstore was *the* after-hours place for all the artists in Barcelona. Halfway across the street the girls were enthusiastically met by a gaggle of other late-night performers. I said "performers," but "artists" is what they really wanted to be called, whether dancers, singers, acrobats or jugglers. And from what I'd seen and what I would see, they damn well *deserved* to call themselves artists. During these exchanges I couldn't understand everything, since much of it was in Spanish. Hugs and kisses galore. Lots of good-looking guys (making me feel a little less special). June said they were dancers from other shows in town, and almost all gay (*whew*) but "quite nice chaps," always looking out for the girls and doing nice things for them. Several of them, still wearing their stage makeup, whisked the girls up in their arms and carried them in.

The interior of Le Drugstore was bizarre: ultra-modern décor, all white—the walls, floor and twenty-foot-high ceiling. It was sterile looking like the interior of a hospital lab. Halfway up both side walls, and spanning their entire length, ran a narrow, one-table-wide clear acrylic balcony. At the far end of the room—halfway up the rear wall, at the top of two chrome spiral staircases were two eating areas, each with a table. This place may have been *called* a drugstore, but it was a neo-something eating establishment that just happened to sell a handful of cosmetics up front.

I was embarrassed as June proudly introduced me to everyone in sight. I was being shown a respect I knew I didn't deserve. The conversations between the girls and the other artists were admirably wholesome. I was surprised at the camaraderie and caring expressed by everyone. One skinny guy with a struggling mustache was showing everybody a leather purse he had bought for his "mum." The girls fawned over it and told him it was beautiful, and that his mother would love it, and how sweet he was to have gotten it for her. These kids were all willing to spend the time to make each other feel good, feel important—feel a part of something. I could see it. *What right did I have to be here,* horning in and trying to get my kicks out of something in which I had no investment. They were a large, kind, and protective family. I felt out of place and I should have, though I had the kindest and most respectful feelings for June and her girls. And if time and some luck were on my side, they might someday see the sincerity of my affection.

Once again it was a pleasure to watch June and the girls celebrate eating, discussing each entree with much ado; their eyes lighting up as one of the specials was explained. Done ordering they'd slam the menu shut, look up with an expression of absolute confidence, and begin the rubbing of stomachs, licking lips, and kidding each other about gaining another kilo. When the food arrived I could readily see (as I would every time to come) that June had picked the most savory dish in the house. As it was set down in front of her, she leaned forward, encircled it with one forearm, acting like it was going to be necessary to protect it from me. Time to "dig in." The fork was in the air and down, and she was after it. This girl knew how to enjoy a meal, let me tell you. Your own worries disappeared at the sight of her. She relished the moment without being concerned with her appearance. No second thoughts. I think because she knew she was always doing what she *should* be doing. No falsehoods involved. No ulterior motives. Life for June was simple. No regrets. Tears almost came to my eyes, watching her and thinking of all the duplicity, "what ifs," and "play-acting" going on in my life.

It was over. Dinner (breakfast) was over. It was after three now. Boy, was I going to be exhausted tomorrow. Most the girls had left—alone or with members of another cast. June, Laurie and I were finally alone. Paid the bill (not too bad, considering) and exited Le Drugstore. Waiting for a cab on the sidewalk I realized June and I were holding hands. Laurie and June were roomies and had their own apartment. Laurie was ready to call it a night. I agreed and rode along with them back to their place. Out of the cab Laurie kissed us each goodnight and was gone through a black metal gate. It had been a long night and I knew I should have just given June a goodnight kiss and caught the next Shore Patrol launch back to the ship. I was out on my feet, but it could be happening. I was being invited up for a coffee. Up the stairs—a lot of stairs. (With no elevator the rents go down the higher you go.) I got coffee—that's all I got, but I didn't mind. Several times I dozed off while on my feet. I met June's two cats named Tony and Maria (from *Westside Story*), and we listened to a 45 RPM record of that song we had heard together in the decrepit old seaside hotel in Valencia—the one by Cilla Black, "You're My World …every breath I take, every move I make."

If I didn't get horizontal quick, I was going to collapse. While talking I was visualizing scenes that had nothing to do with anything I was saying. While listening, I could see lips moving, but wasn't hearing any sounds. *We're talking critical fatigue.* I stood up, thanked her for the evening, got a great kiss on the lips, and pledged to do my best to be at the theater tomorrow night, same time. (But knew this might be a problem, since it would not be a liberty day for me.) She insisted it wasn't necessary to sit through the show, just meet her in the same café at quarter to one. I stumbled out the door, hoping to find a cab at this hour. I did. Arriving at the dock a Shore Patrol shift boat was just cranking up. *I was going to make it—this time!* On the ladder, into the forward passageway, and towards my stateroom. Pitch Black. Jim's snoring. Shoes, shirt, trousers, off, one, two socks off. In the rack. *Thank you God—again, for everything."*

Before falling asleep images of June, the girls, the guys, and Le Drugstore flashed through my mind. I had suspected as much weeks ago, when I first met Ardith in Rome, and then Erica in Cannes, but now I knew I would never be the same. My real life was on more and more shaky ground. It was becoming less real than the one that was rapidly taking shape. I couldn't make myself think about both lives in the same moment, though at any given time—in my defense (or perhaps to further debase my character) I was viewing this new world with Sara's face in the foreground, and condemning myself for betraying my good wife's trust. It was a very bad feeling, and worse—I had chosen to live with it. The adventures I had always fantasized about—in strange new places with exciting new people, were happening! Perhaps any day now (and it was a scary thought) I might find myself no longer just imagining but planning steps that would have me changing my work and domestic situation when I returned to the states. Maybe even leave the Corps and hire on with Air America; achieve the separation; freedom of movement, without needing a divorce. Changes that would very much affect the family, and caused real fright just to contemplate.

The Start of an Evening to Remember

Was awake at 0800, but sure could have used a couple more hours. Hit all the shops and spent time listening to the troops. Mid-afternoon got some bad news. Tripp had already swapped for someone else and couldn't swap with me, and it was too late to intercept anyone else. *I was screwed.* Nothing to do now. Just sit here and stew. It was a bummer night, wondering what activities the girls may partake of after the show. Jim was ashore, which was good; needed some solitude. Wrote a letter to Sara (now finding it difficult to make my twice a week schedule). Didn't know how it would sound when she read it a week from now, but here on my desk in front of me, it appeared a pitiful effort. *God help me.*

Wednesday—my liberty day today. But I'd made no special arrangements for where to meet June. Around noon they usually hit some local restaurant (for a stevedore's brunch), then interviews and publicity appointments after that. I'd never be able to find em. I'll just have to wait and meet them at the theater. Took a short nap—knew I'd need the rest if I was going to have another 3 a.m. night. But that Cinderella liberty boat that I was consistently missing; one of these days I might get called in about it. I think all the other guys are actually coming back by midnight. (Or earlier.) Fortunately, my good work aboard was being noticed. Our aircraft had been up and flying like never before. For the past ten weeks as the Officer in Charge, the *head* of the Maintenance department, reporting to no one, I'd managed to keep our fleet of aircraft 100 percent available. The Skipper was genuinely pleased. Only six weeks until we steam westward (out of my world). It had been a successful cruise; no accidents (involving our squadron anyway) and we'd be home before we knew it. *The thought of this threatened a cold sweat.*

At the theater. (Just one seat tonight.) Decided to attend the performance in spite of June's assurances that I could just skip it. (I'll bet her previous boyfriends would have taken her up on the "just meet me in the café.") Same routine. Same great performance. Finished at twelve fifteen. Out and into the cafe. June and the girls were there in no time. June took over as tour director. The pressure was off me to come up with some great idea. Five of us piled in a cab and once again I was ensconced in female-kind. After having turned down an unlit and deserted city street, we stopped in front of what appeared to be a row of locked up darkened store fronts. Time to pile out, but the girls were listening to a great song on the radio, by a currently popular Spanish vocalist—Raphael. It was a romantic sounding ballad with evidently moving lyrics. The girls made the driver wait for his fare until it was over. Now on the sidewalk in front of shadowy doorways, we ventured through one into a dark, tunnel-like club that could not have been more than fifteen feet wide, but fifty feet deep from front to rear. There was a bar along the first half of the left wall. It was so dark that although I was aware of a blur of light- colored shirts in front of it; no figures or even reflections off the mirrors behind it visible. Nothing was distinguishable. At the far end of the room against the rear wall (only fifteen feet across) was a small stage upon which an Italian rock band was going full blast. The male vocalist was another hoarse-voiced, long-haired, macho-looking guy, with his head back and eyes closed—wailing away. The girls were about swooning over him. I'd give anything to swap places with him (maybe just for a week—to see how it went.) The only light in the entire club was what was reflected back from the three colored spots over the bandstand. We sat in the dark on a long, cushioned right-wall bench.

The place was owned by a chunky Lebanese guy the girls had met when they first arrived. He was a swarthy guy—about 45, with a cigar stuck in his mouth and pinkie rings on both hands. (To me kind of phony looking.) Seeing the girls he hurried over. Lots of hugs and a few kisses. I wouldn't doubt these club owners vied with each other to adopt the "Staffy girls." They knew it was damned good for business to have this lot come crashing in each night. If this guy wasn't a card-carrying member of the Middle East Mafia, nobody was. (An hour later, I'd meet Marcel!) A long row of small tables were set in front of us and in ten minutes each had its own tray, holding an assortment of pastry-wrapped "somethings." bread and dips. It looked inviting, but I'm not big on eating things that I can't see and identify, even in this *Boite Beirut*.

Out of there, on the sidewalk, flagging a cab again. Only four of us. Claire stayed. I could see that the other two with us did not approve of her attraction to the lead singer (and particularly June, who had a heart-to-heart talk with her while we were inside). I don't know what it is about singers and drummers, but geez—*do they get the girls!* I would see it time and time again. Hot affairs while they lasted, but they never lasted, and when they fell apart, they really fell apart. And here I was (again) jumping in another cab and racing across Barcelona at two in the morning. I didn't know what the other guys did when they were on liberty, but I couldn't imagine they wouldn't have wanted to be in my shoes right now. *Who'd believe this?* After some time the driver turned through a pair of wrought iron gates, into what looked like a large and well-maintained private estate. We traveled about a hundred yards along a curving sand drive, edged by neat little lanterns. On either side, manicured lawns and shrubs extending as far as the eye could see. The cab stopped in front of an imposing, large, swanky-looking, single-story, white brick building. I think—the only structure on the grounds.

We made our way up a half dozen shallow but fifty-foot-wide steps, then across a veranda-like foyer. The girls did this like they did it every day. Me? As confidently as I could I followed them across the marble floor, past overstuffed floral print furniture, and up to a large white archway. Through it I saw the dining area—a sea of tables inside a large, perfectly round *greenhouse!* The outside walls were curving, side-to-side, floor-to-domed ceiling *glass panels,* which were reflecting all the lights and images back inside a hundred times over. The dance floor was racetrack-shaped, encircling a white-tuxedoed orchestra in the very center. Tables with linen and candelabras ringed the circumference. This was the strangest club I'd ever been in! The manager approached us. *I was about to meet Marcel.*

As usual, June was not one bit embarrassed about introducing me; proud we were an item—let the chips fall where they may. But this time it was different. I didn't have a good feeling about Marcel. He was one of those guys of uncertain origin; from his facial features and physical appearance, perhaps of middle-eastern heritage; from his accent, perhaps from Algeria or Lebanon. Balding at a young age, I'd say he was not much over thirty. Although he was only about five-foot ten and 175 pounds, you could see he was a powerful guy. Strong neck (and a two-inch scar on his forehead). It was obvious, in spite of his overly polite—almost fawning façade, that this was one "tough cookie." He shook my hand and by the excess pressure he exerted, it was a private attempt to intimidate me—to show his strength. The second I felt it occurring I tensed my hand to block the compression, as best I could with my small hand; may have at least balanced it. Never let myself wince. I concluded I'd just met a rival for June's affection; someone who had recognized by her bubbling smile and exuberant introduction of me, that whatever chances he had previously, might be in jeopardy.

Although June and I danced several times, I never did get comfortable in that place. The girls danced with each other most the time. Occasionally some Spanish guy would get the nerve to come over and ask for a dance. It was a swank place all right, well-appointed and in a choice location, but I had my doubts about the clientele. The bulk of the patrons looked like cast members from some Hollywood Mafia movie. Each time I caught a glimpse of Marcel he seemed to be looking over at our table. *Spooky.*

Observing June and listening to her, I suspected that in spite of her striking appearance, bold walk, certainty in almost every situation, and these uninhibited good times, for whatever reasons—she wasn't counting on any great things happening in her life. It was as if it weren't her place to expect any miracles. They hadn't happened for her mother or her older sister. Her birthright was hard work and being satisfied with the lot at hand: a wet newspaper, left-over foods, chapped skin, a broken purse strap. Was it possible that all this was *before she met me?* Could it be that now she was daring to hope something special was about to happen in her life? And if so, no matter how I admired her and felt towards her, I didn't deserve such a place in her life. I was saddled with a too-early commitment (of permanency). I had lied and was at a loss as to how I could still be in the picture in another month, but I could not help feeling she was allowing herself to imagine a future for us. Had I at last met someone with whom I could be a good and true person (*for the first time*). I was almost sure of it, but tragically she was not that one woman who could turn the key. What have I started here and where can it go? June was a person you could count on! She deserved the best and it's true I dared to consider I might have— however slim, the chance of being that one, but again, *how?* I didn't know what was in store for her, and I sure didn't know what was in store for me.

Another Try at Spending the Night Together

It was almost four before the girls began to wind down; never running out of things to chatter about. Except June. While she listened attentively to the girls and made a few comments, she mostly just sat there beaming at me. *God, I never felt so good, so important (so undeserving).* I think she would've left in a minute if I would have suggested it. When we did leave, we said goodnight to Marcel (whose countenance told me the same thing it had upon our arrival). We took one cab. Dropped the other two girls off. They all claimed to have had a great time and were pleased that June and I hadn't left early. We continued in the cab to the Manila Hotel. A respectable but comfy-appearing old wooden hotel I had seen the first night—just off the plaza atop Las Ramblas. I was going to do it right; got one of the expensive suites. We'd earned it and had the time now to lie undisturbed in each other's arms. To share and think and wonder.

The room was first class—hardwood floors with oriental rugs, brocade silk wallpaper and ornate tables with ceramic lamps. Alone in the suite, once again a most unsexy encounter. June didn't flirt or tease. Knowing beforehand that my chances to succeed with her were slim (my record with her now defying any other interpretation). I was resigned to hope for no more than the opportunity to show her the affection and tenderness she deserved. To show that to June would (perhaps for the first time for me) not be difficult. Deservedly I had elevated June above all others. My feelings for her were good, and true—*a new experience*. Now, in this room and better known to each other, I had left a light on and was able to observe her smoothness and newness lying there next to me. My eyes settled on her most female part. It was dwarfed by the silky-white expanse of her powerful belly above hugely muscled thighs. It was surprisingly small and innocent and closed; squeaky clean with just the slightest bit of soft fuzz, like the head of a small baby. It was what God had meant it to be, and it had that same pure fragrance.

I wasn't sure what I felt for June, but it was good, and I knew she deserved the best from any man (and that I certainly wasn't worthy). Why she would have any similar feelings for me was yet unexplained, but she seemed joyful and well content just to be with me. And this was causing in me a kind of feeling I'd never had before. She wasn't sleeping. She was lying on her side and looking straight at me; and not with a strained emotional fixation (that could well have been expected in a situation like this). Rather it was a look of happiness—an "*ask me for the moon*" look; if you could imagine that, in view of my inability to give her any assurances. That night in bed, the best I could say is that by my efforts, she may have recognized my intentions.

Reflecting on my recent activities during the cruise, I felt a pain in my chest. Now laying here in the aura of June, sampling her body, her pure white skin against me, her darkly dyed red hair across my shoulder, I could feel the tears welling in my eyes. For June it wasn't fair that I was even presenting myself to her, and for me—I was probably racing headlong down a steep hill, picking up speed and thrilling to the wind in my face, while there was every chance a giant pit awaited me at the bottom. I didn't know where I was going, or how I would get there (if I would get there at all) or what I would do when I arrived.

Barcelona, a Summary

The whole in-port stay was a whirlwind of varied excitement. Not a single bad scene. Besides the established metropolis I'd seen the first day, June and the girls showed me all the fun places: castles converted into hotels, monasteries turned into restaurants, wine cellars made over into after-hours clubs, and my favorite, for a midnight trip back to the 1500's—the Old Quarter. It was a hugely spacious, spookily unoccupied, stone-paved square—several hundred feet across, lit only by the moonlight. All four sides were buttressed by twenty-foot-high stone walls. Nestled in the bases of the encompassing walls were an inviting selection of bistros, wineries, and darkened enclaves of unknown specialties. I would conclude that the *joie de vivre* of Barcelona and the affluence of its population were a Spanish birthright; a perfection that never wavered.

I was now going ashore alone every time, slipping in and out of cabs, hurtling through the night, bursting into theaters and then afterwards riding the high-flying coattails of the Stafford Ballet. *June's guy!* Back in town out of nowhere. And surprisingly the girls approved of me. To my amazement and gratitude, they had given me a "thumbs-up." I was an invited guest. And the girls of the Stafford Ballet, they *were* "Barcelona after-hours!" Where they were was where it was happening; where they went so went the excitement—laughing, singing, arms flying, hair tossed, long legs everywhere, band playing, dancing the night away. No pain, no strain, nothing but the good times. *They were gonna live forever!*

Repeated days, meeting them for a giant brunch, a newspaper interview at two, a "telly" interview at four, and the theater at eight-thirty. Out of the theater at quarter to one; then tearing across town—six deep, in one of Barcelona's rigid black cabs—racing by spacious parks and big buildings behind high wrought iron fences—giant silver trees and old iron streetlamps streaking by. Speed runs full of merriment. The Beatles, Tom Jones, Stevie Wonder. They knew every word to every song on the Top Twenty, and sang them at the top of their lungs (especially "Hey Jude"). At least twice a night, piling out at a great little, all-night club or restaurant! An hour later, on the other side of town hurtling down the steps to another after-hours club. These girls knew how to live. *And I just wished there was some sense, or reason for me to learn how.*

But what I had said earlier—about my activities and relationships ashore occurring in a "parallel universe," and not really going to affect my marriage on my return; well yes—that's what I thought then. Originally, they were the desperate focus of a necessary search; and if I continued to fail, be no more than a terribly humbling, but must-be-forgotten experiment. How could I possibly think now, with all that was haunting me, and having met sweet brave June, that I could ever return to the states and step back in as the same guy who left ten months ago? My activities thus far on the cruise—for the first time, caused the word "divorce" to cross my mind. (Not yet my lips!) The thought of it struck terror in my heart. *Help me God.*

Chapter Twenty-Five
PALMA DE MAJORCA

The End of the Cruise

The Russians hadn't called our bluff. We were still doing our daily training flights, albeit now in an android fashion, not with the "teeth-to-the-bit" attitude we had upon arriving. (Although even in our present state of mind we would have been a lot more effective.) But it was over. No soviet ships, no impending war, no reason to bomb the Eastern Bloc into rubble. For ten months we had been the threat of horrible and instant retaliation. (If I'd been the Russians, I'd have been worried.) But now it's time for reflection, and I could tell—not just for me, others would never be the same.

Four more days of flight ops before they're over for good! Friday noon we'd drop anchor off Palma, on the island of Majorca, 125 miles off the Spanish coast. There we'd have a short 36-hour liberty, because at midnight Saturday we'd up-anchor and steam up to the north end of the island (where I first laid eyes on the European landscape): Pollensa Bay. There, the next morning—Sunday, would be the "Change of Command" ceremony. We'd be the old hands turning the task over to the new arriving carrier. As soon as the ceremony was complete we'd turn south to begin our trip across the Med and then the Atlantic. In a little more than a week I'd be looking at the Carolinas! *You think the thought of that didn't strike fear in my heart?*

My Critical Last Liberty

And during that 36-hour mooring in Palma on the island of Majorca I had big plans—*very* big plans; a rendezvous with June; our last meeting—a goodbye, perhaps a *final* goodbye. As soon as the anchor chain got wet I was going to be in a liberty boat on my way to the dock, hail a cab to the airport *and catch the first plane back to mainland Spain*—a thirty-minute flight to Barcelona to see my June. The visit would be short, hectic, and require precise timing. I'd have Friday night and most of the day Saturday with June. But I absolutely had to be back here in Palma by Saturday evening, *since at midnight we were starting up and around the island to Pollensa Bay for the Change of Command ceremony Sunday!* I'd fly from Barcelona back here to Palma about six or seven Saturday evening, catch a quick cab to the dock, thump my way out to the carrier, and drag myself aboard about nine, ready to accept my fate. Thursday evening now, the island of Majorca on the horizon. Tomorrow we'd arrive there. I could hardly taste my supper. mulling over all that would have to come together. Was hoping there were frequent flights between Palma and Barcelona.

A Staggering Announcement

Friday morning, just a few hours before dropping anchor in Palma: *"Mandatory"!* That's the word the speaker kept blaring out. *"0800 hours on the hangar deck. Every single hand"!* We guessed it would be a litany of "well dones" and presentations. Oh well, none of us had much to do anyway. I filed up to the hangar deck with Tripp and Ernie. We kidded a little bit. (Not something that was easy for me at this time.) The hangar deck had been marked with tape to specify which units assembled where. I met Jim and the other guys in our designated area. I must say, a pretty well-disciplined bunch. A few thousand guys and only a minor din. On the platform were all the tactical squadron commanders, and, *the ship's captain!* I was right. A whole bunch of statistics, number of sorties flown, flight hours, etc. Then a long string of congratulations and unit awards. Lots of good news. (No reference to Norm or the kid killed on the elevator.) Some plaques handed out. More handshakes. And then the ship's captain took the microphone (for the first time on the cruise).

His few words were more of the same, and as expected—real nice. That is to say, *real nice up until the part that froze the blood in my veins!* Palma would be our last in-port visit. The Captain had completed a whole ten-month Med Cruise without losing a single hand to the allure of the Cote d'Azur, the Greek Isles, or the girls of Naples. He was about to make a "first": *Returning home without losing even one sailor to the temptations of the Continent.* Having a perfect record up to this time, he was not going to let some guy with latent wanderlust screw it up. So, he said that during this one-and-a-half-day liberty, no one, repeat—*no one was going to be allowed to leave the city limits of Palma!*

I couldn't believe my ears. I was stunned—reeling. If the ship's captain had known the urgency of my plans he would've never considered such a restriction. My cars were ringing. This decree would ruin everything for me! I couldn't believe the lack of concern displayed by the other guys. How come there were no moans, no outrage or indignation? Guess it didn't make much difference to anyone else. (Who else would have had plans to catch a plane out of Palma?) Ernie was saying something to me, but while his lips were moving no sound was making its way to my brain. I couldn't ask the Skipper to grant me an exception. If he said no and I still went, I'd really be asking for it—direct disobedience. I'm just going to have to do it on the sly and make absolutely sure to be back on board by 9 p.m. Saturday.

Not an hour after the announcement, at 1100 hours when I heard the familiar deep metallic rattling of the anchor chain rumbling out, heart was racing I was on my way. I managed to miss all my squadron-mates on the way to the liberty ladder, so no explanations necessary. (Though the harried look in my eyes would have discouraged anyone from asking me anything.) Down it and into my bumping escape craft, overnight bag in my hand, heart in my throat, face into the wind. This time no frivolity present.

A Clandestine Flight to Barcelona

Once ashore, to disguise my pending absence I rented a room in a hotel not far from the dock and left a bunch of clothes in it. I wouldn't use the hotel of course, but it would make it *look* like I was staying in the city. Had a cab in two minutes. At the airport in ten minutes. The small terminal looked like a concession stand at a lake. Got a ticket for the three o'clock flight. So far so good (but about an hour behind schedule). The flight was called and I was on board; excited, but unable to shake the awareness of the risk I was taking. Forty minutes we later touched down in Barcelona. Got a taxi and was on my way to the Manila hotel, where June and I spent our last night together. Got a room; my refuge for the next twenty-two hours. Took a deep breath (my first of the day). Called June's number but no answer. At her apartment at six but found the metal gate locked up tight. Alone in an abandoned neighborhood, standing in dead grass by a peeling wall, collar up against the wind. *Things have got to get better—soon!* I'm just going to have to attend the performance and meet June afterward.

Got an idea that used up every minute till show time. Began a search for a flower shop. Found one. Picked out a nice bouquet. To make the delivery even more special, I cut a big star out of a piece of cardboard, covered it with aluminum foil, and with a magic marker and my growing Spanish vocabulary, inscribed it: *Por la Inglesa June. Una estrella para la estrella.* ("For the English girl June. A star for the star.") I gave the shop owner directions to the artists' entrance, and he guaranteed me they would have it delivered during the performance. To the theater. Same show. Soon as the curtain closed I was out of the theater and around to the artists' entrance. The lady in the guard booth had not forgotten the jerky young American who had appeared just a few weeks ago. I was waved in with a big smile, and she referred to me as June's *novio*—June's "fiancé." (To the Spaniards we *were engaged*.) And the girls with high hopes for their captain, were more than willing to refer to me as such. They wanted to believe that good and lasting things did happen to girls on the road, far from home. Down to the first landing, then into that same hallway. In range I now heard the girls howling.

"June! It's me, Rog." Once again she was out in two shakes, with a giant hug, and those kisses again. She was barely holding the tears back, but not because she was so glad to see me; rather because the night's big incident had them all in hysterics. When the flowers arrived, the stagehands saw the silver star and assumed it was for Lola (Tony's leading lady with the huge bazooms). The whole cast was crowded around her as she admired the bouquet and the star. But her delight was short-lived when she read the inscription and realized the flowers were not for her. *They were for the red-headed Inglesa!* With precious little time remaining, we were going to have to get some place alone—quick. There were lots of things to talk about. (Not that I was at all ready to tackle that task.) I was on shaky ground in every respect: my wife, my family, the Marine Corps—and the course my life would take. We excused ourselves as quickly as we could and grabbed a cab for the Manila Hotel.

One Last Visit to the Manila Hotel

In the elevator. Into our room. Safe. A small ceramic lamp was spreading a warm glow. June gave me a kiss and went into the bath. I plopped down in an over-stuffed chair to wait; nervous for at least two reasons: primarily, aware of hard explanations that were way overdue, with no solution on the horizon, and second, a repeat of my non-performance our last time in bed. It was as if I needed a good cry—and felt like I could if I let myself. June came out of the bathroom in the same comfy old bathrobe I'd seen before. She sat down on the carpet alongside me and looked up with the most loving and trusting look one could imagine. She had a hairbrush in her hand. I don't know what possessed me. I took it and began to brush her hair. The look I was getting from her continued; one I did not deserve, but one that tore at my soul. The warmth and hope in her eyes that moment is indelible in my mind today.

A kiss and I was out of the chair and to the bathroom myself. Finished, I was afraid to come out; nervous about the coming physical intimacy and dreading the requirements of the confessions I would soon have to voice. I was a "basket case." I'll bet June could have stayed up all night, but maybe just to keep from putting me on the spot, she feigned exhaustion as well. She *had* to be expecting some explanations, some hint of a plan. But I offered nothing, knowing it was the one thing I should have been doing. I owed it to her. *I hated myself.* Whatever her thoughts, she didn't verbalize them. We were together, but in silence. I wasn't sorting anything out. I was a mute.

Again our bodies were together under the sheets, and now—the one time I would have given anything for a landmark performance, I was equally unspectacular—as in Valencia and here a month ago. In spite of me missing the mark, she wrapped me in her arms. The objective of my initial sexual encounters was to find that one female who would turn the key and unlock my manhood (and I was sure she had to be out there). But now here I am in this new and wonderful relationship with June, feeling as I do about her, and she is *not* that woman! Not that it would ever occur, but what future could we have? My inability could cause any union to fail, and I couldn't bear that to happen with June. For sure there was at least one tear in my eye when I slipped off into a fitful sleep.

Don't think I'd ever slept till eleven, but that's what I was saw on my watch. June appeared to still be sleeping, her head motionless on the pillow. I was startled as while examining her face, one eye popped open and she was staring straight at me. She opened the other eye and a wonderful, easy and comfortable smile spread across her face. I felt her hand move under the sheet (scaring me), but she was just searching for my hand. There was no tension, no threat, no regret on her face. It was a reassuring countenance and exactly what I needed.

A placard in the room advertised a celebrated brunch being offered in a gabled top floor restaurant. We took advantage of it. Made our selections and carried our plates to a table in a private alcove. As you might imagine I couldn't taste anything. My *plan* was, in view of last night's inexcusable lack of communication, to try to bring things out in the open now—right here this morning. Be a man about it; confess and then try—at least *try,* to verbalize some possible eventualities. *But as the married man I was, what eventualities were possible?* I knew for our relationship to have a future, painful and unimaginable changes would have to be brought about in Sara'slife, changes that on only fleeting occasions could I bring myself to consider, and when I did it caused me to shudder with fright.

I barely have the courage to admit it, but I failed again here in this restaurant, to take advantage of what might be our last opportunity to get anything resolved. Oh, I started several times, but I didn't commit to anything. I got off on tangents, spoke in abstracts, kept finding myself off track. June watched and listened patiently. *God bless her.* She never asked any hard questions (ones she had every right to ask). Instead, she just waited for me to say something that would make some sense. As close as it came, we once talked about her starting a dance school in the states (leaving it not real clear *how* it would come to pass that she would be in the states). Brunch was finished and we were back up in the room. A little past noon.

I don't know if it was the late night, too much breakfast, or the mental burden of constant and deservedly critical introspection, but I was overcome by a great weariness as soon as the door was closed behind us. June encouraged me to rest. She allowed me to escape, close my eyes (and let the real-world slip by without an attempt to sort it out). Lying on my back exhausted and looking straight up at the ceiling, I felt as if the skin on the sides of my face was going to sag and drain off onto the pillow, till just a skull was left. June stroked my forehead for a while and then lay down beside me. I fell asleep. Don't know if June slept.

Woke from a dream, into what in a few weeks, could *itself* be no more than a dream. I only had an hour and forty minutes to catch my flight back to Palma! *Have to get moving.* Like a punch-drunk fighter with one elbow on the canvas trying to get a knee under his weight, I struggled, exhausted from talking without saying anything, avoiding explaining away what truthfully had a very simple explanation (but one I was too cowardly to verbalize). For ten months I had been keyed on my own plight and how all this would affect Sara, but I never considered how it could affect anyone on *this* side of the Atlantic. My ramblings must have been frustrating to her. I had proven my weakness. I failed to make a commitment. *Running out of time!* Dialed up the main desk, gave them my room number and told them I'd be down in five minutes and would need a quick checkout.

As I moved about the room gathering my belongings, June sat on the bed, back upright against the headboard, not moving, not blinking. The dark green of her plaid slacks and an olive turtle-neck contrasted prettily with her fair skin and red hair. Her arms were folded across her chest, long legs stretched out in front of her, one ankle over the other. No doubt about it, she was a handsome young woman. Sure would have liked to know what thoughts were going through her sweet head. June watched every move I made, as if she was taking photos with her eyes and storing them away. No tears, no asking for promises. She was a real trooper that was for sure, I think ready for the worst and afraid to hope for the best. Everything in the bag, we made for the door, out of our little world, in the hall, down the steps, and into the lobby. A quick checkout, in the street and hailing one last cab.

The Ride to the Airport and Leaving

As you might have suspicioned, the ride to the airport was also void of any valuable conversation. She sat close by my side, holding one of my hands in both of hers—from time to time patting it and giving me a courageous smile. Inside the terminal things did not get better. I was one confused young man and it showed. From brave June no signs of regret or worry; not a tear. Maybe—just maybe, this time she was willing to believe it wasn't necessary. Perhaps because of the level of energy I'd put into this campaign from day one, maybe she was daring to think long term thoughts about this American guy. Maybe she held hope. Waiting in line to check in she stood by my side like a statue. Got a boarding pass for the five-twenty flight to Palma. We didn't have a drink or do anything worth relating, just strolled hand in hand together sensing an unspoken, mutual, solemn pledge. At least that's how I felt.

The moment I was dreading was upon us, the flight was called; time for one of those strong bear hugs and another one of those great kisses—unashamed and full of love. June's kisses were like I said, unafraid and without other motives, an example of her unconfused life. Not meant to be sexy, not meant to arouse. They were meant to tell you something, and they did! And none had told me as much as this one. She knew what she was all about, and now, what she wanted this kiss to show. After it only a fool would ever think he had reason to question her. None other could match it. All others, forever, would be no more than dutiful.

If I was feeling ill earlier, I was really sick now. For a short time we could watch each other through a glass partition. But then I was ushered into a departure area where squinting between two room dividers I was able to see her finally give up on catching a further glimpse of me, turn, and begin her walk out of the terminal, and likely out of my life. I lost sight of her, but knew I'd not soon forget that tall proud figure cutting a straight path towards the exit. With each strutting step her long red hair bounced upon the black shoulder cape she wore over her suede vest and wool slacks. With her high-heeled boots she appeared even taller than she was. In this world, she was someone to be reckoned with. My heart hurt. Reader it truly hurt.

The Flight Back to Palma

I held onto the thought that in this one case—just perhaps, it wasn't over with June. But if not, it would have to be put on hold for an indefinite period. Five o'clock now. Could be back in Palma by six-fifteen. Catch a cab to my unused sacrificial Palma Hotel. Pay my one night's bill, run to the dock, catch the seven o'clock liberty boat and be back on board with hours to spare. Should work out okay. *I'm just not sure the rest of my life will work out okay.*

Five-fifteen came and went. Five-thirty also, and they had not yet called for boarding. I was becoming concerned. This is one time I absolutely positively could not afford to be late. We were going to up-anchor at midnight, although the last liberty boat may have been scheduled for as early as eight-thirty. This was going to be close. Five forty-five. I latched onto one of the airline reps and asked what the heck was going on. They had cancelled the five-twenty flight, but not to worry, everyone would get seats on the next scheduled flight. I counted my blessings when they announced a Palma departure at six o'clock. Not great, but I still should make it okay, just thirty or forty minutes later than planned. My nerves were frazzled enough from the situation with June, I sure didn't need the flight cancellation. I felt part of a scenario over which I could exercise no control. I was experiencing a distressing melancholy. One part of me was saying, you shouldn't have left June like that. Everything has not been said. There must be more. But for now I just had to concentrate on making it to the dock in time!

The plane was fully boarded but we were just sitting there. What the hell's the delay? The engines should be running by now. Christ, six thirty-five already. Forty plus minutes to Palma; that makes seven-twenty at the earliest. Shit! Even if we took off right now, it would still only leave me forty minutes for the cab ride to town, hotel checkout, and a mad dash to the dock to catch what perhaps would be one of the last liberty boats. Okay we're taxiing. Thank you God. Into position at six forty-five. When we were finally airborne, I breathed a sigh of relief (but not a big one). It would be close. Anything else going wrong, I could still be in serious trouble.

Getting Back to the Ship

Descending into Palma the aircraft was being severely buffeted. The water was swept with white caps, and in lieu of its famous blue, it was steely gray. On the ground in Palma at seven thirty-three. Leaden skies and almost gale force winds. I had to lean hard into the wind to make it to the terminal. Pieces of trash were flying across the ramp and plastering themselves up against a chain link fence. Geez, I'll bet there's one hell of a sea-state. Grabbed a cab and was on my way to the hotel.

Out of the cab, room key out of my pocket, up the hotel steps two at a time. Inside. Into the room. Jammed my stuff into the already full bag. Down to the desk. "Yes, checking out, right now, please. I'm in quite a hurry." Paid the bill and was out into the damp air and full speed towards the dock. A strange, foreboding, isolated lost-soul feeling was coming over me. I wasn't seeing any other servicemen; in fact I wasn't seeing *any* other people! Palma was a ghost town. Globs of foam and spray flew at me from over the sea wall. Eight-twenty. At the dock, fully expecting to see at least a couple boats, but not one! *Nothing!* Not even a Shore Patrol boat (or a Shore Patrol guy)! Not a sole indication that the *Forrestal* had ever used this dock. It was deserted! Straining to see through the mist and low hanging clouds, my heart stopped as I made out the carrier—on the distant horizon. *Oh my God!* For some reason they had pulled out early! Surveying the area I realized the entire waterfront was deserted and all the shops were closed (some even boarded up). I was at a loss. It wasn't like I was thirty minutes late; *it was like I was a year late!* Now I was *really* worried. There was nothing to indicate the liberty boats had *ever* been running. *What am I going to do?*

Squinting into the wind, through the tears (and big droplets now pelting down), about a half mile down the shoreline I saw a bunch of masts protruding over a breakwater with a lot of small boats anchored alongside it. Maybe I could hire some boat-owner to take me out to the carrier. I ran all the way. When I got there a sign read *Palma D. M. Yacht Club.* Who knows, *maybe.* Into the building. Found the office.

"Good evening." My presence was acknowledged by two guys, well dressed. Looked like officers of the club.

"Good evening. I'm afraid I may need some assistance. I'm off the carrier, and I have a big problem."

One of them spoke perfect English; an old but handsome white haired guy in a black turtle neck sweater. He took a pipe from his mouth and spoke, "And you're here for some help?"

"Yes sir. I was hoping I could hire a small craft to take me out to the carrier."

A nervous laugh, and then: "In *this* weather? If we could—we would, but even your own boats stopped running about six. The seas were too rough. Can't help you son."

Well that explains it and might help! There *was* no boat at eight-thirty (or even seven-thirty). This turn of events could disguise my late arrival. Evidently nobody got out to the ship after six. But if not, where the hell are they? I could make up a story that I was on the dock by eight, and still missed a boat. Luck might be with me. But I still have the problem of getting out there now.

I'm screwed. Nine twenty-five. In real trouble now! Holy shit, can you imagine if they *left* me!? But maybe some other guys missed the boat. I sure hope so. *Had to think of some way to get to the carrier!* I decided to seek help back at my unused hotel. I strode into the lobby. Empty, except for one clerk. Not another soul; deserted like the rest of the waterfront. I looked across the foyer into the lounge, a vacant lounge. Just a sea of unoccupied black Formica tables strewn with napkins, small plates and half-finished drinks. There I stood, overnight bag tucked under my arm, and fresh out of ideas. This could be the end of my career. Scanned the empty room again. *My heart almost stopped when my glance got to a barely lit far corner.* At a single table was a cigar-smoking American businessman with his frumpy, martini-wielding wife, and their beautiful young daughter *sitting on Nick Cassopolis's lap!* And Nick was in rare form. Even half in the bag sporting a foolish grin he was one good looking guy. Evidently he'd drawn today's Shore Patrol duty. He was in his uniform—such as it was (his hat being on his head crosswise). He was wearing the tell-tale black and white arm band. What a sight!

He saw me! A double take, and then he jumped to his feet, nearly upsetting the table. He teetered for a second before steadying himself. He flashed a smile to the parents and was on his not very straight way to me. Once to me he blurted out the least believable statement I ever heard: "Rog! Boy have I been worried about you!" It was a cinch that Nick Cassopolis hadn't been worrying about anything for quite some time.

"What's the skinny Nick. What the fuck is going on?" He didn't answer right away. Steadied himself with one hand on my shoulder. Started to talk, then broke into giggles. (I sure was glad to see someone who wasn't worrying.)

"Sea state Rog. Too rough. Cancelled boating about six. Each of the squadrons have a shore patrol detail to round up stragglers. I'm it for our squadron."

"You mean I'm not in trouble? Yet? There's others?"

"Well maybe. So far just you, but I think there's two guys missing from the Crusader squadron. Was just talking to their Shore Patrol guy."

"What's the plan Nick, what are we supposed to do?"

"Gonna rent a taxi Rog. We're going drive the length of the island, up to Pollensa Bay" and be there when the carrier arrives tomorrow morning. It's a small island—will only take a few hours. We'll be there by dawn. When the carrier arrives we'll hop a boat out. No sweat. Don't worry. We'll be out on the ship before the Change of Command ceremony even starts." For the first time (in twelve hours it seemed) I just let it all hang out. I was mentally and physically empty. I hadn't needed it to end this way. At midnight we still hadn't left; were just waiting under some trees by a little gazebo. Can't remember when we left or how long it took. We ended up with three other guys; didn't know any of them. The sky was turning pink as we arrived at the north end of the island, the town of Pollensa.

Out of the cab. Nick paid (which was good). We sat alongside each other on a smelly sea wall, feet dangling, like a bunch of homeless bums, hungover and tired, waiting for a miracle. I was content to leave Nick in charge. I was pretty sure we were somehow going to make it back on the ship, could have been a *lot* worse. At 0900—there it was, as big as you please, the *Forrestal* came steaming around the point; cutting a handsome shape for us to ogle (and dread the consequences of our tardy arrival). The ship probably had a plan for our pickup, but Nick wasn't going to wait. He made his own arrangements with some fishermen at the end of the pier. We were about to be brought out in style. You should have seen it; an old scow loaded with nets, oily tarpaulins, crab traps and drying fish innards. What a mess. (But probably no less than we deserved.) Five of us packed in. I not only looked like death warmed over, I smelled like dead bait. I was one bedraggled-looking USMC captain. (And I looked better on the outside than I felt on the inside.)

Leaned and got ahold of the wet vinyl handrails of the ship's ladder. Up the rungs. The usual ritual salute to the colors (that I felt unqualified to render). We were officially piped on board. Only one squadron mate—Bob Harmon, the crew scheduler (and my last remaining confidant at this time) was waiting for me topside. He had a hand-scrawled sign that said, *Bien Venido, Senor Fortunado.* A reference to me being like the leading man on the "Mr. Lucky" TV series, miraculously surviving another in-port stay. Scanned the rest of the flight deck and heaved a sigh of relief when I didn't see the tall silhouette of the Colonel. No one else waiting for me. *Whew.* Headed for my stateroom, tail between my legs.

Chapter Twenty-Six
TIME TO FACE THE MUSIC

It's Done

The Change of Command Ceremony was over at 1500. Our ship's Captain was piped aboard. Thirty minutes later the anchor links began notching their way around the turnstile; starting up from the bottom for the last time. I feigned a squadron member joyful returning home for a grand reunion. I couldn't escape taking some ribbing about my tardy arrival that morning. In my head was a collage of faces and scenes from the Cote d'Azur, Rome, Barcelona, Milano, Bulgaria, and frightfully—Beaufort, South Carolina. I mulled over multiple courses of action upon arrival; none seeming the slightest bit plausible. It was going to take more than six and a half days to get my head and heart back in order. I was the same person who had stood on this deck in Norfolk that first gray and windy day. But how could anything look the same for me now.

A Dread-Filled Trip Across the Atlantic

I wandered to the fan tail and once again marveled at the pounding, turbulent wake this monster spewed rearward. She wasn't afraid. Like a horse on the way back to the barn, nostrils flared, it could smell the states. I feared it was going to be a much too short trip. I was gripped by woefully complex feelings of loss and guilt. Decided to face it; walked forward to the bow, hair plastered back, forehead damp from the wet salt air, I was the sole lookout—a weary sentinel. Our gray monster was plowing westward under a full moon, white water leaping from her bow. For the last time I would see the eerie luminescence of those sparkling phosphorus-filled waves. I was a tiny flea on the back of a big dog; helpless to affect direction or speed, with lots to think about. Tomorrow's another day (although I could not imagine it presenting any solutions, and thus worse).

Monday: There were rumors circulating that Air Ops was going to order one last launch while we were still within 400 miles of a coast (and could get to land in the case of a broken tail hook.) Wisely it got canceled, meaning we'd made our last carrier operation! The rest of the crossing would be mostly paper shuffling interspersed with mutual congratulations. We'd spend our time getting things in order for the squadron reorganization upon our return to Beaufort.

Tuesday: Spent the better part of the day touring my shops like I'd done a hundred times; mostly helping the guys with their next-duty-station requests. Back in the stateroom Jim was working on his own next-duty-station request. "Rog, what are you going to put in for?" Still in a turmoil about whether or not a life with Sara was possible, and if it wasn't—would I even stay in the Marine Corps, where among our married friends a divorce between Sara and I would be untenable—unthinkable. I managed to answer:

"Not sure Jim, I know I should think about the 'Boot Strap' program." (A helluva deal where the military sends officers back to college to finish their degree—on campus, at no cost to the individual.) "Maybe now is as good as any."

He gave me a thumbs-up and bent back over his own form. Once again I was saying one thing and thinking another. My lips were moving and I could hear apparently rational sentences coming out of my mouth. And this tact with Jim was downright risky. But it's what I'd been doing for the past ten months. No matter what the activity, nothing dislodged the major issues that had me so abstracted. The weight of it was there all the time. As if gremlins were filing away the top of my brain, rasping off the cells. I felt increasingly weary as I sought to come to some rational conclusions. *Ten months to get in this fix, less than a week to sort it all out.*

Wednesday: I passed most the day alone in my stateroom, going through Sara's correspondence with renewed attention. I was encouraged noting the revival of a capability I didn't think was in me. I found myself getting involved and sensitively so—feeling a bit excited as I read and re-read the letters. I even hazarded to think I could do it; like maybe we'd be able to make it. Then curses! Thirty minutes later—like an addict I would put on one of my French, or Spanish, or Italian tapes, hear the music, look at some photos, glance down at the silver bracelet from Rhodes or the Super Dakota, *and just plain get sick!*

But (*Thank you God*) I might be beginning to feel an increasing positive anxiety to see Sara and the kids. I reopened the shoebox full of photos, studying each one. I saw personalities that just leaped off the paper; handsome kids—broad smiles, white teeth, square foreheads, and thick locks. (Sara's good Hungarian heritage. Not from me.) Even looking at the recent photos, it was hard not to visualize Samantha and Mark's faces as they were when I left. I missed them both and was very ashamed of myself (and deservedly so as I need not tell you). I had regularly sent them cute cards and little gifts (mostly picked up running through train stations). But certainly had not given them the priority they deserved, that I saw being rendered by the other officers.

Thursday: We had a ship-wide volleyball tournament on the hangar deck. VMA 331 had two teams, an enlisted team and a team made up of the officers. I was on the officers' team of course—with Jim. (If you were involved in anything with Jim, winning was almost a foregone conclusion.) And I gotta admit there were moments—albeit brief moments, when I think I forgot my plight. In the midst of a lunge for the ball, a good save, or a successful spike, I was just "one of the guys." It felt tearfully good (but it was tearfully temporary). I had a monumental problem, and for me exercise was not going to lessen it.

The Colonel wanted all the officers to plan on taking the evening meal together. We'd meet in the wardroom for one of our last, special times together. The Officers Mess was a formal place. Its tables spread with white linen looked all the more immaculate as they were contrasted by the dark wood-paneled walls. On the walls hung colorfully embossed plaques boasting the emblems of previous USS *Forrestal* tactical units. One could not help but be aware of a long-running involvement and feel proud to now be a part of it. Fitting decorum was not difficult. It was a great evening. Many good stories retold. Rave reviews and expressions of camaraderie.

And thank God for small favors. In spite of my philandering ashore and onboard concern with other things, I must have put up a good front, because after the Skipper finished his nostalgic recap of the cruise, he commenced a "roast" of each of the officers. When he got to me, I was obviously worried, then surprised and gratified, as the sincerity of his accolades, left no doubt about him believing I had made a fine contribution both as a Flight Leader and the Maintenance Officer. This only made me think, *what in God's name would the Colonel have thought if I had really made the job a priority.* The finale and perhaps high point of the evening was the singing of the Marine Corps Hymn. There wasn't a tearless eye. It was hard for me to comprehend that for so many, life could be so uncomplicated, so honorable. I would have given anything to have mine that way!

Friday: (Two more days) I felt queasy, in fact nauseous, each time I thought ahead to my face-to-face meeting with Sara. *Dammit!* Everything was still desperately up in the air. Five nights of laying in the rack hashing things over, and I was no closer to a course of action than when we left Pollensa Bay. I knew I needed to have a plan—one way or the other, *before* we arrived. I *had* to come to a decision. If I arrived in my present state of mind it would be a disaster. I still had no idea if I was going to wrap Sara in my arms committed to our future, or hand in my resignation, and try to get on with the airlines. I was a wreck (and don't know how I thought I could come to some decision in the 48 hours remaining).

Mercifully, in the past week and the thoughts of Sara and the kids were more and more actual; I *think*, the fragrance and intensity of my adventures in Europe might be receding. I've heard—we've all heard, how *time heals*. Even in this short period it might be the case. Part of me knew that forgetting it would be for the best, since I saw no way that I would ever be able to renew the associations or recreate the lifestyle I had sampled. *How? Where? Doing what?* While weighing two mutually exclusive lives, I realized going back over Sara's letters and the photos had indeed helped. I went over them again. She'd done a great job keeping me up to date on the kids, their activities and signs of their growing up. And the photos; *stare* at those kids! I was making a valiant effort to re-instill within myself something which had never been present; that which had never been dislodged from my squadron mates.

Samantha, our first was now seven, and according to Sara, a lovable hellion. Knowing her own mind (and expressing it loudly when things weren't going her way.) Sara said Sammy had become the little girl in the poem: "There once was a girl with curl, and when she was good she was very good, but when she was bad she was horrid." Sounded to me like she might be a real challenge as she grew into adolescence. I would abandon her again—twice; and yet, many years later see her stick up for me and by me—repeatedly, when my actions did not merit that support. (Later bringing me to my knees by naming her first child "Roger.") Now five years old, Sara said Mark was always trying to do the right thing; intent on approval. You could just see it in his face. Recent photos indicated he was still small—not much bigger than when I left. Like me he would be faced with striving each day to overcome the stigma of being the "littlest guy" in the room. (Hated myself for giving him those genes.) According to Sara he was unusually perceptive, probably too sensitive, but often demonstrating a wisdom beyond his years; able to frequently add an unexpected, wise comment.

I had ineptly exercised my ill-prepared right to bring them both up, having not read a single book on parenting. Instead (and embarrassedly) primarily using the tactics of a Marine Corps drill instructor; just raising my voice to an ear-splitting level when I wanted to discourage them from some act. *Damn.* I was justifiably ashamed of my performance in that regard. Soon, in addition to facing their mother (the thought of which weakened my knees and turned me mute) I would have to look into these children's eyes while trying to convince myself that a man like me could be their father. How could I think I deserved any love or respect from them. I didn't. Not by a long shot.

Saturday: The schedule and details of our forthcoming return flight to home base was in the throes of final coordination and gaining hoopla. Tomorrow, Sunday *(tomorrow?)* crossing 74 degrees west, two-hundred miles out of Norfolk, the USS *Forrestal* was going to shed its Marine Squadron. Our last launch; all twelve aircraft—direct to USMC Air Station, Beaufort, South Carolina. An 0915 launch would put us overhead the airfield at 1045. A gala "Welcome Home" ceremony was scheduled to kick off upon our arrival at 1100. I was shaking in my boots. Twenty-four hours to go and still not the faintest idea of any words or actions that would paper over my deep and deserved guilt. Not a single idea of what I was going to do. I was not proud of myself. My weakness was despicable to me.

Our return—a twelve plane formation, was going to be an appropriate and dramatically staged arrival. The Colonel of course would lead it. (My first job was to make absolutely sure that all twelve airplanes were up and ready for the trip!) We received "Well Done" messages from the Group Commander at Beaufort, which included a diagram for the areas to which we'd taxi and park. Right in front of where we would park the chairs were set up, where our family and friends would be sitting. I was unwell, a significant stomach problem, and had a hard time concentrating on any of this. The plan was we'd come in over the field, lined up with the southeast runway, three divisions of four aircraft, do a three-second break, touchdown with short (too short) intervals (perhaps six aircraft on the runway at the same time), and taxi together. *One more day.*

An Inescapable Final Flight

Sunday morning: The last hour of my ten month's hapless experimentation. Minus me the Ready Room was a joyous place. I wasn't part of anything good. All too soon for me, but what everyone else was waiting for—one last time, booming out of the squawk box it came: "Marines, man your aircraft." I accompanied the other pilots as they excitedly commenced their last journey through those now familiar passageways and up those narrow ladders, to emerge into the bright daylight of the flight deck. I would be the Division Leader for the third division. Jim had the second, and the Colonel of course, was leading number one.

The ship's company was particularly respectful and gave us lots of salutes and earnest handshakes. I was again made aware of the mutual respect and bonding of personnel aboard one of these flattops. I was experiencing a ton of emotions as I strapped in for the last time. Real tears, and I didn't care. Sergeant Parker gave me a hard slap on the shoulder, said something complimentary, and pulled the canopy down. Like so many times before, alone in this acrylic bubble, about to be launched into whatever—gray, blue, black, wet, cold. Who cares? This is what we're trained to do. I think I could have done anything, except what I'm going to have to do after we land.

The launch went flawlessly. The same helmeted and goggled Launch Officer, the same pants legs flailing in a thirty-knot wind. Readied my head, pressed it backward against the head rest. There's the windup signal; eased the power lever full forward, hard against the stop. Wanted every last pound of thrust. Same unbridled roar. Whoa! Off. Sinking. *Rotate. Got it!* I'm goddam away again! *Catch me if you can!* Course set 240 degrees. We'd go "feet dry" at Charleston, then turn due south to Beaufort.

MCAS Beaufort South Carolina was in sight! I could see the expanses of its concrete ramps, the nearby swamps of Parris Island Recruit Depot, could even make out my old neighborhood. We were letting down, 250 knots indicated, passing eight thousand feet. Lined up with the runway. The Colonel gave the order to drop off in trail. Beaufort tower was on the air. We were heroes. *Some hero I was. I didn't even belong in the same airspace as these guys.* Overhead, I saw our ramp set up just like the messages had said; with all the chairs, making a sea of heads and bodies; wives, kids, families and friends, straining upward as we streaked in.

The pitch! The Colonel racked it over in his left break. Counted to myself, ...two, three, there goes Ken, ...two, three, there goes Nick, nice interval. So far so good. It was a perfectly timed break. I glanced over to the downwind and saw the Colonel wings level, gear coming down. Ken right behind him. Nick in about a sixty degree bank, arcing across. There goes Jim, ..two, three, Tripp's gone. One more. Last one. ..two ..three, *I'm over!* Oops, I may have pulled it too hard. Shallowed out my bank a hair. That's it, looking good now. Out of the corner of my eye, acres of tarmac were visible beneath me, occupied by the expectant family members, dignitaries, and other interested personnel. We had messaged the aircraft sequence to Beaufort Ops, so the wives would know which plane their husband was in. One of those heads craned back would be Sara, searching for her husband. For me, *I could barely voice the word husband.*

It was a pretty sight, twelve birds taxiing in, in three tight diamond formations. As we taxied closer, through my wet eyes I could make out more detail than I wanted. Blobs and bodies were rapidly becoming faces and people. I was searching for a dark-haired woman with two kids. Maybe all standing, maybe one in the arms. I was ill. I'd never been this nauseous—ever. Onto the ramp. Pulling into my slot. We were going to open all the canopies simultaneously on a signal from the Colonel. For just a moment more I would be protected. Still had time. Still in a world I knew. Not vulnerable. *There's the command.* I hit the latch and let the canopy swing upward.

A breeze that should have been refreshing struck me face on. I was only a hundred feet from the chairs. The hangar was draped in brightly colored banners. I spied Major Burnham on the ramp. A band was playing. Someone was testing a loudspeaker. People were hollering. I was terrified. I stood up in the cockpit. *There she was!* I spied Sara and the kids in the second or third row. Knee up. Stumbled on the canopy rail. Leg over the side. Where's the first step. Got it. Down the ladder. *Who stuck it in?* Never felt it go in. It was just there in the side of the aircraft. Don't trip. On the ground now. On my feet. Swaying. Scenery changing. All the guys running. Things passing me. I must be running too, but not feeling the pavement. I am running. Heart pounding. Through my blurred eyes I could make out Sara. She was waving while holding Mark. Yeah I'm running. Don't fall. Oh God. *God help me here.*

Chapter Twenty-Seven
ONE LIFE OVER, ANOTHER STARTING

The USA, My First Day Back

The panorama of chairs and bodies were a mirage, no more real than the kaleidoscope of images still in my head. Everything that had infused my being for the last ten months was over. And I feared—as the imposter I was, it would only be a matter of hours before I was exposed. But I kept moving towards the waiting families—staying abreast my running, joyfully innocent squadron mates. I was afraid to imagine the expression on my face—or lack thereof, which had to be broadcasting my guilt. In spite of my fright, churning stomach, and worst fears, I hopped over a row of chairs to Sara and the kids. It's happening—now! Can I carry it off? *Lord help me.*

Sara and I were in an embrace, a big hug and kiss. Some rushed bubbly greetings, a couple expected comments, and then an awkward silence. *Quick, grab the kids.* Hugged them both and scooped up Mark. And then the euphoria—what of it there was, quickly faded. Surprisingly, all too quickly Sara and I found ourselves making small talk—talk about buying trash bags when we passed the 7-11, and what I would want for supper. Not what one would have imagined, but it was a diversion and so far I didn't think I'd been discovered. *Don't think about the adventures, particularly the Barcelona late nights.* I forced myself into the midst of the reunion and listened with my best show of enthusiasm. The kids began a chorus of commentaries on their present activities, while just under the listening a riptide of contrasting emotions lurked. I was being handed Sammy's hand to hold. Mark was talking a blue streak and shoving a piece of paper to me. How could I feel so much confusion on the inside, and not have it glaringly apparent on the outside? At least twenty minutes now. I may have pulled it off so far.

Bob and Don sauntered by. Our eyes met. *They knew.* For sure they knew. I was no more than a walking stick-figure being pulled along—

the returning hero being escorted home. Our Ford Esquire station wagon looked like I just stepped out of it yesterday. Sara got in the driver's seat; never offered me the keys. Guess by now she's used to being the chauffeur. I heard words coming from my mouth that I didn't realize I was forming. Was hoping this afternoon would be the worst of it. Tried not to visualize the Carlton hotel in Cannes, Leo or June, or a year's fruitless experiments. I'd sold my soul. Now I was here face-to-face with reality and what I was sure was as good a wife as anyone ever had. When the din subsided I heard Samantha: "Daddy, Daddy, I'm getting perfect report cards."

"No she's not," added Mark non-committedly, only commenting as a disinterested bystander.

"I am too," she shouted, twisting around and glaring at Mark. He slunk back into his seat apparently satisfied with a sole remark. Samantha continued disputing Mark's input, while making a horrible mess with some sort of chocolate snack. Soon, between the two of them it was approaching bedlam. My heart was racing. Sara looked at me with a sheepish smile. She glanced at the kids, then back to me and just shrugged her shoulders. I could feel a rushing in my ears. The noise in the car was mounting. Sara looked over and smiled again. A chorus of voices was mounting from the rear seat. Sara gave a rote command to quiet them, to which they paid no attention. Her callout sounded like just part of an oft-repeated non-binding script. Like so many other perfunctory things she said and did, I now remember these responses. As it continued, she made some "waving off" motion with her hand. I could see she had immunized herself to this sort of confusion. My shoulders were cramping and I realized I was rumpling Mark's drawing in my hand. If the car stopped I might open the door and run. I hated myself. I had been in over my head before, but this time it could not be ended by jumping in a liberty boat and returning to the carrier. This was permanent. *This was my real life!*

In the driveway I scanned an already packed carport, the bad lawn, the ripped screens, the stained brick front, the peeling white paint. It was the house I left, but not necessarily one I could live in now. Inside, I noticed cracked tiles, chipped enamel, soap-ringed bathtubs, corroded faucets, torn shower curtains and loose corner moldings. At least I would have a bunch of projects to occupy my mind. I retreated into our bedroom feigning a prolonged unpacking. Sara made a light lunch while I played with the kids— could do that. And they were looking up at me so admiringly my heart could not do other than be heavy with remorse. Sara hollered in with local and family news—the latest updates on our neighbors and relatives. That was okay, I could handle that; keep it coming. *Just don't ask about the cruise.*

Sara cooked dinner—a special casserole she said was my favorite, which while this was typical of her thoughtfulness, I couldn't remember that I had any favorites. After the meal I helped her with the dishes. Before putting the kids to bed, I went through snapshots of the carrier and I gave the best running commentary truth would allow. That accomplished, Sara and I watched a little TV, and then what I was dreading since my arrival: *bedtime*. As you might imagine, I knew I was almost certainly in for trouble. My recent trysts—however incomplete, would be sufficient to keep me from being the love-starved husband I should be. And the deserved weight of shame would no doubt play a role in me not being able to consummate the act. You can bet I was praying to the good Lord to gift me with what would be necessary—even if only for this one night.

Now there was even more at stake. Over there I had been experimenting—searching for that one woman. Now I was where I should be and that could have made it right. But it didn't and it wasn't. I felt a deserved respect for this woman and knew the debt I owed her. But once again, what I didn't have—was what the male partner needs. I kept imagining being someplace else, anywhere else. Sara was unusually aggressive, moving her pelvis in hard thrusting movements that would have excited any other man, but only succeeded in intimidating me. But *thank you Lord,* I was gifted with just enough to accomplish a passable union, although I suspect for her, as it had consistently been before I left, certainly nothing worth any woman waiting ten months for. Though I felt no better than when I climbed down from the cockpit, I was pretty sure I would eventually fall asleep.

The Old Grind, Almost

The squadron was now undergoing a complete turnover of personnel. VMA 331 wasn't tactical anymore, just the remnants of a previously formidable fighting force. The cycle starts all over again; an influx of new, "green" pilots replacing us, ready to begin their Phase One training. Each of us would be plucked out—for new and non-tactical jobs such as a Building and Grounds Officer or the Base Fire Marshall, which none of us felt we deserved. So now, a cavalier attitude prevailed among us. I was afraid that no matter where I was assigned, it would be a substantial letdown—a term of incarceration. And if I was going to do something about it, it would have to be soon.

I was taunted by an assortment of images: cities, train stations, restaurants, cab rides, places and faces—most frequently June, whose every move—everything she ever said, was exactly what I would have anticipated and understood. These reminiscences were of such intensity that I often found myself unknowingly shaking my head or worse— emitting a moan (which more than once provoked a quizzical look from whomever was next to me). I foolishly believed that over there I had made a difference in other people's lives and was thinking now (ridiculously) that things were somehow 'on hold' over there until I could get back. *But how and where, and for who?!* What in the hell was I thinking? The discontent had me stumbling robot-like through these first days, and deservedly so.

Memories Revived. Exactly What I Didn't Need

One night when Sara and I were watching the Ed Sullivan show, he introduces a new sensation from England: *Cilla Black!* On the stage right here in the USA. My heart almost stopped when she commenced to sing "You're My World" (June and my special song from our times together in Spain). Two minutes later the phone starts ringing off the hook; one after the other of my cruise buddies telling me to quick turn on the TV. (Evidently the awareness of my activities during the cruise was more widespread than I thought.) Seeing and hearing Cilla Black again made forgetting the memories of the cruise even more difficult. I feared I might soon be investigating ways to alter my domestic situation; find a way to live at least some of the time separated from Sara. Shameful. And to do so—striking terror in my heart, would likely mean leaving the Corps. And as a "lifer" resigning one's commission is no easy thing! Along with sacrificing all your retirement benefits, your fellow Marines view you as a traitor—dissatisfied with the Corps and them. On rare moments I had allowed the word "divorce" to cross my mind (but not for long). Broaching that to Sara and the consequences were unthinkable. And a divorce in front of our military friends would be something I couldn't face. As far as the kids were concerned it was like I had never left. To Sara I'm sure it was as if someone other than her husband had returned. Or perhaps she had always tolerated this selfishness on my part; this distancing of myself from her. Maybe I'd always been this way, in which case her excellence as a loving wife is even more laudable.

A Possible Plan

The DC return address read *Air America Inc.* Remember? The CIA covert aviation operation in Southeast Asia that I heard about on the carrier (and to whom I had sent a query). I had already mentioned it to Sara—sort of readying her for that possibility, telling her she would experience a lavish lifestyle in some exotic city and that I could make a lot of money—assuring college for the kids. The single page said little else besides I could come for an interview, but it caused my heart to pound. Suddenly the idea of resigning my Commission and a less culpable way to affect a physical separation from Sara might be possible. This could be the light at the end of the tunnel. A scary tunnel and a faint light; one I might never reach, or reach and sorely regret.

It was just about the hardest thing I ever did. I can't imagine how I got the courage to state I wanted out, especially to Major Burnham. But I did. The biggest hurt was I dared not voice the *real* reason behind my wanting to leave the Corps. My fabricated explanations did not justify my intended action. I felt terrible because I had inflicted a hurt upon the Major and my squadron mates. The paperwork was sent off. I'd persevered, but I wasn't at all confident in the wisdom of this decision. My legs went weak every time I thought about it. I prayed that my memories of the Continent would not fade; now needing them close by to see me through this. A week later (surprising everyone and especially me) my resignation was accepted and I was a civilian. *Had I known the emptiness and loss that would have accompanied it, I doubt I could have gone through with it.* I guess in my naiveté or reliance on providence, I was just assuming I'd be a Marine pilot one day and a gainfully employed Air America pilot the next. The following week I flew to Washington, took the shuttle bus to 1725 K St. N.W., *and was hired!*

Leaving

And when I shared all this with Sara? As usual she went along with everything. If I thought it was for the best, she would not argue. I didn't know if her passiveness was because of a great inner tranquility, or that she never understood the genesis of my machinations, or that she doubted she could make a difference if she tried. *Sara! Speak out! Please make your thoughts known.* I don't know how she ever let me go through with it. Perhaps she was numbed from years of inattention and my lack of prioritizing what might be important in her life. Perhaps having never experienced a devoted husband she had accustomed herself to me—this kind of interface being the norm. Her calmness in this instance wasn't due to my confidence or enthusiasm. Just under the surface I was experiencing grave doubt, in fact downright fear! The kids—what do they know? They don't know about separations, either temporary or physical ones.

The night before my official separation, my carrier buddies threw a hell of a party for me. The punch was potent (a variety of fruit juices, ice cream, and rum), but tasted like fruit slushies. I drank way more than my share. I don't know how I was allowed to drive home (or made it)! This was before the war on DUI. No one even blinked at me staggering out the door. I remember patches of roadway, an occasional yellow line, tree limbs streaking by, going airborne after passing over humps in the road, before in what seemed like three minutes—mercifully finding myself in our driveway. *God was I lucky*.

Sara hadn't yet accustomed herself to my return and here I was bounding out of her life again. I told her that even though I was taking a job halfway around the world, as soon as my probationary period was over she could join me, and we'd have a great life abroad. I'm not sure she felt at ease with my explanation. (I know I didn't.) I was whistling in the dark, alternately feeling moments of excitement and then waves of breath-taking apprehension. I was saying whatever I had to, to make this exodus go calmly. Sara's feelings I could see were not so complex. She was worried. She was watching all this come together with absolutely no understanding of why, or what would evolve. As I reflect on my selfish departure, if she would have shed even one tear I doubt I would have been able to carry it off. But she didn't. She just stood there the expression on her face saying, *I guess you know what you're doing*. I didn't. Good thing she didn't know.

The drive to the Charleston airport was quiet, minus my assurances that after 90 days they'd be coming over, to live in a big house in Bangkok (where most the Saigon-based pilots domiciled their families). And that she'd be introduced to a new and privileged lifestyle, with a maid, a cook, and a personal driver. And that the kids would be attending a new and modern International School—which was bound to be a once-in-a lifetime experience for them. I was throwing out a lot of facts when I wasn't sure of anything. Maybe the reality of my suspect motive was such that while this hyping up might be working on Sara, it fell flat with me. Somehow the awkward wait, the check-in, and the goodbyes were accomplished. I made it inside the terminal, to the gate, to the aircraft, and collapsed onboard; in no way capable of putting into any perspective, what I was about to do.

Chapter Twenty-Eight
ARRIVING IN SOUTHEAST ASIA

Taipei, Taiwan

Boarding the flight from San Fran to Tokyo, and musing on my future, I couldn't help but wonder if this was the beginning of that other more exciting life I always felt I was destined for. It would at least constitute a huge change for the indefinite future. Twenty hours later I arrived in Taipei—the S.E. Asian headquarters for Air America, discretely housed inside the Civil Air Transport offices (the flag carrier of Nationalist China). CAT was begun after WWII by retired Army Air Corps General Claire Chenault, the head of the storied "Flying Tigers." He, Chiang Kai Shek (the military leader of the old Republic of China), and all the other opponents of Chairman Mao had fled from mainland China to Taiwan (then Formosa) in 1949. Unknown to most, *CAT had been covertly purchased by the CIA for intelligence-gathering purposes.*

In Taipei I and a few other new hires were instructed in Taiwanese aviation regulations (in spite of the fact we weren't going to be flying in Taiwan). Observing and listening to our Chinese instructors, it was easy to see they worried every day about an attack from the mainland. Most of them had been pilots in the Republic of China Air Force in their loss to Mao's revolutionaries. To the man they believed they would confront Mao's soldiers again, defeat them, and retake control of the mainland. The aviation regulations stated huge fines, long sentences, and even the death penalty, for any pilot caught making radio transmissions to the mainland (just 110 miles away, across the Formosa Straits).

Bangkok, Thailand

After finishing in Taipei we boarded a flight for Bangkok, aboard CAT's top-of-the-line *Mandarin Jet*—the airline's *only* jet; a many-times-over refurbished, old Convair 880. The aircraft was highly polished, trimmed with white and gold, and boasted a dragon stretching the length of the fuselage. In no other airline did one plane spend less time on the ground and more time in the air. It seemed to be in Bangkok, Hong Kong, and Tokyo the same night (and usually was). The stewardesses wore silk brocade, sheath dresses, with the high slit up the leg. There were hot towels, spring rolls, rice bowls, and chop sticks. It was my first glimpse of Oriental hospitality.

What would I find in Bangkok? (*The massage capital of the world!*) It was two in the morning when we taxied up to the arrival gates at the Don Muang Airport. When I stepped out of the airplane the temperature and humidity were in the high nineties! And I had my first exposure to the unmistakable fragrance of Bangkok—the fragrance of sweet flowers. Once having smelled it (I think Frangipani) you would forever be able to identify Bangkok even without opening your eyes. I got a cab and was bound for the city on a 10-mile long, straight and abandoned road. The moon reflected off the muscular backs of water buffalos in the canals on both sides of the road. Brightly colored cabs with multiple chrome ornaments continued to shoot past us, loud Thai music blaring out their open windows. In the city I noticed an unusually large number of girls wandering the streets, shapely young girls, in high heels and short dresses.

Downtown: The corner of Silom and Sukhumvit—the crossroads of Bangkok. Only two blocks up Silom, a right turn onto Pat Pong Street, and there was the Air America office. This street was in the process of gaining world acclaim as a hangout for mercenaries, journalists, and horny single guys (having its share of girly bars with upstairs massage parlors). There were one or two bars that still had some innocence: sporting darts and shuffleboard. I would discover that before CNN, in these bars was the best place to get the latest Southeast Asian news. There was a bar for Germans with a giant pewter stein mounted above the door; one for the Swedes—the door being a carved, brightly enameled Swedish flag; and an Australian bar with its "yard of ale" decanter over the entrance; and a bar called The Red Door which you can guess how it was distinguished. And finally: "Tigers"— the bona-fide watering hole for all the Southeast Asian soldiers of fortune. (To this day you might find an old Air America pilot there.)

I found a room around the corner at the Suriwongse hotel and had an experience which typifies Bangkok. Being exhausted, I didn't shower, just fell into the rack. I was just drifting off when there was a knocking on the door:

"Who is it?"

"*The Manager.*"

"Yes, what?"

"Do you have a girl in there?"

"No Goddamit, I don't have a girl in here!"

"Do you want one?"

The following morning I checked-in at the AAM office with the other new pilots. We sat through a few days of company indoctrination while waiting for our duty station assignments, and the visas to go there. The heat was oppressive. Some tropical cities have chosen to coexist with it, opting to leave the doors and windows open. But not in Bangkok. Whatever establishment you enter seemed to be near freezing. The motto was "Step in our place and see your breath." Every building trembled beneath a mega-ton air conditioner rumbling on its roof.

Now, as if You Didn't Know – Why I Chose Air America

Bangkok was the main "safe haven" city where most the married Saigon pilots kept their families. In Saigon there was always the threat of Viet Cong terrorist act: a satchel charge here, sniper fire there, or a car-bombing; so keeping your family in Bangkok—only a one hour flight away was an accepted procedure. (My intention.) And Bangkok *did* have all those perks I had told Sara about. On the surface, keeping the wives and kids in Bangkok looked like the reasonable thing to do. (No one interpreted this as a result of questionable marital preferences.) It was hard to believe Sara would balk at this setup. I should be able to swing it. Though now after many years, *I can't believe I drug my family through so much—just to meet my ends.* I get a pain in my heart reflecting on my behavior and selfishness. Just a couple days of foolishness and our Saigon duty station assignments came down.

A Pensive Flight to Saigon

Bangkok was sweltering—as usual. The temperature must have been 100 and the humidity the nearly the same. And inside this old French Caravel it was worse. Myself and my new hire friends were in an aluminum oven, stuck to the seat, neck soaked. This hour and a half flight to Saigon would be a chance to mull over the decisions I'd made during the past year, *where in the hell my life was going.* As we descended into Vietnamese airspace I sensed some of our bravado fading. The asides were forced as it began to sink in that we really had no idea what to expect. A week ago the headlines in the Bangkok newspaper announced that the Viet Cong had blown up the old US Embassy, and yesterday it said they had hit the famous *My Canh* floating restaurant—killing nine US personnel. *This could well turn out to be more than we bargained for, or the beginning of that other life I always strove to imagine.*

Tan Son Nhut Airport

Gray skies and rain showers filled all quadrants as we descended into Tan Son Nhut airport. I peered out alternate sides of the aircraft as it banked from side to side—seeing mostly just a sea of rusted corrugated metal roofs. Surprisingly not much greenery, just a few trees in and around the shacks. Most structures were tilting or shored-up—appearing as nothing more than battered shacks. Lots of fields with trash. Lots of narrow red dirt roads—all rutted and cluttered with puddles. Not many cars, but a million scooters and bicycles. Tiny figures clothed in black were scurrying in all directions. Smoke was drifting up from the center of numerous neighborhood "soup and noodle" stands.

On the ramp. Parked. Dead quiet. We emerged into a pelting rain, cautiously descending a slick and rickety aluminum stairway. Inside the terminal we became part of an unanimously concerned group attempting to bear up while being herded one way then another; directed first into a queue on the left and then being yanked out of it and sent to the queue on the right. Very-much-in-charge officials (all thin as a rail and with gaunt faces) scanned us suspiciously—seemingly just waiting for someone to question their authority. Immigration and customs were being accomplished using decades-old French Colonial procedures. From behind high counters immigration officials were shouting to each other in noisy and nasal staccato bursts (sounding like a bunch of ducks quacking). We were a captive audience to a non-stop cacophony of indecipherable chatter and rubber stamps banging on passports.

The Vietnamese people were just skin and bones, apparently accustomed to hard work but not a whole lot of food; didn't see one that couldn't use another twenty pounds. Every man that wasn't in a uniform was dressed in a long-sleeved white shirt and black trousers. And they must sell only one size belt in Vietnam—too big, because a foot of belt hung down beyond every buckle. We decided it might be wise to view the procedure as a drill to be played according to their rules; be very patient then very responsive; still and silent as a photo, then spouting answers and handing over documents on cue. The wartime activity was not close, but everyone appeared to be taking its presence seriously. I felt a vibrant energy in the air; sure I'd arrived at a place where things were happening. Time seemed to be the overriding consideration. One could feel the urgency and sense that at least in this place, things were barely under control. The terminal, which was the only public service building on the airport, was wet straight through, from the aircraft ramp to the small parking lot in front.

Our New Duty Station

One new hire said the Air America ramp was right next to the airport parking lot; just on the other side of a vine-entwined chain link fence. In spite of the rain and puddles we set off on foot; a band of strange-looking American gypsies lugging their Samsonites. Our travel orders were enough to get us past the Vietnamese guard stationed at an apparently rarely used side gate. Once through it I had my first view of what would be my workplace for some time to come; an almost level, pot-holed, puddled and patched tarmac ramp that boasted a wide variety of propeller aircraft—perhaps about 20 (including some I didn't even recognize). Each had the words *Air America Inc*, emblazoned on the side and (even in the rain) were being wiped down and polished by Orientals in dark blue coveralls. I was to learn that while the mechanics were Filipinos, the men cleaning the planes, sweeping the ramp, and doing odd jobs in the area were Vietnamese laborers. Attached to the maintenance hangar was a two-story white wood building that appeared to be an administration building. We struggled up a narrow outside stairway to a second-floor door that said "Operations." Inside we met Les Stroud, sitting at a desk that said "Chief Pilot." He was young—about my age, and even smoking a cigar he did not appear old enough to be behind that desk; as if he was doing this while the real Chief Pilot was out of town (which turned out to be true). In spite of the fact that I did not consider him to be the manager, he commenced to give out information and instructions without faltering.

A Ride to Town I'll Never Forget

About six o'clock Les sent us to Transportation where we crammed ourselves into one of the Air America silver and blue vans for the trip to town. We were joined by a burly Captain who had just finished his day of flying. The driver set off on what would be a wet and eye-opening trek to downtown Saigon. There was a lookout tower and guard station every hundred yards. Rolls of concertina wire lined the road. Every building was behind a wall of sandbags, and behind them were Vietnamese soldiers manning mean-looking automatic weapons. Prepared or not, we were likely to be part of a chapter of history.

The barrel-chested Captain who joined us was an outspoken red neck from Texas, with strong opinions on everything, especially the Vietnamese.

There appeared to be no love lost between Stan and the locals. We new guys were talking about domiciling our families in the safe haven city of Bangkok. Les Stoud had told us that pilots who did so, would get ten days off a month to visit them. Stan overhearing our conversation growled "Show me a guy who won't have his wife here in Saigon, and I'll show you a guy who doesn't love his wife." Hearing this I thought *what a ridiculous statement!* And a couple of the other new guys challenged him on it. As the months and years went by, I found out that old Stan was "right as rain." The case for keeping your wife out of harm's way was frequently just a smokescreen for some middle-aged guy to have a chance to experiment. (Unfortunately—like me.)

The streets were choc-a-block with two-wheeled vehicles. Bicycles, motorcycles, and mopeds, struggled to hold their own amidst the other vehicular traffic. Vietnamese of both genders and all ages were guiding these spindly vehicles in and out among the bigger traffic. Mostly they stayed to the side of the road, striving to keep their balance in the rutted and puddled patches alongside the road. Most had large bundles lashed on the backs of their scooters, with a bulging plastic bag hanging from one hand, and a section of newspaper held over their head with the other. As we approached one such poor soul on a moped—barely succeeding in negotiating his way in the narrow area between the passing traffic on the left and the ditch to his right, Stan—with some snarling words of contempt, waited until our van was abreast the moped, then swung his door open, slamming it into the driver's side, sending him cartwheeling over into the refuse along the side of the road. We were shocked speechless at this, glancing back and forth at each other in disbelief. Our trip downtown was arranged so as to be able to drop off Stan at his house. His dutiful Mexican wife was waiting outside (in the rain) to meet him. *Good riddance.*

Saigon City

It was quite a sight when we finally descended into the steaming, smoky, drenched and bustling city center. Under low hanging clouds and through the fog and lingering drizzle we were able to make out all manner of vehicles bumper to bumper and door to door. Pedestrians of all sorts and ages were dodging between them, each carrying a variety of bags, boxes, or even large car parts. Three out of four cars were taxis—Volkswagen Beetles painted bright blue with yellow fenders. In front of every other storefront was an outdoor cookery under a makeshift canvas awning. From each one smoke was drifting up about ten feet, then spreading and hanging there. All kinds of smells were making their way into our van. The sidewalks were also lined with hawkers who had set up low-rent places of businesses: tables spread with wallets, sunglasses, belts, ivory-carvings, and "you-name-its." And small children were everywhere—more than half of them taking care of even younger children. What appeared to be six-year-old girls were carrying their infant brothers or sisters on a jutting outward hip—the infant sitting astraddle this bony perch.

A Hotel Check-in to End All Check-ins

The driver stopped in front of a narrow, stand alone, three-story, building; an apparently abandoned store with empty glass fronts. On each side of it was an empty sand lot. We tumbled out of the van, into the drizzle, each of us looking left and right for what must be our intended lodgings. The driver continued pointing at the lone building and nodding. The building was only 20 feet across and at best could hold two small rooms on the second and third floor. It likely had just been converted into a makeshift hotel (to house a handful of the thousands of US military streaming into Saigon daily). Inside, the left and right walls of the lobby were the actual exterior walls of the building. No doorways, no windows, no hanging pictures; nothing on or against the maroon and black walls. Halfway down the right-side exterior wall was a door (which according to my calculations would have opened up onto the vacant sand lot next door). However, it was marked *Ascensor* (elevator in French).

We gathered up our soaked possessions and followed the sole employee to the *Acensor*. Even before our full weight was on the floor I wondered if it would be up to the task. We rode upwards in silence, eyes downward, praying that the creaking was not a forerunner of total failure. It went up some amount and stopped. But then a big surprise—the *back* wall of the elevator opened (which according to my calculations *would have spilled us out into airspace above the sand lot to the right*). We were in a small, darkened area with no windows that led further away from the building. We must have been in an enclosed, airborne walkway that would take us across the void below, and into the building on the other side of the lot.

Stepping out of this tunnel (into what must have been the building on the other side of the lot) we proceeded down a hallway, and up three steps—onto the roof! (In a pelting rain.) There, three long trellises supported a network of grape vines. Scanning the horizon, we could see the tops of other buildings poking into the gray wet clouds. Our leader—sorely affected by the rain, motioned for us to follow him towards a three-foot high concrete-block wall. We stepped through a cut in the wall onto a two-foot-wide ledge *surrounding a putrid rooftop swimming pool!* Single file we followed the clerk around the first two sides of the pool, gingerly placing our feet to avoid crushing fingers and hands. One wrong step and we would have been treading water next to our floating luggage.

Halfway back up the third side he went up three steps, through a door, and into *a fully operational Chinese laundry!* In a maze of hanging laundry four or five old men were sitting cross-legged on wood tables, ironing and folding. A large mechanical device was cycling and wheezing. The occupants did not take much notice of our intrusion as we quickly exited through a door on the opposite side. Into *another* hallway. At the end I could see a set of glass-paned French doors, with tied-back lace curtains. The best-looking thing I'd seen since entering the hotel. We might have arrived. Up three steps, through those doors, and we were there: our room for the night.

As grateful as you'd think we would be, it was nothing more than a large cell; only fifteen feet deep, about thirty feet wide, and starkly unfurnished. The only light was coming in through two small windows, almost to the ceiling; too high to look out. All four walls appeared to have been recently poured; the cement not yet cured—still that greenish color. The whole floor was the same rough concrete as the walls. No rugs. No tile. Not a stick of furniture other than five metal cots (with no mattresses)! No tables. No lamps. A demoralizing queasiness overtook us all. There was an enclosed toilet and wash basin in the far-right corner. The entire left side of the room was a shower area. A row of ugly showerheads lined the wall. A three-inch-high cement curb spanned the center of the room— ostensibly to keep the shower water from running into the right half of the room where the cots were positioned. I was having serious misgivings about the viability of this Vietnam experience to be. The five of us sat on what support was available; not talking, heads in our hands, listening to the street sounds, each to his own thoughts. I could smell smoke, and fish, and other strange smells. It was still pouring. I was a little nauseous. *This may be gonna take everything I got.*

A New and Sobering Thought

As I and my similarly-stunned new comrades sat there perusing the bleak surroundings and the soaked clumps of our belongings, my eyes came to rest on mine, including a plastic bag of letters from my female Continental acquaintances. For the first time I had to recognize another critical shortcoming (in addition to my glaring problem, which had already dictated my every thought and action since I was twenty). This second realization was of an additional grave flaw: an inability to make a *sole* commitment; to obligate myself to a permanent situation—with *one* woman! The thought of doing so had always struck fear in my heart; that I'd be quarantining myself from other possibilities, for the rest of my life. Admittedly, I had no idea what these possibilities might be!

Here I was with a collection of letters from June, Ardith, Ingrid, and Erica! What kind of true partner could I ever be? Don't most men settle on one woman: *one woman, special or not*. Even if I were to find that one woman who would unlock my manhood, could I still be doomed? Could I be lacking the ability to love; love *one* woman to the exclusion of all others? I just hoped that finally achieving sexual prowess would negate this second disturbing flaw. I did stay there that night. I did not stay a second night. I think Rob stayed there a week, but I don't think Rob was used to a lot of comfort. Ed quit the following day, was on the first plane out. The third guy spent most his time picking up Vietnamese bar girls and therefore did not spend much time in any one room. Me, I found a room in a small hotel, and would move on many times before finding suitable living arrangements.

Chapter Twenty-Nine
MY NEW DUTY STATION

At Last, Getting the Real Lowdown

The next morning we were picked up and brought to the airport for a detailed rundown on what we would actually be doing. In addition to MACV (the US Military Assistance Command Vietnam) that was arming, training, and fighting alongside the ARVN (the Army of the Republic of Vietnam), there was a large complement of CIA "Case Officers" working with members of the Vietnamese civilian population to assist in acquiring intelligence and engaging in guerilla combat with the NVA (North Vietnamese Army) and the VC (Viet Cong). These case officers were covertly assigned as staff at the U.S. Embassy or USAID (the "U.S. Agency for International Development")—supposedly as experts in agriculture, livestock, water supply, medicine, local law enforcement, etc.

Air America was under the Dept of Defense, and they got our operation approved in-country under the guise of providing humane airlift missions (such as bringing rice to needy areas, resettling thousands of Vietnamese who had been denied their villages, and delivering medical supplies to needy areas). But we had a much more important mission: *we were responsible for all the airlift requirements of the previously mentioned CIA case officers.* Day in and day out we would be delivering weapons, ammunition, food, water, and actual armed troops to wherever they were needed. We were told to never use the word CIA. If we had to refer to it, we should say *"The Company."* And the case officers (whether they were carrying powdered milk or an automatic weapon) were to be called *"The Customer."*

The Air America Fleet

For heavy cargo and parachute drops there were WWII C-46's and C-47's (stalwarts that flew the "hump" between India and China twenty years ago). For carrying six to eight staff from the embassy or USAID, there were several smaller but nicer twin-engine C-45's. For direct support of the missions of the CIA case officers, there was the Swiss-built Pilatus Porter, originally designed to land and takeoff from short and unprepared strips in the Alps. For getting into and out of even smaller jungle clearings, there were the Huey helicopters (Bell 206's) just like the ones being flown by the Army (except ours were polished aluminum with white and blue trim). I was assigned to the single-engine, single-piloted Pilatus Porter. It had Swiss language airframe manuals. The engine was French, so had French language engine manuals, and all the mechanics were Filipinos who spoke neither of those languages and only broken English.

Checking Out in the PC-6 Porter

There was no training syllabus. I was just told to be at the airport at 0700 the next morning and get in Frank Reynold's Porter, and do so every day for the next week. He would show me how to fly it. Not yet issued a uniform, I showed up at the plane in my Levis and a Banlon shirt and introduced myself to Frank. He looked just like Gary Cooper and talked just like him (on the rare occasions when he spoke). Supposedly, Frank had already been told he was to check me out in the Porter. What ensued was five days of breathtaking flying; skimming low through driving rain across rice paddies in the Delta, buffeting through teeth-jarring thunder clouds, wing-tipping around mountain peaks or slicing through a fifty foot-wide cut in a ridgeline, and finally diving through low hanging clouds and fog to put the aircraft down on a tiny, rutted, well-disguised small flat spot that was going to be our runway! To say the least I was wondering how anybody could do this type of flying on a regular basis.

Thank God For Small Breaks

After sitting in the copilot's seat for five days, not once did Frank ever let me touch the controls. And my captain's check flight was going to be in two days! I suggested that *me trying a takeoff or landing might be a good idea.* It met with a quizzical look. Turns out Frank's briefing had not been so good; me being in civilian clothes he thought I was a newly arrived CIA case officer and his job was just to give me a countryside familiarization, *not* show me how to fly the airplane. The last day of scheduled training, Frank was sick and I flew with a Captain Wogman. *Thank the Lord for small favors.* We had about twenty short flights, none with passengers—all just cargo. Ron said I could fly them (while he sat on the fold-down back seat reading his Zane Gray paperback). I viewed his decision as potentially hazardous but knew I couldn't pass up my one last chance to master this critter. I got in about twenty landings at a wide variety of strips.

My Captain's Flight Check Plus

I passed! Thank God for that one day with Ron Wogman. The day I had my flight check, another new hire—Bruce Clark, a retired Air Force Colonel had his flight check (administered by that burly Texan from my first day's van ride). I overheard Stan say he had just failed Bruce on his check flight, and that Bruce *had no more idea of precision flying than the man in the moon!* I found out later that Bruce's last assignment in the Air Force was as the captain of the "Thunderbirds"—the Air Force's precision aerobatic demonstration team!

My First Flight as a Captain

Arriving at the aircraft for my first solo flight, an Australian Warrant Officer was there waiting for me. (On his upper arm he had a tattoo that said *Malaysia, Never Again.*) He warned me we were going to land at "the worst strip in Vietnam." (When Ron let me fly I had to land on single lane dirt roads. What could be worse?) Arriving at our destination, he pointed at a 500-foot long, fairly straight *oxcart path*, and he was right, it was bad; only a few feet wider than my landing gear. There was a large pasture on its left, its right side fence paralleled the strip. There were no nearby enemy positions so I made a couple low and slow passes to examine it. The path was a raised mound with a flooded ditch on each side. The most crucial thing on landing would be to stay in its center. If either wheel slipped off the edge we would end up mired in a muddy canal, and if the spinning propeller struck the ground, the engine would be torn from its mounts. If we weren't injured we would be stuck there until a helicopter airlifted us out (and I would probably be fired after my first flight).

After two fly-bys, I went for it. Yanked off the power, plowed onto the hard dirt path, hit the brakes, threw it into reverse, and finally brought the airplane to a shuddering stop, without going off either side (only 30 inches outside each wheel)! Stopped, I looked over at the Australian officer who was aghast, his face ashen, his eyes and mouth wide open. He points across the fence at the wide-open pasture and shouts "That's the bloody strip! That's the bloody strip!" I couldn't believe he would have told me earlier, that the large flat area next to the ox-cart path, was our intended landing area. That pasture to this day is still one of the easiest landing sites in the country. The bad news is, when I reached the end of the oxcart path, it wasn't wide enough to swing the tail around and point the plane back for takeoff. We recruited a half-dozen locals to help us lift the tail and hold it up while we splashed a half circle through the canal, to reverse the plane's direction.

Flying in the Midst of a War

The landing described above was not unlike most our daily challenges. Almost the same—day in and day out. We'd usually launch out of Tan Son Nhut at 0700 and reposition at a tiny dirt strip fifty or more miles away, to work for the assigned CIA case officer at that village. This usually meant at least twenty flights a day; loading our plane with weapons, ammunition, food, water, medical supplies, and delivering them to a nearby area of active enemy contact, and on many trips bringing back the wounded. (The sight of some of these wounded troops was enough for me to believe in outlawing land mines.)

In my first couple months we'd already lost several aircraft; some due to enemy action, some due to bad weather, and some due to pilots just trying to accomplish that which was beyond his or the aircraft's capabilities. When these crashes occurred our Air America common radio frequency would be buzzing with comments the rest of the day, and upon returning to Saigon, the pilots would gather in animated groups sharing their opinions of what had happened. Two days ago (what we all dreaded) one of our pilots (another former Marine) landed his Pilatus Porter at a tiny grass strip in an oft-contested area. On exiting the plane he was captured by North Vietnamese soldiers who had taken over the strip the night before. Though we didn't know it then, he would spend the next seven years in a cell in the "Hanoi Hilton" (with John McCain).

Maybe Saigon IS Dangerous

I found an apartment in a relatively safe neighborhood, and on a rare day off—being the sun freak I am, I carried a lounge chair up onto the roof to get some rays. I stretched out contentedly in the piquing bright sun. Dozed. Was brought back to consciousness by a fluttering sound of what I thought was a bird flying close by. Sat up. Nothing unusual around. Laid back down. A minute later something that sounded like snapping a taught cord. Looked around; still nothing or anyone near. Laid back down. But it wasn't another minute before another crazy sound—this one a warbling whistle. *What the hell is going on around here?* I stood up, turned a complete circle scanning all around me. Above the trees I could survey the top floors and roofs of the surrounding buildings. About 300 yards away, on a glinting slanted metal roof, was a guy with a rifle, down on one knee, *shooting at me!* Needless to say this ended my sunning.

Chapter Thirty

THE FAMILY ARRIVES

My 90-day Probationary Period Completed

Iused my ten-day Scheduled Time Off (STO) for a trip to Bangkok to meet my arriving family. Temperature-wise Bangkok didn't let me down; stepping out of the airplane was like stepping into a sauna. I was quite sure Sara and the kids would be impressed by the large new home I had found and leased for them. It was in the neighborhood where other Americans lived. Not only that, it was on a quiet street where two other Saigon pilots had their family's houses (and only a half mile from the American School).

Don Muang airport, a little after 1 a.m.: I positioned myself where Sara wouldn't miss me coming out of Customs. Gotta admit I was anxious to see her and the kids. They were coming with a minimum of baggage and had shipped no furniture since the home came furnished. If we needed any furniture we would just buy here. (The least expensive and most beautiful rattan furniture in the world was made and sold here in Bangkok.) *There they were!* A bit bedraggled but okay. She spied me. The kids saw me. For the next few minutes we all stayed locked in a big embrace and in reserved anticipation of a new life.

The cab ride to town was quiet but understandably so, since they had just finished twenty hours of grueling flights halfway around the world. In spite of their fatigue a cautious interest was aroused when sighting the shining backs of the water buffalos in the canals lining the road. Got to the house and thank God for small favors: As we pulled into the driveway I could see an expression of pleasant surprise on Sara's face as she looked up at her new ultra-modern, two-story home. Inside she appeared equally pleased, seeing the glistening wood floors and the modern rattan furniture accented by brightly colored plaid Thai-silk cushions. Needless to say, after a long day we all bedded down in a matter of minutes, leaving further investigating to the morrow.

Next morning, Sara made a list of the food staples she thought she would need (not yet realizing that the cook would also take care of the shopping). The kids to my gratification, seemed as if they were looking forward to this new adventure. I introduced Sara to Sandy McInerny and her two kids. (Sandy was the wife of one of my best Saigon pilot friends.) *Miracle of miracles!* Sara and Sandy became instant friends, what's more—Sandy's son was Mark's age, and her daughter was just a year older than Samantha. It was obvious Sara and Sandy and the kids were going to be immediate (and as it would turn out) lifelong friends. The boys made a fortuitous discovery: at the end of this little travelled dead-end street was a small hotel that had a neat swimming pool surrounded by rock cliffs, as if it were in a jungle cavern. (And available to the general public.) Though I surely did not deserve it, all the indications were the family would have no problem adapting to this new life. I was much relieved.

During the week, using the readily available cabs we explored Bangkok from end to end (which was about five miles). The city was brand new—gleaming white; in the process of adding shopping centers, huge glass office buildings, beautiful new hotels (and more jewelry shops than any city in the world)! Combined with what the city had to offer there were luxurious beaches just an hour south. Thailand was becoming a prime destination for European vacationers, so in addition to meeting the wives and families of other Saigon pilots, Sara and the kids were daily being introduced to English, German, Swedish, and other European nationals. It was new and exciting. I took Sara and the kids to the American School and enrolled Mark and Sammy. There was no need to consider purchasing a car; cab fare was nothing. And why risk an accident, in which the foreigner was always at fault, no matter what.

We visited the famous Bangkok Zoo (even its renown Snake Farm) and took the 6 a.m. Floating Market boat tour (a bunch of tourists in long canoe-type boats) that motored past all the fruit and vegetable vendors, restricting essential waterborne traffic. In Bangkok there was no excuse for not eating your share of fresh fruit, especially pineapple, mango, papaya, kiwi, and a bunch of other delicious and readily available fruits.

Sandy told Sara that her cook, a very pleasant Thai woman—about 30, had a younger sister that was looking for an American lady to cook and clean for. Sandy arranged a meeting, and Thalee was a hit—a smiling, gracious girl about 25. Not yet sure how she could cook, but the comfort level was so high, Sara hired her on the spot. (All the houses in Bangkok have a small structure behind the main dwelling, where the cook lives.)

A couple nights we went to a movie in one of Bangkok's giant theaters. They all had two or three tiers and must have sat a couple thousand viewers. Sandy bowled and asked Sara to be on her team and even ordered her a monogramed shirt. Once again, although I certainly didn't deserve it, things could not have gone better. After a few days Mark was making regular stops at the food stalls (two-wheeled wagons), of which there was one at every corner in town (including our street). They all seemed to be run by a guy in a white and black plaid sarong, no shirt, no shoes; busy cooking a variety of seafood or pork or some other braised meat served on a skewer. Of course there was always an ample assortment of fresh fruit. Irrespective of Mark's not caring, Sara was justifiably worried about the cleanliness of the food.

When I boarded the plane to return to Saigon I was relieved and happy that my family's transition to becoming "expats" had gone so smoothly. My renewed presence with Sara and the kids had been genuinely pleasant, and surprisingly satisfying. My dilemma—the search, the resulting longings, and destiny wonderment, refreshingly took a back seat that week, though I doubted it could be permanently side-lined. With my flying duties since arriving in Saigon I didn't have much time to reflect on my Continental adventures, and I wasn't wistfully thinking of June, though I was constantly aware of her existence; another person in another place going through their daily routines. Even with this greatly improved family situation, it was hard to imagine I would never see June again.

Chapter Thirty-One
ADOPTED BY A CIA CASE OFFICER

Flying For "Juliet Bravo"

As the months wore on, some of the case officers got to trust certain pilots more than others. I had been adopted by Jack Benefield. He was in control of Ban Me Thout—a rugged plateau of red dirt in the Vietnam highlands, inhabited by tribes of the US-friendly Montagnard natives (and where Teddy Roosevelt had a still-standing large hunting lodge). There between the ridges and dense woods, most of the flat land was French Michelin rubber plantations—thousands of tall trees in razor sharp straight lines.

Today Jack had re-supply missions for me—taking explosives to a small Montagnard village. As a rarely visited locale it had no radio beacon to help a pilot find it. You found it by knowing and memorizing nearby terrain features. There, I'd land on a tiny (400-foot-long) runway composed of 6ft by 6 ft pieces of pierced steel planking that had been parachuted in. The runway was laid in an east west line. On the trip there from Ban Me Tout I held exactly 165 degrees, flew exactly 120 knots, and held it for exactly 19 minutes—at which time I was over the middle of a small lake, where an immediate left turn to exactly 090 degrees (due East) would have me directly lined up with the runway. This final leg to the end of the runway took exactly 25 seconds and was only a hundred yards past the edge of a swamp (in which—today, a herd of elephants were milling around). On landing my altimeter read an elevation of 1,760 feet above sea level.

During the morning hours I didn't need all these "headings" and "times." It was a beautiful day and I could see the village when I was still five miles away. However about noon, with four trips under my belt, the weather made a change for the worse. Taking off from Ban Me Thout I was now entering dense clouds at three hundred feet of altitude—leaving me with no visual reference to any terrain features (what pilots call "solid instruments"). But no sweat, I had memorized the precise headings (to the degree) and the exact leg times (to the second).

Midafternoon Jack meets me with a white-haired, Army colonel. "Hey Rog, Colonel Dawkins is going with us on this trip. He wants to check out my Montagnard troops." The weather was even worse—we entered gray nothingness at just 200 feet of altitude! I made the same turn to the 165 degrees heading. *Time now 15:04, plus 19 minutes, I should be over the small lake at 15:23.* Seated right behind me the colonel was understandably worried, since it was as if we were inside a milk bottle He knew I had no ground features to navigate by and that we were surrounded by peaks *that were higher than our flight altitude!* On this southerly heading I let down to 2,300 feet MSL (which I knew from previous trips to still give me good ground clearance). At 15:23 (the 19 minutes having expired), I knew I should be over the small lake, and made that left turn to due East. I knew the end of the runway would be 25 seconds on this heading. 10 seconds gone. Started a let down to 1,960 feet MSL (which would have us 200 feet above the runway). We were still completely engulfed in grayish-white, wet clouds. Out of the corner of my eye I could see the justifiably worried colonel rising up out of his seat, straining his eyes ahead through the water-streaked windscreen and into a blank wall of white nothingness. While he was looking *ahead* I snuck a peek, not ahead, but *straight down*. Though I could barely make them out, I knew the gray blurs I saw were the elephants in the swamp. 20 seconds elapsed. Pulled the power back and continued down. Three seconds later, at 1,850 feet (90 feet above the runway) we broke out of the clouds—and two seconds later slammed down on the metal planking that had suddenly (to my passengers—miraculously) appeared directly under us. The colonel looked at Jack, shaking his head in amazement, and said, "Jesus Christ Jack, your fucking pilots *really* know this country!"

A Completely Unauthorized Flight!

One morning the Ops Manager told me to forget my scheduled assignment, just get up to Ban Me Thout—now! Fired up my Porter and made it up there. Got Jack on the radio, landed, and parked on the red laterite ramp. His jeep came careening around the last turn and speeding towards the aircraft (in fact so fast I feared he was going to ram the plane). Jack got out—in "cammys," wearing an M1941 Field Marching Pack, carrying an Armalite 15 rifle (magazine inserted), and with a .45 strapped to his waist. *Whoa*, this was going to be a special mission. "Here's the plan Rog. You're gonna take me about 50 miles west of here."

"Say what? That will put us inside Cambodia!

"Right."

"Jack, we just got an Ops Order saying under no circumstances were we to let our case officer talk us into doing just that."

"Well today you're gonna make an exception." He motioned towards a small oriental guy getting out of the jeep with a PRC-25 (portable radio) on his back. "You're going to take me and Nguyen to a critical recon location." What's more I learned there was no strip. *We were going to land on a supposedly straight stretch of a dirt road.* Jack briefed me using a folded map showing an area only a mile either side of the route (which if I could stay on it, included all the terrain features I would need to get us there).

They boarded, I fired up the new 750 HP Garrett turbo-prop engine, swung onto the strip, jammed the throttle full forward and we were airborne. Well accustomed to recognizing and picking out the smallest landmarks, navigating was no problem; a small stream, a slight terrain rise, a crooked ridge—all I needed, though it felt a little eerie being over forbidden terrain. Pol Pot and the communists would not officially take over this area for another year, but even now the ground beneath us would be harboring platoons of vicious Khmer Rouge soldiers. We arrived at the designated and thankfully presently deserted stretch of road I was to land on.

I couldn't circle overhead to verify its acceptability. This would draw a crowd, and if so we'd be captured (or shot) as soon as we landed. With no "look-see" I could not be sure there were no obstacles on the road that would disable the aircraft, marooning us there for certain capture. I picked a spot where the road went straight for 500 feet, racked it around, yanked off the power, dove in, and touched down on the road—which could not have been more than fifteen feet wide. Once again this only left a couple feet outside each main gear, before a wheel would slip over the edge of the raised road, causing the whole airplane to slide down the embankment into a ditch on each side. I brought the plane to a stop utilizing full reverse (wondering how many ears were hearing that noise piercing a previously silent jungle). Jack grabbed me by the shoulder, pointed an index finger in my face and told me in no uncertain terms, "Two days from now, Wednesday, at 4 p.m., be here! 4 p.m. exactly! And I may be on a dead run—I may be being chased, so keep the engine running. We matched watches and he leaped out. I knew I had to get out of there ASAP! Any minute the Khmers or pissed-off armed civilians could come bursting out of the trees and I wouldn't stand a chance.

Big Trouble
My heart froze! As I peered ahead—down the road, I saw with horror that the trees grew closer to the roadsides; their foliage touching overhead. I couldn't make a takeoff from where I was. *The wingtips wouldn't fit up between the trees!* Okay. Stay calm, they may not be here for several minutes. The Porter has a reversing propeller. I'll back it up 400 feet and takeoff from the same spot I just landed at. Tried to back up once. Tried it again. Big problem: The tailwheel kept swiveling to the right, so the result was I was angling off the raised roadway. I jumped out, ran back to the tail, crouched down under the horizontal stabilizer, put my back up underneath it, put my hands on my thighs and then raised up—lifting the tail wheel off the ground, and hefted it back to the middle of the road. Ran to the cockpit and gave another try backing up. Damn! Same thing—the rear of the plane was on its way into a flooded ditch. *Backing up isn't gonna work!* I had no choice but to just start taxing down the road—straight ahead, as long as it would take to find a stretch where the trees were further from the edge of the road, giving me enough clearance to get the wingtips through. I must have taxied for three miles, and spent ten, loud turbine-whining minutes doing it! And I must be the luckiest man alive (or we were in the most unpopulated area in eastern Cambodia), because miraculously not once did a single person come into sight. I poured the coal to it and was outa there!

Speaking of Cambodia
Besides this trip *into* Cambodia I made many trips to dirt strips right on their border. On several trips a freelance photographer bummed a ride with me. He wasn't with the government. He was on his own mission to expose to the world the brutality of the rising communist red tide (the Kymer Rouge) in Cambodia. We became friends and I put him up several times in my tiny apartment in Saigon. Two months ago I dropped him off at one of these border strips and he hasn't been seen since. An MIA later to be classified a KIA. He was Sean Flynn, the son of the 1940's famous movie star, Errol Flynn.

Did I Get Caught?
Got back to Saigon and was told to get upstairs and see the Manager of Flying. *Oh, Oh, did they find out I went into Cambodia?* He spoke: "Well Captain Yahnke, are you ready for some more responsibility?"

Not knowing what was in store, but knowing the expected answer, I responded "Sure."

"We've been checking with the Customer on what kind of job you've been doing, and we're ready to promote you to the position of Assistant Manager of Flying—Chief Pilot of the Porter program."

Wow, caught me by surprise. I knew as a program Chief Pilot, I would end up flying less, spending the bulk of my time keeping the aircraft flying and keeping the 28 Porter pilots in line (on and off the airport). It would also involve training new pilots, assume the role of Safety Officer for Porters; and most importantly, administer the six-month "Line Checks" to make sure the captains were competently carrying out their operational missions. This check flight was real serious because *if they failed, they weren't just demoted, they could be sent home.* I'd lose the opportunity to accumulate excess flight time for the generous overtime bonuses, but it'd be offset by an increase in base pay—almost a washout. I accepted.

Chapter Thirty-Two
A NOT-SO-ROUTINE LINE CHECK

More Realism Than We Needed

I was scheduled to give one of my pilots his six-month Line Check; the one where the captain has to prove he can fly a long, hard, frustrating day; determine what might be the only safe routes; unload the airplane himself; fuel it while it's running, and make it into and out of the most dangerous landing sites. Today I was going to give one of these checks to a guy named Jack Spencer. I already knew he was doing a great job so anticipated an uneventful day.

We were going to a strip only 40 miles southwest of Saigon: Bao Tri—famous for being controlled by friendly forces at sunset and held by the enemy at daybreak. So I was keen to see from what direction and at what altitude Jack would approach it, and how he would determine if it would be safe to land. The strip was only 500 feet long. Only the Porter could land and takeoff from it. Today (fortunately) we wouldn't have to be on the ground long; just quickly unload about ten crates of .45 caliber ammo cans onto the ramp. Full, the metal containers weighed about 30 pounds each. Empty—no longer useful, they became "collectibles." The strip was an east-west oriented strip and we would be landing to the west. As we over-headed it nothing appeared abnormal on the ground, minus the fact we couldn't see a single soul within a mile of the strip. That *was* unusual, but not a definite indicator of enemy presence.

Landing and Unloading Cargo

Jack made a tight spiraling descent, landed and got the aircraft stopped in half the runway, allowing him to turn off midfield and take a short taxiway to the basketball-court-sized ramp (saving us two dangerous minutes taxiing-back had he rolled to the end of the runway). On the ramp Jack spun it around and put on the parking brake. He stayed at the controls—engine running. I jumped out of my seat, through the cabin, swung the doors open and began the unloading. If the Viet Cong had observed our arrival (which they likely did) we might have just a couple minutes before they started shooting. Got the ten crates off and stacked on the ramp in record time. Jumped back in the aircraft and shut the door. Sweating and out of breath I flopped into the copilot's seat. Unfortunately, instead of first moving straight ahead, Jack locked the left wheel and began turning the airplane, which caused the tail to swing to the right, becoming caught behind the nearest pile of ammo boxes. *We were snagged.*

I was out of the aircraft in a second, grabbed the problem pile of wooden crates and walked backwards, dragging it away from the aircraft. Once I had it far enough away from the tail I started back to the aircraft, when *Holy Shit!* Two yards from my feet several rounds hit the pierced steel planking—loudly! While stunned in the realization that I had been shot at, several more rounds went zinging past me. As I was preparing to jump back in the aircraft, Jack having seen what was happening jumped out of the aircraft, bringing our single M16 rifle with him. It was loaded with one magazine of 20 rounds, which if you're scared enough, you can empty in the first twenty seconds (and if so, the only thing left is to run)!

Into a Water Buffalo Hole and Out of the Line of Fire
Just a matter of yards from the west edge of the parking ramp was a round, water buffalo pond, about fifty feet across. (The natives dug these next to every tilled field so the water buffalos could cool themselves during the day.) Amid the snaps of the passing rounds, we somehow made it to the water hole and jumped into the dark slimy water. Once in and upright we found our feet mired in goo and the water level halfway up our backs. We plastered ourselves side by side, chests pressed against the black mud bank that faced the incoming fire. We stuck our heads up just high enough to peer over the edge of the hole. We were able to see—about a hundred yards past the east end of the strip, from within a hedgerow, the muzzle flashes as they continued firing. Must just be a few of them; could only see four muzzle flash locations, probably a rag-tag group of untrained VC. Their rounds were going by either high or wide. And (thank God) it appeared they had not thought of disabling the aircraft, which was still parked with the engine running. We knew the VC always had a limited supply of ammunition and would most likely run out in the next few minutes. Luck was with us. The shots became less frequent then stopped altogether.

Jack and I failed to get the nerve to make a break for the plane. *We'll just hide in the hole for a little while longer.* We waited about ten minutes. No more shots. We decided it was now or never. Time to make a break for the plane. We were still propped up there side by side, up to our belts in black water, our chests pressed against the steep mud bank, staring to the east, when before we moved—about the loudest noise I ever heard! Fired from somewhere *behind* us, a single bullet slammed deafeningly into the mud between us! In the six inches between our shoulders a single round cracked into the black mud. While frantically scrambling out of the water and up the bank, we turned our heads to look at the far side of the pond. There, standing on the west bank of the water hole, silhouetted by the late afternoon sun were four VC firing at us! *Thank God one lousy marksman fired too soon.* If they would have waited and all fired together, this story would not be being told. And God knows how, between the rounds passing us on both sides, over and under us, we got to the aircraft without being hit! In a second we were in our seats and moving to the runway.

Besides the scare in the water hole, I got another when Jack—instead of taking the metal taxiway to the runway, chose to take a shortcut across soggy wet grass. (You never do this because of the chance the tires will bog down and you'll become permanently stuck.) But we made it! Onto the runway with only half of it to use for takeoff. He crammed the throttle full forward, and we were on our way out of there, barely becoming airborne by the end of the runway; our wheels ripping through the foliage where the VC had first begun firing at us *(before they walked all the way down the north side of the runway, crossed the west end of it, and advanced up our side to the edge of the pond—right behind us)!* While I can't say this kind of thing happened daily, or even weekly, in Vietnam. I can say that every pilot has at least one or two stories like this for each year he was there!

A Female Introduction

Due to Sara being in Bangkok, my demanding flight schedule and no female candidates in Saigon, my experimentation was put on hold (allowing me to avoid more embarrassments). However I did meet one reasonably attractive American woman (referred to over here as a "round eye"). She was about my age and single—a civilian secretary assigned to MACV downtown. I knew right off she was not going to be *that* woman. However, here—for most guys, any female partner (especially an American) was a welcomed diversion; occasional dinners, evenings of Scrabble, and other joint activities that would make Saigon more livable. And for her it meant having a gentleman escort, who from time to time could take her to one of Saigon's French restaurants (which at this time—with the influx of US troops, were able to sustain a profitable business). After several weeks of not showing any signs of considering a physical relationship, one evening I found myself cornered (or let it happen). One more try, as you might imagine without success. The one thing I do remember, is—on this only encounter, her exhortations: *"You can do it! You can do it! I know you can do it."*

Chapter Thirty-Three
WHAT WE DIDN'T KNOW THEN

The Never Understood South Vietnamese Mindset

I had a flight to a village that was safe to visit during the day, but "off limits" at night, likely infiltrated by North Vietnamese soldiers or Viet Cong after dark. There in hidden clearings they held classes about the invading foreigners (*us*) who were desecrating their land and defiling their ancestors. This was an effective tactic, since having lived through decades of Chinese, Japanese, and French occupation they were now the bloody and maimed recipients of our presence. If the truth were known, 95% of the rural Vietnamese did not believe they were fighting their uncles and cousins from North Vietnam. All they knew was that it was the US military that was blowing up their roads and bridges, burying mines alongside their rice fields, and napalming their villages. Each time Army Intelligence visited a village they would yank out a dozen young males as suspected enemy sympathizers (never to be seen again). The locals understandably thought *we* were the enemy. Most if not all the rural Vietnamese *were VC in their head*. They *all* feared us—it was just that only a few were willing to face certain death by taking action. And then when we did kill that one guy who just shot at us, we chalked it up as a *single* VC who had been hiding in that village, not realizing *the entire rest of his village* was of the same mindset, just not as daring.

A Matter of Numbers

Yesterday, at the village I was going to now land at, all the North Vietnamese and Viet Cong had been killed or run off. My passengers were two army colonels and one enlisted man going there to supervise another "Body Count." General Westmoreland's theory to winning the war was this: North Vietnam could only send down about 4,500 soldiers a month; so if we killed 4,501 a month, mathematically we would eventually win the war. (I'm not kidding, that was our battle plan.) The objective was—everyday, to kill as many enemy as possible, count em and then *declare every one of them to be Viet Cong or a North Vietnamese soldier.* To my eyes, the assortment of very young and very old, barely clothed, emaciated bodies I saw, did not look like enemy soldiers. But to the Department of Defense, each one was a hard statistic numerically proving we were on our way to winning the war.

The Real Reason So Many Soldiers Returned With PTSD

I landed and let out the passengers, resigning myself to a day's wait at the aircraft while corpses were gathered and counted. Surprisingly, the officers—accompanied by the young corporal, motioned me to follow them. We traipsed single file down a narrow path that led to what little remained of the village. There were craters everywhere. Before the overwhelming ground assault by US and ARVN forces, it had been pummeled by airstrikes and then artillery barrages. It was now a lifeless, devastated area (and probably already was when our troops made their assault). Not one in ten huts was still standing, and everywhere you looked, there were bodies (of all ages and both genders). I was not feeling well, watching while the bodies were assembled and counted. The task finally completed, an Army helicopter landed and left with my two officer passengers. I would be making the flight back to Saigon with just the corporal, who looked too young to even be in the service.

Together, the two of us left the village and started back that same narrow path we had used to get to the village. Two-abreast, the jungle foliage on each side brushed our ears as we made our way down it. About halfway to the airplane, we hear a strange creaking noise a short distance behind us. We both whip our heads around and alongside the path behind us we see what appears like a picnic basket lid swinging upward out of the ground; a lid that had been covering a small underground hiding place. Also visible was the head of an emerging person. My young corporal, as a result of his training reflexively swings his weapon towards the figure and lets go a burst. The figure makes a gurgling sound and slumps back into the hole. The corporal is visibly shaken, his eyes full of wonderment at what has just happened, or more particularly—what he himself had just done. I'm sure a soul-shocking "first" for him. Together we approached the dugout. The splintered lid is still wide open and splattered with blood. We look into the hole and are sickened at the sight of an old Vietnamese man, *with a whimpering couple-month old baby in his lap!* One could easily conclude he was its grandfather or some village elder, just trying to hide the baby from the carnage until everyone was gone.

The corporal was incoherent. One could not miss the effect his actions had on him. He was looking left and right (as if for someone to question or give him approval of his actions). He tried to speak to me, but even though I understood the words, they did not arrange themselves into sentences. He leaned forward as if to pick up the baby, but then stopped, unable to get closer to his own handiwork. He didn't get sick but gagged and appeared on the verge. I told him I'd been to these apparently wiped-out villages before, and every time at least half the residents were in hiding nearby. The baby's mother or family members would likely be here within the hour.

We were the last two Americans in the village, with no alternative but to hurry to the airplane and get out of there. We knew special mission troops would soon be arriving. The flight back was without a word of conversation; just the almost constant moaning from the corporal and his indecipherable utterances. Sitting on the aircraft floor, his back against a side bulkhead I could see him trembling, the whole way back. He was indeed a shadow of the 18 year-old blonde, blue-eyed, farmer's son from Iowa who had come to Vietnam just three months ago. This day would no doubt forever live with him.

A Frequently Occurring Heart-Wrenching Scene!

A week later (as had happened a hundred times) a Vietnamese village was declared to be enemy-infested and we destroyed it, requiring the relocation of its remaining inhabitants. In the Orient, parents and grandparents become deities, and are they buried just yards from their children's huts. And in our well-meaning evacuations, not a single Vietnamese was able to bring their parent's remains with them. And many were relocated multiple times, away from this most sacred ground, and to an area completely unknown to them. One day I was watching a US Army helicopter doing this evacuating. A frail and elderly couple, holding hands and shivering together were yanked on board. It was probably their second or third relocation, by now having lost all their possessions. The man was holding a stick with a bundle on the end, containing the last of their valued possessions. In order to make more space on the chopper, the army sergeant grabbed the stick with the bandana, *and chucked it out of the plane!*

1968, the Year of the Monkey

Chinese New Year's Eve, 30 January: Nothing to us but a really big deal here in the Asia. By mid-afternoon a minute did not go by without the sound of fireworks. In the streets around my building kids were lighting off bottle-rockets, cherry bombs, and those long strings of firecrackers that snapped and leaped like a crazed snake. New Year's Eve here didn't take a back seat to anything stateside. Unfortunately it kept up through the night. At 05:30 in the morning, walking to my faded green Datsun, instead of the normal pre-dawn silence, there still was the sound of those damned firecrackers, distant celebrating or shouting, and strangely—cars "peeling rubber."

At the corner ahead I would turn onto the street behind the new US Embassy (a gated, well-guarded monstrosity of a building). At this ungodly hour, I was almost hit by a truck careening around the corner; *a truck whose bed was filled with ARVN soldiers firing in all directions!* Further down the road I saw dark figures running across it carrying rifles! Uniforms were not recognizable, so I was not sure if they were Vietnamese soldiers or civilians. (I could see they weren't Americans.) No idea what in the hell was going on. Passing directly behind the US Embassy I pulled over in front of a house across the street. In front of it was a five-foot high wall behind which I decided to take cover till whatever it was, was over.

It was almost nine, before I heard commands in English and knew the US military had the situation under control. Assuming the disturbance had been just an unsuccessful attack on the US Embassy I got back in the car and resumed my trip to the airport; in so doing I was shocked when each time I started down a new street it was strewn with dead bodies. And while some may have been bodies of North Vietnamese soldiers, they were mostly Viet Cong (Vietnamese civilians) who had arisen at three in the morning, retrieved their hidden weapons, and taken to the streets. Inside Air America operations it was abuzz with stories and explanations of what had happened. As is well known now, it wasn't just a local attack on the US Embassy here in Saigon, or even the whole city. It was the precisely planned "Tet Offensive," widespread attacks on US Military installations, Vietnamese Army garrisons, and U.S. supported police headquarters, all over the country—*beginning on the same day at the same minute, in every city and village in the country!*

Now here is the thing of great significance (which should have had us leaving Vietnam then in 1968, seven years before we did). The unavoidable and hugely discouraging take away from the "Tet" offensive is this: To have carried it off, more than half the population of the country had to have known about it, and known about it for weeks if not months! And with thousands of these same civilians working as laborers, translators or advisors, closely, daily—often one-on-one with their US military counterpart, *not one, not a single one of them ever uttered a word about the scheduled uprising!* This single fact will give you some idea of the extent of animosity the civilian population of Vietnam had for us. At least half the South Vietnam population viewed us as the enemy.

It's hard to believe—impossible for me, to comprehend, that after our experience in Vietnam, years later we would allow ourselves to become involved in multiple civil/religious wars in the Middle East. Talk about not learning anything from history.

Chapter Thirty-Four
I CAN'T BELIEVE SHE PULLED IT OFF

I'm Going to See June!

Since arriving in Saigon I had been sporadically able to send and receive letters from June. Most recently I learned that the Spanish vaudeville tour was over and the Stafford Ballet was now part of *The Circo Magico Tihany* performing in Jakarta, Indonesia (where the girls were locked in their hotel and brought to the theater in a police-guarded, tractor-drawn cart). In the circus, besides dancing, June was a female centerpiece with clowns, elephants, and even one with lions. These roles and her character established her as the spokesperson for the performers. Her letter almost fell from my hands when I read she had convinced Mr. Tihany that since they were already in the Pacific and there were 50,000 American troops in Saigon, he should schedule performances there and pull in a bunch of revenue in just one week. She succeeded! *The circus was coming to Vietnam in the middle of a war.*

She didn't know when they'd arrive or where they would perform but did know the name of the hotel that would be putting them up. Waiting for the circus's arrival I checked out their hotel and discovered another not-yet-completed wet concrete structure that (if it could get some water and electricity in the next two weeks) was going to be their hotel. On the way to the airport I saw an abandoned soccer field on which American soldiers were setting up chairs. I asked them if they were getting it ready for the circus. They answered they were, but said that here wasn't a good idea: "Right here, a couple miles from the center of Saigon, just six feet under the surface, there's miles of tunnels full of North Vietnamese soldiers! Right now, while we're standing here!" I thought to myself, how can these soldiers be that brainwashed, to actually think that? To win the war all we'd have to do is grab a shovel.

Fifteen years after the war ended, on a trip back to Vietnam I availed myself of a tour called "The North Vietnamese Underground Complex."

Yup, the van took us to that same soccer field. Within twenty feet of where I'd been talking to that army guy, were the steps down to miles of tunnels! *The damned guy was right!* While I had been standing there discounting it, all kind of activity was going on right under my feet!

June's Arrival

Minus the elephants the whole circus arrived and I was there when their plane landed. When Customs and Immigration was through with them I was thrilled (and humbled) at the unbridled joy and enthusiasm June showed just to see me. She ran all the way to me and once again gave me one of those rib-crushing hugs. "Roger, Roger! You look just great! Oh, it's been so long. I'm so glad to see you"! She introduced me to all the girls—half of which I knew from Spain. Wendy and Laurie seemed almost as happy as June to see me (and once again see their captain with her special guy). During the bus ride to their hotel June held one of my hands with both of hers and never stopped looking at me (and I have seldom felt less worthy of such a show of adulation).

Most of the circus members spent the first few days building a large wooden stage and backdrop. I was impressed seeing the acrobats and unicyclists utilizing power saws and drills. The girls' hotel was off-limits to guys, but for their captain the girls made an exception for her *novio*. Though I never stayed overnight we had fun-filled late-night parties, with French tarts and ice cream, and plenty of café au lait (not great to drink at midnight). I felt privileged (and guilty) as I was made a part of each evening's festivities, held in one of the girl's rooms. Ten minutes after they arrived their makeup was off and their faces covered with white skin cream. With this facial covering and in their loose fitting, wild patterned flannel pajamas it was as if I was in a room full of clowns. I remember the bedspreads being strewn with 45 RPM records, and that every other one they played was the current hit "Reach Out, I'll Be There."

A Belgian named Arnaud did that act you've seen many times: the man running up and down alongside a table, just barely able to keep six plates spinning on top of three-foot wooden dowels. After having me practice it one afternoon, he talked me into trying it in front of a live audience that night. I had fairly well mastered the technique and the farcical display of panic you had to show when you almost didn't reach one in time. (The art was seeing how far you could let the dowel lean and the plate wobble, without letting it fall.) I managed to get all six up and spinning, and make my several dashes to rescue one. But I didn't get to complete the act. A U.S. Army helicopter flew over too low and the downwash from the rotors sent the plates and dowels flying in all directions.

I am saddened that the details of this short week mostly escape me. I can remember no romantic trysts (successful or not) with June. My job and events displaced more serious times we could have had together. We had such a history and she had done so much just to get here. It was surely true that I had June on a deserved pedestal, but when given the chance I failed to demonstrate it. When the circus pulled out (and it did all too soon) I realized my time and intimacy with June had been terribly insufficient, sadly non-committal. In spite of June maintaining her wide and constant smile, I knew she was disappointed; like an opportunity had been missed—like it should have been a much better time together. And she was right! Still, like all our greetings and salutations, our good-bye included a massive hug by her, a kiss that actually hurt my lips (and lets you know the person on the other side means it with all her heart). She told me they were bound for Singapore and were going to be there for at least a month. You can bet I had my next mission! *Get to Singapore on my first "Scheduled Time Off."*

A Reunion like Never Before

I knew my next "Scheduled Time Off was not going to be my usual trip to Bangkok. Shamefully I phoned Sara that my coming STO was cancelled. My plan was to use this time to visit June in Singapore, and show her the consideration she deserved, that I failed to demonstrate in Saigon. Unfortunately my STO got delayed a week, but the day it started I was Malaysia-bound. Unlike the acrylic and stainless-steel megalopolis it is now, in the late sixties Singapore was still the sleepy, palm-fronded town that one could cross in a ten-minute cab ride. And I did, visiting every theater and two stadiums trying to locate the circus, *but no luck!* Nor did anyone I asked know their whereabouts. It was nine at night and I decided to make the rounds of the big clubs, on the outside chance the ballet was performing on their own. One club after another; and finally—in one, my heart leaped! On a big stage there were several scantily dressed dancing girls, and one in the middle of the stage, in a bubble bath, apparently naked, *and it looked like June!* I think I was more relieved than disappointed when I realized it was not her or the Stafford Ballet. (I should have known. They never did any routines like that.)

I plopped myself down at an empty table, head in hands, tired and without ideas. I realized a waitress was standing alongside my table waiting for a drink order. For a short breather and hope to come up with another plan, I ordered. When she returned, appearing ready for some small talk, I thought why not ask one more person.

"Young lady, are you by any chance aware of a German circus in town?

"I haven't been to it, but I heard about it."

"What! *You have?* Where? Where is it?"

"I think out at the old armory."

"The old armory? What's that? Where is it!

"You know, up past Yishun, at the old Brit airbase in Sembawang."

"Sembawang you say, Sembawang?

She nodded an okay. I could've hugged her, but just paid for my drink and ran out of the club. A long three minutes waiting for a cab. Finally, waved one down so frantically I'm surprised the guy even stopped. Head in the window and with an urgency I doubt was lost on him, I shouted, "The old Air Force Base. The one at Sembawang! Do you know it?" He didn't answer but nodded. I was in and we were off. We stayed northbound, a long time, out of town, less populated and lots of shanties. Finally, a mile or so ahead, against the night sky I could see a control tower with a circling beacon, and then as we got closer, other buildings which appeared to be hangars, and finally parked airplanes! *This has to be it.* But I didn't see any parking lot filled with cars, or any people coming or going. The place looked deserted. The driver located the main gate and got us over there. I jumped out and approached the Royal Air Force guard on duty: "The circus! The circus, where's it at?"

"The night before last was its last night. There's nothing left, not even a pallet. Everything was taken down yesterday."

"Where are they staying! Do you know where they were staying?!"

"No, but let me ask the sergeant."

It was now almost eleven. When he came out he handed me a scrap of paper—with an address! I thanked him profusely, and trembling with anticipation jumped back in the cab. After looking at the address the driver did not seem certain of the location. After studying it for several more minutes he responded to my urgent requests to *get this frigging cab moving.*

I would have thought the circus company would have been staying near the venue, but no. We drove for some time, winding our way into an even less populated (deserted) area. He finally slowed to a stop in what I would call the "middle of nowhere," in front of a single, isolated three-story building. Its only neighbor was a 20-acre fenced-in lot with two gravel piles as high as the hotel and glinting in the full moonlight.

The complete lack of activity was causing me to consider a terrifying thought. Only two windows in the whole place were lit. I leaped out of the cab and ran into the ground floor entrance, which was unlit and bore no sign. No rooms on the ground floor I bounded up some nearby stairs. I raced down the second-floor hall. Every room empty. Up another flight. The same thing on the third floor; every room was empty. The place was deserted. No—wait. I heard voices coming from a room at the end of the hall. I was down there and into it. What I saw was not encouraging: a starkly empty small storage room with two old guys—one of them maybe Tihany himself, playing cards at a rickety table. I gushed out my mission and dire question. The skinny guy smoking looked up at me and said, "No mate. You missed em. The whole lot took off outa Paya Lebar airport at three this afternoon. Going to Sydney."

Chapter Thirty-Five
HURT, BUT NOT BAD

Got Everybody Out (Except One)

We would often be contacted by the Customer to divert to a strip that was under imminent attack, and he needed his operatives evacuated before the village fell to the North Vietnamese Army or the Viet Cong. We rarely knew which till afterwards. The NVA wore uniforms and had automatic weapons. The VC were usually in rags, their footwear often just rubber shower shoes, and they only had a pocketful of ammo. I was flying west of Danang and got such a call—instructing me to divert to a strip (in the A Shau valley right next to the "Ho Chi Minh" trail) where the case officer's people would be waiting for me. We never held any territory within ten miles of it, for more than 24 hours. I told him I'd be there in about 25 minutes, and asked him when was the village supposed to be overrun? He answered, "Not till noon if we're lucky!" Checked my watch: 10:45! *Geez.*

When I was still a mile out I heard two or three loud snaps, as small arms fire penetrated the skin of my aircraft. Overhead the village I saw individuals running in all directions, lugging bundles of who knows what. I knew if I dallied over the strip I'd be seen and when I landed there would be a hundred villagers already on the strip. So I did a tree-top approach—hoping that most of those panicking in the basin wouldn't see me approaching, and those few already up on the strip would be Mule's guys. If they didn't get to the plane first, there may not be an inch of space left inside. I landed (missing the ones wandering on the strip), threw it in reverse, and brought the airplane to a stop. Here they come! *Please God, make the first ones my Customer's guys.*

The first guy to the plane looks in and says, "Good job. Mule said you'd be here!" *I lucked out*—the first villager to the plane *was* the Customer's guy. He pushed his wife on board, and then handed her a large bundle of something. I leaped out of my seat to help him load, yanking his guys into the plane and shoving others backwards. Within a minute I had put about a dozen persons on board my seven-seat aircraft. Clambering towards the cockpit over a sea of sweaty malodorous bodies, I saw one of them *sitting in my pilot's seat!* I succeeded in hefting him up and over the top of the seat, unceremoniously dropping him on top of the other bodies. I reclaimed my seat, poured the coal to it, and with the sound of mortars impacting behind me, was roaring down the runway (dodging dazed villagers still wandering across the strip).

Ever since I closed the door and especially while lifting off, I could hear one guy in the back screaming and shouting at me in a desperate (and what sounded like a considerably demeaning) tone, that I of course could not interpret. I heard a couple more rounds snap by, which must have been through the tail since there were no screams inside (minus that one guy way in the back who was going ape shit). Going through 200 feet and starting my turn towards Danang I (first) sensed that something was suddenly wrong with the world; next (second) I heard the shot—inside the plane! Then (third) I saw my left hand was no longer gripping the stick, and my arm was lying across my thigh—bleeding, though I still felt no pain. I then became aware of a commotion in the cabin as a couple of Mule's guys overpowered the soldier *who had just shot me!* On the instrument panel in front of me was a splattering of what looked like pink oatmeal, which I realized was pieces of bloodied bone or cartilage. Still didn't hurt—just numb, and my whole hand as well. On course for Danang. I noticed a hole in the instrument panel where the bullet had gone through the center of one of the gauges. Cabin quiet now. Another twenty minutes and I'd be at Danang, where there were several medical facilities. *Please God, let it just go okay, not have me pass out.*

I did get there and landed (or at least put the aircraft on the ground). Mule was there to meet me and off-loaded his guys—including the crazy one who had shot me (which I learned was because in evacuating the strip, *his son did not make it onboard)!* In the clinic at Danang ("Charlie-Med") I was treated respectfully—for a civilian, sometimes erroneously viewed as a mercenary or worse, a drug runner. (Don't know who started those damned stories that seem impossible to squelch.) My wound was cleaned and stitched. The bullet had split a piece off the end of my ulna bone. According to the doc, the piece that was missing was from the outside and should not limit extension or flexion. (Good thing, since it was stuck somewhere on the instrument panel).

So Many Young, Wounded or Dead

That night at the Officer's Club in Danang, I heard an account I have not been able to forget. As much as I thought I knew about this war, I never really understood the scope of the ultimate sacrifices being made by our troops, every day and every night—especially up here in what they call "I" Corps, the furthest north sector of operations in Vietnam, right next to the Demilitarized Zone. Instead of the rag-tag Viet Cong encountered 300 miles south in the Delta, up here there were multiple battalions of well-trained and well-armed North Vietnamese soldiers who had just left the comfort and security of their own barracks the day before.

"Grunts" is a term used in the Marine Corps (with utmost respect) to describe the non-aviation, back-pack-wearing, rifle-toting, hand grenade-carrying officers and men slogging through waist-deep rice paddies or hacking their way through six feet high elephant grass; the ones actually doing the day or night, face to face or hand to hand combat with the enemy—the real veterans and true heroes (*not* clerk typists in some safe headquarters). And if you needed a better idea of why these battles were so ferocious, remember this: *The enemy were born and raised here and held the conviction that it was their homeland, and that we were the invading foreigners attempting to occupy it. They were—to the man, ready and willing to die defending it.*

Shortly after entering the club I met a helicopter pilot named Marion who had just finished a physically and mentally disheartening week; up close and personal with the sacrifices being made by these grunts (as well as the numerous injuries and fatalities suffered by his fellow pilots). The military brass had decided we should occupy a certain burnt-out, bombed-out, artillery-scarred, bald hill (number 208), not far from Dong Ha and the Cam Lo river—only 7 kilometers from the DMZ. It would be a choice lookout to monitor the North Vietnamese making their way southward in the ravines alongside it. Marion's job—everyday, was to bring the new grunts in and bring out the ones he dropped off the day before (be they alive, dead, or wounded). He said they all looked 18 years old. Bringing them in they just sat in muted silence with the proverbial 1000-yard stare, in no way able to comprehend what the next 24 hours would hold for them. And the next day on the way out—even more demoralized, having just witnessed things they'd never imagined. He'd do these drop-offs and pick-ups as quickly as possible; before the NVA mortars started raining down on his aircraft (usually about 60 seconds after setting down). Many of his fellow chopper pilots did not return from these missions; killed when their aircraft was hit by one of these incoming mortars or shot to death in the cockpit. One was Bernie Terhorst, a close friend of mine from my first Marine Corps squadron.

Marion never once straightened up—his gaze fixed on his shoes. It was apparent that he had been part of an unreported ongoing tragedy. What was new to me was the *extent* of the casualties. If the American public would have known the level of this massive youthful sacrifice then in 1968, we would really have had protests. When the NVA launched their advances on the hill (at least twice every night) the best estimate was the marines were out-numbered at least 5 to 1! Marion said yesterday he had left off the new grunts at 4 p.m., and in picking up the 18 Marines he had left off the day before, seven had been killed, and of the remaining marines, half were seriously wounded—dying. And he had been something similar for the past three weeks, witnessing the same extent of casualties on every trip.

Today, after landing atop the hill, and while under a mortar attack and taking constant small arms fire, the platoon leader—a 22-year-old First Lieutenant, would not let Marion takeoff until he had personally drug every last one of his dead and wounded (that outnumbered the living) on board. When he finally did, the lieutenant stuck his head up in the cockpit and gave Martin a "thumbs-up." It was then Martin was shocked to see that evidently during the night the young officer had taken a round through his left temple that exited where his left eye had been! He had done this last minute gathering up of his men—with just one eye! Needless to say, I was awed and deservedly humbled.

Then Marion hesitantly told me that this afternoon, after several weeks of this carnage, the powers to be (whoever and wherever they were) felt we no longer needed hill 208, *and it was left to the enemy*. This account helped confirm my conclusion that the war was not going our way. Now well understood, this same conclusion was held by many others, such as Daniel Ellsberg who went on trial for publishing the eye-opening "Pentagon Papers," finally leading to our withdrawal.

Chapter Thirty-Six
SHOT DOWN AND A TRIP TO SPAIN

January 31ˢᵗ, 1969

Remember that overly realistic Line Check I took with Jack Spencer (ending up in the water buffalo hole)? Well this morning I was scheduled to administer one to a pilot that I flew with in the Marine Corps—Chet Falk. Having just flown with him last week I decided we'd pull a sly one: I would write it up as a standard "Line Check" for him but would sharpen my own skills by doing the piloting. Let *him* sit in the co-pilot's seat. Chet's nickname was "Black Cloud Falk," that he earned regularly. If something was going to go wrong, it went wrong with Chet. After never taking any time off, a bunch of us convinced him to treat himself to a week in Hong Kong. Stepping out of Baggage Claim at the Kai Tek airport he's hit by a cab and spends the whole week in the hospital. His first year in Saigon he just took cabs. We finally convinced him to buy his own transportation. He chose to purchase an Italian motor scooter. His first day on it his toe catches the curb, yanking his foot rearward, breaking his ankle. And those are only a couple examples that perhaps should have been a signal to me.

We were dispatched to a strip in the Delta, with an airplane full of money—the payroll for hundreds of Vietnamese soldiers (which always had the airplane several hundred pounds too heavy. Arriving overhead Cao Lanh we could see no reason not to land. I began my descending left 180 degree turn to final approach—the standard landing pattern for all fixed-wing planes (to be strictly avoided by helicopters)! On short final, a hundred feet in the air, just a couple seconds from touchdown, an Army helicopter swoops in from the side to land *right in the airplane touchdown zone* (prohibited for helicopters). I had to abort my landing, pour the power to it and struggle over him.

By the far end of the runway I'd climbed to about 500 feet of altitude and was beginning my left turn for another try. But I never did get to start it. There was a loud ping, a gushing sound, and then terrible vibrations, followed by silence. *I'd been hit by ground-fire and lost the engine!* With the nose up and no power, I was rapidly losing the airspeed necessary to sustain flight! Chet was hollering "Watch your airspeed! I shoved the nose over immediately—*way* over, to gain airspeed and avoid a fatal stall. (Nose down, even without an engine you will gain airspeed, but of course, lose precious altitude.) If I had been a half second later lowering the nose we'd have lost three or four knots, stalled, spun, *and gone in upside down!* I had to nose over so steeply, that looking straight ahead there was no sky visible, just ground! I held it as long as I could—diving almost vertically towards the ground to gain the airspeed necessary to make the flight controls effective. At what I judged to be the last second—about 100 feet above the ground, I yanked the stick back to arrest our plummeting descent and we hit flat; like a ton of bricks. I have no memory of the impact.

When I came to and opened my eyes I saw only a totally gray screen. Worse, the wings had ruptured where they joined the top of the fuselage and fuel was pouring down on the top of my head. And at the same time I felt the gas drenching my body, I heard the loud "snap" "snap" of the 8,000-volt emergency igniters sparking in the engine—just 30 inches in front of me! (The first step in an engine loss is to turn these igniters on, and I had done it when the engine quit.) But right now—still firing, they were seconds from causing the fuel to ignite, enveloping Chet and I in flames! Although I could not yet see, I knew where the igniter switches were, and had them off on my second swipe. Still blind and numb, I felt rough hands all over me, dragging me out over the jagged edges of the windshield which had been broken out.

I lay in warm mud hearing voices—all in a different language. I had been hauled out by members of a South Korean platoon. My eyes were open, but I still couldn't see. (We'd hit so hard, I was later told I'd driven the legs of my pilot's seat through the bottom of the airplane.) I was fearful I might have damaged my spinal column. One at a time I tried to move my legs and was gratified to be able to slide my heels a few inches forward and back. And my vision was coming back. I could now see patches of blue through the gray. I spent another hour in a Korean Army field hospital tent getting stitches. When that was completed I boarded the Air America helicopter sent to bring us back. In the chopper I was able to get a look at my airplane, and it reminded me of that phrase in the Jim Croce song: *Leroy Brown looked like a jig saw puzzle with a couple a pieces gone.* For sure it'd never fly again.

It was the next day before I realized the extent of one injury: A huge hunk of cornea had been gouged out of my left eye and I was now 20/500 in that eye. For several months I managed to stay on flight status by cheating—memorizing the letters on the eye chart. Myself and most the other pilots had a "Loss of License" insurance policy from Lloyd's of London. With my now disqualifying vision I could claim the insurance settlement. A US Army ophthalmologist told me qualifying flight vision might be restored, but only with a total corneal transplant; an operation he said was only done by two doctors: Ramon Castroviejo in NY Presbyterian Hospital, and Joaquin Barraquer in Barcelona, Spain. Castroviejo had a waiting list in excess of eight months so I discounted him. Perhaps Barraquer would be less busy. At least that's what I thought before learning he *invented* the operation, and people from all over the world traveled to his clinic. But there was another factor: the Stafford Ballet and June were now in Madrid, just 45 minutes from Barcelona. I'll bet you can guess where I chose to go.

England, Spain, and "Decision Time"

Embarrassedly I planned my departure without bouncing it off Sara. In England, Lloyd's surprised me by saying they would honor my policy, or if I chose to try to restore my vision—*they'd pay for that special transplant*. I decided to hear what Barraquer would say so flew to Barcelona. Got a cab and gave the driver the address. The clinic was a massive and intimidating edifice. Two sets of heavy double doors, and then directly behind the second set—the reception desk. When greeted I stated my case. Shock and disbelief would best describe the expression on the girl's face. She excused herself, returning in a few minutes with a stern-faced administrator. I learned no one ever arrives here without an appointment. Although I was guilty of this very thing (not any previous contact) the fact that I was (sort of) a United States airline pilot—must have carried some weight. After a short conference among themselves, I was given a check-in date the following week. (Keep in mind, I had not yet come close to making the decision to actually go through with the surgery.)

I found a comfy, old wooden hotel—the Hotel La Rotunda. It had been a large and old private residence, perhaps even historical. I was lucky in getting a comfy third floor suite, with a balcony that looked down into a most interesting walled-in back lot of a nunnery. My task here: eight days to come to a decision *whether to do it or not!* But the days came and went without me being able to come to a decision. One night I decided to get a good night's sleep, order a big breakfast sent up, and then—when I had eaten, I would make the decision. Just make it! *Right or wrong,* figuring I would likely never be more clear-headed, and thus that decision should be the most sound. Well, I did just that, or almost just that; *everything except come to a decision.* The next night—about 10 p.m., having skipped lunch, I went to a nearby bistro and had June's favorite *"entrecote y espinaca a la crema."* In addition to it I ordered a bottle of Rosé wine (in a tall, three-sided bottle). About midnight the restaurant played Frank Sinatra's famous hit, "My Way" ("Mi Manera" in Spanish) and that did it! The perhaps reckless but reflective lyrics seemed to say "What the hell," and pushed me over the hump. *I'd do it!*

The Clinica Barraquer

I was escorted to a private room on the third floor. The whole fourth floor (top floor of the building) was the permanent residence of Dr. Barraquer. He operated four days a week, from midnight till 6 a.m. On those days he spent the afternoon and evening studying the charts of the patients he would be operating on. During this time he listened to classical music (that we on the third floor could hear well enough), and he never sat—just continued pacing his residence. His floor (our ceiling) was made of thin white marble supported by a metal grid, and allowed us—looking up, to track the shadows of his feet as he meandered. He was a recluse, only leaving the building once or twice a year, when he went on holiday or had to appear at a seminar.

My room contained only four articles of furniture: a narrow bed, a sturdy black pipe chair, a chest of drawers, and a mammoth, round, black marble table. (As I found out later—so did every room.) All the patients ate their meals in their room, delivered three times a day on a hostess trolley by a butler in a white frock (who when he showed up the first afternoon, I thought he was the doctor). On top of the table was a large circular crocheted doily covered by a protective piece of glass. Each meal, prior to the food being set out, the table would be further topped by an exactly sized felt table cover, which was then covered by a freshly pressed white tablecloth.

My First Office Visit

I entered a dark, high-walled, circular room, about twenty feet in diameter. There was a round black tower in the middle—maybe ten feet in diameter. Perhaps a dozen chairs—all facing the tower, were mounted on a track that encircled the tower. Some were already occupied by other patients, their faces but a foot from the tower wall. I was instructed to take a seat. A few moments later I felt a jerk and realized my chair (the track) was moving around the tower. After several minutes and a couple more jerks, I found myself in front of an open window, looking directly into Dr. Barraquer's face. Inside the tower it was well lit and I could see an assistant behind him. *What a place!* I learned then that for this type of transplant, a synthetic cornea could not be used. All the grafts were from donors who had left this world just minutes earlier. I was therefore going to be in a 'waiting mode' until the perfect cornea became available.

Meeting Meredith

A nurse told me to check a room just down the hall, where I'd find another English-speaking person: a young girl from England awaiting complicated surgery—on *both* eyes. I did. These chance meetings with the opposite sex were occasions I always welcomed. Who knows, *any one of them could be that magical female.* She wasn't alone, her grandmother was with her. Meredith was a pistol; an attractive blonde with a good figure, but only about 17 years old, and totally blind. We spoke at length about current global affairs, and I was astounded at how much this young girl knew about everything going on worldwide. She acquired this information from the BBC and listening to "talking" periodicals every day. She asked me what had transpired with my eyes, and then I asked her to tell me about her situation. What I heard from her was devastating and left me feeling guilty about even being here.

"Well" said Meredith, "I was in the tenth grade. Our science class was studying the earth's crust, and we were going to build a miniature volcano—get to see an actual eruption. I was given a mortar and pestle, three jars of powders, and told to put a spoonful of each into the mortar and grind them. I did, and while leaning over my work there was a loud bang and a sudden intense white flash and realized I had been impacted with a searing substance. I just stood there unable to move. I put my hand up to my school tie only to discover it was a melted blob. My face, hair and clothes were caked with a molten substance. While the exterior of the magma was hardening, beneath it the acidic action of the chemicals was devouring my skin. Two nuns drug me into the hallway where some friends cried out, "Who is it"? I was startled to realize I was unrecognizable. For the next two years my family exhausted the talents of the leading ophthalmologists in the UK. In fifteen months I had five surgeries, none of which afforded the slightest improvement, and may have even further damaged the remaining live tissue. After several conferences, the UK surgeons decided that Dr. Barraquer would be the most qualified to treat me. Dad brought me here a year ago, and I've had four more surgeries."

Fortunately—unable to be seen by her, to supply more live tissue for a transplant to attach itself to, they had grafted mucous membrane from inside her lip. When one looked at her opened eyes, instead of the iris being surrounded by white, *it was all wet pink flesh!* In addition to a valiant positive attitude she could be quick with a witty response. Before they grafted the flesh from her lip, they tried it off her thigh, and she warned them: "If you make a scar to where I can't wear a mini-skirt, I'll sue you into the ground."

A Real Perk From Meredith's Dad!

Her dad was the Director of Entertainment at Granada TV, England's only independent channel that show-cased European and American actors, actresses, singers, rock groups, and other celebrities. Each time one of these people or groups was on her dad's show he would ask them, "If you go to the Riviera this summer, try to hop over to Barcelona and visit my daughter in the Clinica Barraquer." One night eating supper (cannelloni with Porto) in Meredith's room, in walks John Lennon and Yoko, with whom we shared our cannelloni. He gave Meredith a reel-to-reel tape of a song the Beatles had recorded but decided not to release (titled "Where Do You Go To My Darling"). When she left the Clinic, she gave it to me. Much later I gave it to Samantha, and unfortunately it is now nowhere to be found.

The Surgery

Evidently, Barraquer wanted to make sure I got the precisely right cornea, because twice I was wheeled to the prep room, eyebrow shaved, face scrubbed, IV inserted, and my left eye socket painted with a red disinfectant, only to be soon wheeled back up to my room because he did not consider that cornea to be right for me. When the proper donor cornea arrived (from a nine-year-old boy), prior to being wheeled into the O.R. I received a shot of what I think was morphine. From the entry point of the needle, all the way up my arm, over the shoulder, up the side of my neck, and into my skull, I felt a disarming sensation of a thousand icy fingers tickling their way up; leaving a semi paralysis in their wake. This was followed by stark terror as I felt the gurney chattering over the grout lines towards the O.R., *and I was still conscious!* Soon I sensed the blinding white light directly above me. Whoa, this could be trouble. *The anesthesia wasn't working!* I tried to tell them but couldn't speak; perfectly alert and aware, but unable to form any words! *Move your hands or feet!* Let them see your condition! Yup, you guessed it, I couldn't move a muscle. Resigned to whatever was coming and waiting for the pain to begin, I woke up in the recovery room—the operation completed. Afterwards I learned the surgery was accomplished using a sharpened, hollow cylinder (like a miniature cookie cutter) to remove the whole corneal (a plug completely through from front to back) from the donor. As soon as this plug arrived at the clinic, they used the same-sized tool to remove a similar plug from my eye; the donor's plug now the exact same diameter as the hole in my eye. This drastic 'completely front-to-back' procedure is required in cases of unusually deep corneal damage.

What You Might Have Expected From Me

Meredith had a frequent visitor; a comical guy from Ireland who spoke with a brogue so thick I could barely understand him. When I asked what he was doing here in Spain, he replied, "Teaching English at Berlitz." *What!?* (Anyone in his class would have had to send their resumes to Dublin if they wanted to get a job where they would be understood.) To protect the graft I wore a plastic guard over the eye socket. I discovered that pressing in on the center of it caused its edges to press against my eyebrow and cheek and relieved the irritation of the stitches. Several days after my surgery, guffawing at one of Brendan's stories, and at the same time pressing in on my *cascara*, I pressed too hard and it popped inverted—going from convex to concave, slapping hard against the graft and *rupturing a half dozen stitches!* Part of the implant wanted to squeeze outward and in so doing would create a major astigmatism. It was a Friday night and no one at the Clinica did *anything* on the weekends; I had to wait till Monday to see Barraquer, and he was furious when he saw the damage (saying *solo un Americano*)! The eye was too traumatized to consider another surgery. I was screwed. I would be leaving the clinic with perhaps even worse visual acuity than when I arrived.

June, Still in My Life

Wonderful June managed to get over twice, taking the train from Madrid to Barcelona. She was all bubbly each time and appeared thrilled to see me, but what could we do in the clinica? Only a week after the operation, knowing that the Stafford Ballet had a party planned in Madrid, I unwisely snuck out of the clinic, took a cab to the train station and made a trip to Madrid. I felt weak and lightheaded soon after leaving the clinic. While walking in the train station, I twice had to drop to one knee to steady myself. When

I got to Madrid I was shaking and feverish; went straight to a hotel and got in a hot bath, hoping I'd experience a miraculous revival. I did not. I went to the party at 1:30 a.m., and insofar as possible did my best to appear sociable for two hours before we escaped back to my hotel. I doubt June was anticipating having her body ravished, since by now she was accustomed to being satisfied with a half hour of kisses. And tonight even that was out, as I collapsed in bed wholly unable to demonstrate any affection.

Out of the Clinic
After discharge I went back to the Hotel La Rotunda to recuperate before making the trip back to the states. Holding my head erect caused significant discomfort in the eye socket. Only hanging my head (looking down at my shoes) relieved it. This being the case, at night I first tried positioning my head face-down in the pillow, but that made breathing impossible. I had to sleep each night kneeling on the floor with my forehead on the edge of the bed. Besides that, the worst lingering effect was a bad case of photophobia (inability to take bright light). Before turning on a lamp I had to first put my hand on the switch, turn my head away, close my eyes, and then turn it on. Going out of the hotel in the morning sun was not possible. I bought two identical pairs of sunglasses and layered two lenses over my photophobic left eye.

And What's Been Missing These Past Weeks?
Any mention of my wife and kids, that's what. *What kind of person am I?!* Well Sara and I had been in contact by mail, even a couple phone calls. But I admit, as you have no doubt noticed, I have been primarily (exclusively) preoccupied with my own life, rather than things of greater significance, such as my wife and kids and their lives. Once again I was provoked to take a hard look at myself, as a flawed male who besides a devastating sexual deficiency, may be incapable of feeling a proper devotion to just one woman. Shamefully—now, that one woman being my wife! Why could I not feel what so many other good men felt and responded to?

Thinking About "What Next"
Only a few more days before I would be boarding my flight back to the states. And once there I wasn't sure how long it would be before my eye was sufficiently healed to get the FAA vision waiver necessary to revalidate my pilot's license. I would have to do this before being able to set a date to return to Air America. And this could involve some fancy talking, since in a recent communication with the company, I was startled when a new guy in Human Resources (who was not familiar with my past service) made a

comment that best he knew, *there were no pilot vacancies!* One good thing about this trip to Barcelona, it provoked a fascination with the Spanish language, and I would embark on a project to learn it (which you will see plays a major role in future activities).

Chapter Thirty-Seven
MY RETURN TO AIR AMERICA AND LAOS

A Short Stay in Florida

I decided to recuperate at my brother's. Hank was married with two kids and lived in Hobe Sound—a small ocean side town midway down the east coast of Florida. Thankfully (I think due to his unwarranted admiration for his big brother) moving in was never an issue and proved to be harmonious. I contacted Sara, letting her know my whereabouts and my plan to return to S.E. Asia as soon as I could. In fact, the second week there I flew her in for a short visit. Although she and the kids were still living their pretty much stress-free day-to-day lives in Bangkok, I could see that Sara was favorably impressed with Hobe Sound, and I sensed that perhaps she was even weighing giving up her Bangkok life-of-ease for a stateside existence in this town.

Healing and a New License

I was making progress, but not fast. It was a few more weeks before I could hold my head erect, the tears stopped streaming, and the photophobia lessened (to where I no longer needed double lenses in my sunglasses). I still had to put in a drop of Decadron every morning to prevent a graft rejection, which would mean total blindness in that eye. After about a month I felt ready to contact the FAA to apply for the issuance of a pilot's license with a vision waiver. The DC FAA medical staff bent over backwards trying to prove I really didn't need a waiver, but the best we could do was way short of what would be required for a waiver-free license. I had to undergo a flight check with my left eye covered. I passed and was issued a First-Class Airline Transport Pilot's license "By Reason of Demonstrated Ability." I was thrilled at this, but secretly wondered, *how well would a one-eyed guy do if a piece of dust blew into his good eye?* I phoned Air America to inform them I was in possession of an unrestricted ATP license and ready to return. This time I got a guy in personnel who was familiar with my record and cleared me to return, no problem. I was on my way back to familiar territory!

But This Time, Assigned to Another Country

In Taipei I received an update on our current mission in a neighboring country—Laos. The Geneva Accords of 1962 declared Laos a neutral country. *No nation was allowed to have a uniformed militia within its borders.* However, the North Vietnamese uniformed militia did not abide by this, crossing the Laotian border and moving thousands of troops and armaments southward *through Laos* on the notorious "Ho Chi Minh" trail, where they were relatively safe from US assaults. When they had made it far enough south within Laos, they turned east and crossed into Vietnam as a lethal fighting force against us. According to most Air America pilots, in Laos was where the *real* flying was being done, *by the company's best and most daring pilots.* Maybe true. In Vietnam many of our flights were over non-hostile areas, consisting of semi-safe humane missions. Laos was a different story!

Unable to utilize our uniformed US Army in Laos, the Department of Defense appointed the CIA to arm and train the Hmong mountain tribes and lead them into battle against the southbound North Vietnamese troops. Although far from being a notable fighting force, the Hmong were our only line of defense to keep Laos from falling under Soviet control. And we were not only up against the NVA, but their Laotian supporters—the hostile "Pathet Lao" (like the "Viet Cong" in Vietnam). For this huge last ditch defensive action, the CIA required air support for troop movements, weapons and ammunition delivery, medical evacuations, and armed close air support. *Enter Air America and Rog!*

Welcome to Laos

I flew from Taipei to the capital of Laos—the sleepy French provincial town of Vientiane. Ten minutes out I scanned the landscape, searching for some kind of city, but nothing; just an unending uninhabited dirt plain with isolated patches of scrub trees. Five minutes out I spied the snaking, mile-wide, muddy Mekong River, and on the north side of one east-west stretch I saw a small village, which although it was the only populated area for fifty miles, I doubted could be Vientiane. It was and we landed.

At Wattay International Airport there weren't six buildings on the whole airport. The terminal was only two stories, all wood, and a well-faded pink. Just a few hundred yards from the terminal I could see a couple unmarked hangars and the familiar silver and blue of parked Air America aircraft. One of my old Saigon pilots now in Vientiane met me with a robust two-armed hug. "Rog, you son of a gun, you're a sight for sore eyes!" (Eliciting a couple of guffaws.) He had an old MG that we had a tough time getting my stuff into and onto. On the drive to town (without passing a single building over two stories) he gave me the lowdown: "You're gonna love it here in Vientiane. It's a tiny, peaceful town. You'll hear more French than English—as well as a half dozen other languages. Since it's neutral, every country has an embassy here. You'll be rubbing elbows with Russians, North Koreans, and Chinese." He recommended I stay in the Lane Xang hotel—the best hotel in town, located right on the banks of the fast flowing, murky Mekong. On the way to it we went past a low budget hotel that none of us ever stayed in; a faded yellow, wood-sided, one-story string of about ten rooms. "See that hotel Rog. That's where the Russian pilots stay." *Russian pilots?* "Yeah, and nice looking guys too. I was at the handball courts a couple days ago and two of them were on the next court. According to standard procedure we feigned not seeing each other."

The tour of downtown entailed no more than a five-minute drive down two blocks on one east-west street that was just barely two cars wide, and three or four blocks on one slightly wider north-south street, both lined with cute silver, leather and specialty stores. It could have been St, Germain in Paris! I sensed a cosmopolitan aura and could feel a Southeast Asian version of the Continental atmosphere I had fallen in love with in Europe. I was next shown where most the Air America guys with families lived: a recently built development with well-kept and appealing, stateside-appearing three-bedroom two-bath homes with large grassy yards. I was favorably impressed, being surprised at the tranquility and sufficiency of this charming town. He left me off at the Lane Xang, where I registered, unpacked, and stretched out in wonderment, speculating about what would be in store for me.

Assigned an Aircraft and "In-Country" Area Familiarization

In addition to several large WWII cargo planes, this Laotian operation (even more so than Vietnam), required aircraft able to fly in and out of almost unrecognizable, short and narrow, unprepared valley strips or high spiny ridgeline excuses for landing areas. For this there was a fleet of the "Short Takeoff and Landing" (STOL) aircraft I'd flown in Vietnam: my turbo-prop-powered Swiss-built Pilatus Porter. I was again assigned to it. Before I was allowed to start flying I had to learn the layout of the country (which to do even halfway well would take months). Laos is a landlocked country, stretching mostly north to south and nestled like a buffer zone between South Vietnam and Thailand. The upper half—north of Vientiane, consists of an irregularly square-shaped portion, about 250 miles by 250 miles—stretching all the way north to China, with Burma to the west and North Vietnam to the east. The topography of this northern area was awe-inspiring, comprised of rugged mountainous terrain, a foreboding cluttered array of high rocky ridges, and tall limestone outcroppings (called karsts). I quickly concluded the chances of living through a forced landing would be slim to none. And according to my first day's pilot—if you *did* climb out of the wreckage, your chances of being executed within thirty minutes were excellent. South of Vientiane, Laos was a narrow, flat and arid, southerly tail extending 400 miles down to Cambodia.

I was issued about twenty maps covering the whole country. For two weeks I rode all day long with another Porter pilot, marking my maps with every landing strip (of which there were over 200) and every unusual terrain feature I saw (that I might someday need to orient myself). There were no radio beacons in Laos. All our navigating was visual—by identifying and utilizing terrain features (even fallen trees)! Our maps therefore were life savers. I spent a week figuring out how to best connect the separate maps. Some pilots taped together a set for northern Laos and a set for southern Laos. Some pilots had arranged them in north-south strips and some pilots taped them together in east-west strips. I made a smaller-sized booklet, with a calendar-like binding along the top edge. In the years to come I would arrange them many ways, making hundreds of additional marks and notes on them.

Gratefully, handling the aircraft came back to me quickly, but here in Laos the strips were harder to find, shorter, rougher, and more steeply uphill. Plus in Laos at a higher elevation the winds were stronger, producing sudden (violent) up or down drafts. At most strips, to avoid shearing a wing, collapsing the gear, skidding over the side, or plowing into a rock wall at the end of the landing roll, required bold technique and *urgent prayers to the gods of aviation.* Flying twenty short flights a day was the norm, so every day included at least one date with terror.

I underwent retraining with experienced Checkout Pilots. One—an old hand and a nice enough guy, had a train of thought uncharted by anyone. He was continually blurting out four or five words vaguely associated with something we may have discussed an hour ago, or something in the distant future that just happened to cross his mind. While attempting to become part of the team, I could see there was widely held skepticism about a "Saigon pilot" (me) doing the job here in Laos. Moreover, there were a couple old hands who were just awaiting the day when I would confirm their appraisals by leaving part of an airplane (or better yet—parts of my anatomy) draped on one of their STOL strips. This was a rough group whose fraternity was going to be hard to join.

Important! The CIA Command Post in Laos

About ninety miles north of Vientiane, in a narrow valley between two east-west ridges was the hidden village of Long Chien—*the infamous CIA secret airbase in Laos.* At 0700 every morning, the fixed-wing aircraft from Vientiane and the rotary-wing aircraft (helicopters) from our sister station (Udorn air base) on the other side of the Mekong, in Thailand, would fly up there and get our missions for the day. Our previous secret airbase (Lima Site 20 - Sam Thong), twenty miles northwest of Long Chien, had recently been destroyed by North Vietnamese artillery and troops. Now, here at Long Chien ("20Alternate) we deployed a platoon of Hmong soldiers on top of a ridge just north, to avoid a repeat of what happened at Sam Thong.

The 8ᵗʰ Wonder of the World, the Plain of Jars

About 30 miles north of Long Chien is *La Plaine des Jarres* (French for "The Plain of Jars"). Encircled by steeply rising mountains and karst peaks on all sides, it is a low, table-flat, ellipse of high green grass, stretching about 50 miles north-south, and 30 miles across. Supposedly it's where an asteroid hit the earth tens of thousands of years ago, leveling the mountains and leaving a huge lake of molten material. In the centuries that followed, layers of dust slowly accumulated on the cooled surface. It ended up just miles and miles of six-foot high weeds. Scattered across it are hundreds of huge stone jars, six to ten feet tall, each weighing at least a ton. One theory is they were part of a prehistoric burial practice. Deceased Chinese emperors and their valuable possessions were put into the jars and then hauled hundreds of miles to be sanctified here. It's one of the most important prehistoric sites in Southeast Asia. *But that's not why it's important to Air America pilots!* Since the defeat of the French, the "PDJ" has been the unrefuted property of the North Vietnamese Army, who has many encampments on it with anti-aircraft weapons (for use against errant Air America aircraft). Only under dire necessity would you hazard a shortcut across the PDJ. And if you did your chances of being shot down were about 100%.

Being Released as Pilot in Command

My Captain's Check Ride was administered by the Senior Instructor Pilot for Porters who had flown here since the early sixties. I appreciated that as the best of the old hands, he never made me feel like a new guy (which of course I was—at least here). After we landed at Long Chien the CIA dispatcher directed us to drop off multiple loads of medical supplies at Lima site 32—a tough strip with high ground at each end. Mercifully I made four acceptable trips in and out; never scaring either of us (or at least not much).

Ready to depart on our fifth flight back, there was a gusting tailwind which could *double* my takeoff distance and cause us not to be able to get airborne in the available runway. Okay, this is going to be my first real test. It could make or break my check ride. Gotta think. *If I take off with the tailwind, I might not attain flying speed and end up crashing into the high ground off the end of the strip. But then if I wait too long for it to quit, he may think I don't have the balls to fly in Laos.* There was a windsock at the strip. I watched it, timing the duration of the tailwind gust, and then timing the lull that followed; trying to get a pattern. My plan was to ram the throttle forward right at the end of the gust segment (in hopes my takeoff would coincide with the anticipated lull to follow). The tailwind gusts lasted about twelve seconds, followed by ten second lulls. I eyed the second hand on my watch through two more cycles to confirm my timing. The times repeated. So the split second the next tailwind gust died down I rammed the throttle forward. *It worked!* I accomplished the whole takeoff run during the 10-second lull that followed, allowing us to reach lift off a good hundred feet before the end of the strip and clear the ridge. Ed didn't make a comment, but I think I saw a slight nod of approval. Upon our arrival back at 20Alternate, Ed surprised me by getting out of the aircraft, coming around to my side, reaching up to shake my hand and said, "Well, you're on your own now." *I'd just passed my Captain's check. I'd be solo the rest of the day!* I shut down the engine and walked to the dispatcher's shack to volunteer a new guy's services.

My First (and Almost Only) Captain's Flight
"Hey Jerry, Ed and I finished the med drop offs. Whataya got next?"

"Wait over by your airplane, I'll be sending over some guys for you to take to LS213." *Hmmn, Lima Site 213?* Never went there before, in fact never heard anybody mention it. Just for this type of quandary Air America had a booklet numbering all the strips, giving their geographical coordinates and pertinent data. I found LS213 and discovered it was about 50 miles west, "3,900 feet elevation," "520 feet long," and "*steeply uphill to the north*." While standing there another (unusually clean-cut) Porter pilot named Gar Bogden approached me. He lived alone and quietly in the Lane Xang hotel. To me, he didn't fit the Air America mold; too quiet, too well mannered. A real gentleman and evidently happily married; never left his room in the evenings.

"Where you going Rog?"

"Lima Site 213."

Hearing it triggered a noticeable look of concern on his face. He checked my clipboard to verify I was really going there, handed it back to me, turned and started back to his plane, throwing a "Good luck" over his shoulder. This last remark—coming from Gar, was worth consideration, and went to deflating the surge of confidence I had been feeling just fifteen minutes ago. Behind me I saw four young Hmong soldiers and one stern-faced older guy in fatigues climbing into my aircraft. Satisfied it was the whole load, I started the Garrett TPE331 powerhouse, taxied to the runway, poured the coal to it, and was excited to be in the cockpit, airborne in Laos—*alone, on my first official captain's flight!*

I spied LS213 no problem since it was bright red dirt and perched atop the highest terrain for miles. At 14 degrees upslope it was probably the most uphill strip in the world, and on my first Captain's flight! This far west (almost in Thailand) I was pretty sure there would be no North Vietnamese on the ground and only a few Pathet Lao. So with little chance of taking ground-fire I risked a couple low altitude circles to examine the strip and plan my approach. The wind was not only strong, but unfortunately out of the south. Since I had to land uphill to the north, I'd be doing so with the wind on my tail. This is not desirable. Pilots always land *into* the wind to slow their speed over the ground and facilitate stopping the aircraft. But this strip was so markedly uphill, even with a tailwind I'd have no trouble stopping. But there was another downside: When a strong tailwind hits the rising ground just short of the runway, it is deflected upward, producing a huge updraft just before you cross the end of the runway; at the last minute lofting the aircraft up fifty feet or more.

On final approach everything was looking good. I knew that just short of the runway I would encounter the updraft, so pushed the nose further over. We were now aimed frighteningly low—as if I was going to ram the plane into the face of the cliff, thirty feet below the runway. Held it. Any American on board would have been screaming "For God's sake pull up!" As anticipated, just before impaling ourselves into the face of the cliff, the updraft hit, popping us up high enough that my wheels cleared the runway level by five to ten feet! Crossed the end, set her down (although I can't say gently) and threw it into reverse.

Another problem: This strip was so uphill, if I left it in reverse too long, I could easily come to a stop and maybe even start skidding back down the runway. This could result in going backwards off the cliff at the touchdown end of the runway and cartwheeling several hundred feet to death or serious bodily injury in the valley below. I added power to try to maintain enough speed to make it to the top, and more importantly, have enough speed to be able to swing the tail around 180 degrees—to be pointed back downhill for takeoff. *Shit!* Didn't have enough speed. Hadn't added the power soon enough, only got the plane halfway around. I let my passengers hop out but explained that I needed them to help me pick up the tail and swing it around towards the top of the hill. They turned to and in a minute the plane was pointed back downhill. I was all set for takeoff. The rest of the day was uneventful. I felt proud and justified during the 6 p.m. van ride from Wattay airport to the Lane Xang. Unfortunately, with all my circling I must have alerted the enemy because the next day, one of my pilots trying to land at LS213 had his big toe shot off while on final approach.

Chapter Thirty-Eight
A CHANGE OF STATUS

The Hardest and Most Shameful Thing I'd Ever Done

During my time in Laos, my trips to Bangkok frequently netted at least passable bedtime encounters, but still left me greatly troubled; yearning to experience my male birthright. While the word "divorce" was still something I could not mouth, Sara and I finally began awkward discussions about she and I—justifiably focusing on my consistent lack of prioritizing her (to say the least). Our marriage did not represent what she merited—not by a long shot. She deserved what I was not giving. With considerable awkwardness and hesitancy we somehow *decided to resign ourselves to a Legal Separation;* avoid a divorce but officiate an existing actuality. It was heart-wrenching. Not 100% sure how Sara may really have felt about it; still perhaps just going along with my ideas—as almost unanimously unadvised as they were. (Almost as if she continued to believe *that I knew best*, which of course was not the case—ever.)

Setting Up the Family's New Life as Good as I Could

The separation decided upon I flew back to the States. During my recuperation with my brother in Hobe Sound, Sara had visited and expressed a strong attraction to his small ocean side town, so figured I'd look there first. A quick decision! In it I found a neat 3-bedroom 2-bath home with a pool, and on a canal. Sara agreed to me purchasing it as the sole owner if I signed an agreement to make the mortgage payments, pay the insurance, pay the taxes, and take care of any repairs or upkeep, and that she could live there cost-free until the day she died or remarried. I agreed to this (betting on the latter occurring before too long.) I arranged to have all our great Bangkok furnishings shipped there and parked a Buick hardtop convertible in the garage.

It was a very anxious, nervous, and worried time awaiting their arrival. When they did, I was gratified to see they all were thrilled with the home and Hobe Sound. We spent the first week meeting all the neighbors, experimenting with grocery and miscellaneous shopping together, setting up bank accounts, and enrolled the kids in school. I delayed leaving one more week to make sure there were no lurking problems. Gratefully, all went even better than I could have imagined (or deserved). I was guilty but relieved. Back in Laos I phoned weekly (from an old, dark, outdated telecommunication facility) to make sure everything was going smoothly, which it was. In addition to paying the domicile costs mentioned, I of course was making support payments the first of every month (and would go on to never be a day late).

A First Date in a Long Time

Ashamed to admit it, but it only took a couple months back in Vientiane before I was able to consider myself eligible, and revive the search for that one woman who would change my life. I had several times spied an auburn-haired French woman with an aura of sexuality about her; finding myself unable not to turn my head when she walked past me in her tight, see-through blouses and crimson laced bras. My French expatriate friends told me her name was Danielle Ricard, and adding to her mystique—the rumor was she had been the wife of the famous French mime, Marcel Marceau. They divorced and due to the particulars of French law he got custody of their son. Shortly after that she was hospitalized with a nervous breakdown (or suicide attempt), and when released chose to seek employment out of the country.

Here, she was working for *Compagnie Francaise d'Assurance pour le Commerce Exterier* whose offices were on the narrow, hundred-yard-long quaint main street in town. One day at quitting time I stationed myself on the sidewalk outside the exit from her office. It worked, she almost bumped into me leaving. I found the nerve to nod a hello and flash the best smile I could. Surprising me *she* flashed back a ready smile and replied something that sounded sweet (in French); to my way of thinking—more than would have been necessary. Just *maybe* there was a connection.

Not able to discount this one short meeting, I decided to risk a formal introduction. I put on the most Continental-looking clothes I owned and went to her office. After some convincing and a couple deep breaths I strode in, spying her at a desk in the far rear. She had evidently seen me walk in because she was looking straight at me. Thank God for small favors: her countenance at first quizzical, quickly changed to a welcoming and seemingly pleased expression, almost inviting me to continue towards her. I introduced myself, and while the French men I knew spoke perfect

English, Danielle was in the throes of just learning it. A meaningful conversation became a real task, me being all but overcome with her sensuality, especially from her sultry eyes (which I could only look away from when distracted by the expanse of smooth white skin exposed above her deeply cut neckline). The feelings I was experiencing gave me reason to hope, that the aura of this lithesome foreign creature, might—just might be what I had been waiting and praying for. Thinking about that (as I was right now) and the language barrier produced an awkward conversation. However, I *was* able to arrange a dinner date the following night; my first date in some years, and with an alluring French woman! Exalted, I sang at the top of my lungs all the way home. What would lie ahead of me?

The next day couldn't have passed quickly enough. (And thankfully I had an easy day of flight ops). I once again outfitted myself with my next best European-looking clothes (having already worn my best stuff to set up the date). She gave me instructions where to pick her up. Her company owned the building she worked in and gave her a tiny one-room apartment on the third floor of that building. It contained only the bare essentials. She was obviously embarrassed about it. I made all the positive comments I could. Soon enough we were on our way to the Settha Palace hotel. It was the second-best hotel in town after the Lang Xang. It had a small dining room and a lounge which was fortunately being graced with music by some travelling Filipino band. With the language barrier the conversation was somewhat laborious. She was on a project to learn English, so it did not provide an opportunity for me to begin learning French. (Though I would buy a book titled "Learn French in Thirty Days," and my bedtime foreign language sessions would now include French as well as Spanish.)

The meal was just fine, and afterwards we paid a visit to the lounge where we had a *digestif* and listened to the music. Things had gone so well, I thought it wise to quit while I was ahead; make it a short evening and return her to her apartment. After a few awkward moments on the sidewalk, she conveyed to me that I could escort her up to her room (which of course had me shaking in my boots). *Was she going to invite me to spend the night?* At the moment, while sensing her sensuality, I still didn't feel ready. I was relieved when we parted at the doorway with just a goodnight embrace and long kiss. And I think it *did* cause me to be aware of increasing sought-after sensations—just a bit of heaviness beginning to occur where I would perhaps one day soon need it. This caused me to hope that in spite of repeated failures to find it, my "chemistry" theory was real, and that she may have some of it. This could be the beginning of something that would justify my male existence. Oh, one thing of interest: Me being only 5' 8" her French friends could not refer to me as a "One-Eighty-five," which they did for Americans. (1.85 meters being the height of a six-foot tall guy.)

I Was Right, There IS Something to This "Chemistry" Thing

A second and a third date followed; the third consisting of me inviting her to a homemade dinner at my rented house. I prepared the meal and bought the wine, unfortunately learning that French people do not like sweet wine; the dryer—the less sugar, the better. I thought I was going to have a real treat for her by buying an American favorite—Mateuse Rosé, which unfortunately was just about the sweetest wine you can get! The evening was a gamble. My dinner table was just twenty feet from a bedroom, with a recently purchased queen-size bed. *This could well be the night.* This had a chance to be a "Eureka" moment or another devastating disappointment, which with the international overtone and her expectations, be a huge embarrassment! *I think a valium would have helped.* And true enough, about ten, after girding myself (and loosening Danielle up) with a couple sips of the one liqueur I had, I was escorting her into the bedroom. There, she went into the bathroom to disrobe and freshen up, while I did the same in the bedroom (as well as while praying to the gods of lovemaking, exhorting them to gift me with—if only this once, an erection capable of penetration).

As she approached me—still several feet away, I *did* feel something where I would need it; like I'd spontaneously felt twice before: once when I stood close to that young, succulent, red-headed, freckle-faced new bride on the dock in the Bahamas, or the other time: next to that skinny, big-eyed, rock band singer with waist length honey-colored hair in the Atlanta airport. Getting under the sheets was not awkward. I started by kissing her honorably—her forehead, eyelids, and lips, and then more passionately—everywhere. (In my case, as necessary to excite *myself* as Danielle). And Holy Christ, it may have been happening. I think I may be getting firm; a result of her persona—her sensuality invading me. *That chemistry! I was* going to be able to do it! And I did! And no matter how lackluster, it constituted a breakthrough for me. Perhaps barely qualifying for the claim "Penetration however slight constitutes the act." I was hoping against hope that it would not be a one-time fluke; that I would be able to have a repeat performance should a second opportunity arise. As a result of my weak erection and guarded movements, I'm not sure if she climaxed, although we finished with her making moving exclamations in French, that although perhaps wishful thinking on my part, sounded as if they were expressions of that pleasure.

A Risky Experiment: Trying it as a Couple

It was only a few months before I invited Danielle to move in. We did most things together, although rarely were they without misunderstandings or disagreements (consistently having differing impressions). The sole factor that kept me with Danielle was the new feeling of at last being capable of a male response when it counted. Though nothing to brag about, I could at last talk to other men, on their level. If my performance—however limited, continued, it was going to be difficult to give this up. How could I leave this woman with whom I had *some* chemistry; return to the search for my grail and perhaps never again find a better (or any) chemistry.

I would like to say our life was easy and comfortable, but it wasn't. While I was grateful as hell for my newfound performance, besides completely different mindsets, and her moods, I was guilty of not being as financially generous as I could have been. I don't think I ever gave her "knock around" money in excess of twenty, or maybe fifty dollars-worth of Lao kip. I didn't realize it then, but the foreign women who had landed American men; spent the bulk of their time bragging about the devotion of their man—the uncontestable proof of which was his *financial generosity*. This was the key determinant of how desirable they were to their man. On this score Danielle was unable to prove her desirability. But she did have one bragging point (in addition to the modern apartment and our baby blue Fiat convertible), we went on several fine vacations; a couple times to Paris.

I considered that the intensity of Danielle's responses and unrestrained exclamations just before and during the act, were not so much because of my actions, but because of her vulnerable sensibilities and volatile mentality. I had found out that the hospital stay after the child custody battle was because she *did* attempt to commit suicide, and had been diagnosed as bipolar. It may be that Dannielle; a bipolar woman with a history of trauma, felt heightened sensations and couldn't restrain from responding accordingly.

One thing causing me deserved reservations: she would often ask me what our long-term plans were. I personally (as usual) had not brought myself to think that far ahead; in fact had no idea of my *own* future. I should have at least been thinking about that very thing. I often heard my pilot friends saying how much money they had put away, and I was shocked at the large amounts being bandied about. I had almost nothing put away, but of course half my salary was going to Sara (and I was spending all of the other half). I don't think I ever considered the possibility of Danielle and me settling down—in the states or France, or anywhere. I could think of nothing I would be able to do that would provide the kind of lifestyle we were living. One day, when our future came up in the conversation, she grabbed a piece of paper, told me she didn't care when it would be, but just write down a date when we would get married. Couldn't do it—at least at first (and shouldn't have done it at all) but then wrote down her birthday (about ten months away). Not sure this was convincing. Not sure why she stayed with me. I think it was more the security and status, in that she had landed a "one-eight-five,"

Chapter Thirty-Nine
ONE SOUL LESS

Just Another Flight in Laos

I left the house at six, anticipating another normal day of flight ops, first to Long Chien to fly shuttles in and out of there all day, or be sent off to some remote strip where I'd work for the case officer assigned there. Either place I'd fly about twenty missions moving cargo and troops between the small strips on top of the ridges that looked down on enemy-infested valleys. Some strips were so close to active live-fire positions, flying mud from incoming mortars would hit the side of the plane! When this possibility existed, sometimes rather than land we'd parachute our cargo. Remaining airborne was safer, but would usually still result in us taking several hits every time—usually just small arms fire, going through the tail or aft cabin area. Those kind of hits didn't scare us too much. A good scare is when you're high in the sky feeling safe and relaxed, when with no warning there's an ear drum-shattering airburst right in front of you, you see the shrapnel go by, and smell the burnt powder as you fly through the soot cloud.

Six-twenty, sitting by a window in our tiny restaurant. Cool and gray outside. A real low-pressure day. The ramp looked gloomy. The aircraft looked old. It was windy and the corrugated metal buildings looked flimsy and vulnerable; bad vibes—made you feel antsy. I was having my favorite—creamed beef on toast, when someone hollered "Hey Roger! Jim wants to see you." (Jim Ryan was the uniquely qualified and well respected "Manager of Flight Operations," about whom you will hear much more.)

"Three more bites and I'll be there."

"No, right now!"

William Holden's personal cameraman had arrived yesterday. (Remember William Holden? the movie actor in the classic film, *The Bridges of Toko Ri*. He played Harry Brubaker, a navy carrier pilot.)

His photographer had been hired to do a constructively misleading documentary on the role of Air America in Southeast Asia, titled *Flying Men Flying Machines*. He was here in Vientiane to do the part on Laos. Jim told me to take Mr. Wilheim and one of our Taipei bigwigs to a remote village (Lima site 218) just over the ridge that comprised the north side of the *Plaine des Jarres*. I'd drop them off, do whatever other work I was assigned, and then pick them up about noon. "Geez Jim, why LS218? I'm not aware of any operations up there. I've never landed there or even heard any other pilot mention it. It's no-man's land." To no avail, Jim knew where he wanted them dropped off. I did add: "Of course they'll have to bring a hand-held radio with them, and while they're on the ground, if they see or feel something brewing, they'll have to call me right away."

As every pilot did every morning, I got my intelligence briefing—the latest positions of enemy gun emplacements and the suspected locations of North Vietnamese troops. My plane was in the semi-cargo configuration; just a two-person canvas fold-down against the rear of the cabin, and another five-person canvas fold-down seat that ran the length of the port side of the aircraft. My guys piled in with their expensive molded aluminum cases. Ron Wilheim looked like a Hollywood director. He had distinctive features; was handsomely balding, wearing a faded denim shirt (probably bought on the Champs Elysees) and a suede vest with lots of pockets. Mr. Christiansen—our Company rep from Taipei was a nice fellow, but not sure he needed a white button-down shirt (with a gold Cross pen in the pocket). They joked that Jim had told them they were going to be flown by *the one-eyed guy with the silver bracelet.*

The Standard Morning Flight to Long Chien

After takeoff we buzzed steadily northward, albeit slow and noisily. The large-engined but thick-winged Swiss-built Porter gnawed the air like a gargantuan bumble bee. Lots of power but unable to get out of its own way; not designed for speed, originally designed to get in and out of small flat patches in the Alps. With any semblance of civilization behind us, we went first over densely wooded uninhabited flat land for thirty miles, and then another thirty miles over the river gorge that would lead us to the narrow valley hiding Long Chien. This second thirty miles was over unforgiving rugged terrain, where it would be impossible to make a successful forced landing (or ever be found if you did). A couple months ago coming up in the morning just like we were, one of our planes went down. We were never able to locate the wreckage; some mother's son never to be seen again. Another MIA that is not in a POW camp, just peat moss somewhere. Two miles out I started jockeying for position; making turns to create spacing and get into the queue for landing. In addition to me another dozen aircraft were also maneuvering for landing sequence. After checking left and right, I dove towards the end of the runway while shouting into the mike, "Five-Eight Foxtrot short final, number two behind the one-twenty-three!" With no tower we used a common radio frequency to announce our landing priority (as we saw it.) We were all on the same team, joined by many months of harrowing escapes, so there were few disagreements about who should have been first and who had been "cut in front of."

After parking at LS20Alternate we refueled and received our assignments. (We used to do this while having a cup of coffee in a small cafeteria that bordered the parking ramp—that is up until about three weeks ago when a North Vietnamese DK82 rocket scored a direct hit on it.) Now we just wandered around the debris, but not standing in one place too long.

My Assignment for the Day

First I'd fly north to LS218 and drop off Wilheim and Christiansen for their filming project (whatever the hell that was). Then I'd go to a strip about thirty miles east of LS218, pick up cargo there and bring it to a strip about thirty miles west of LS218. This meant I'd be passing overhead LS218 every thirty minutes and could look down and check on my guys.

I was airborne and up and over the rim of the Long Chien bowl, climbing rapidly to an altitude that would give me maximum glide distance in the event of an engine failure, and more safety margin in the event of small arms fire. Most the terrain was about 3,000 ft. above sea level, with ridges and karst peaks to 4,000 or 5,000 ft. I motioned my passengers forward to the side-mounted fold down seat right behind me, so we could converse during our trek northward. Exciting 1950's Indochinese history (the defeat of the French) was made in this area. I could get to LS218 in twenty-five minutes if I went across the Plaine des Jarres. However that route was a definite "no-no." Numerous anti-aircraft weapons were hiding in its high waving green grass, just waiting for us to take a short cut overhead. *Forget about being rescued if you went down there.* I made a left turn towards the southwest edge of the PDJ. Navigating solely by visual reference to the terrain features beneath me, I levelled at 7,000 feet, just beneath a lead-colored overcast. If I went higher I'd be in the clouds and lose sight of my landmarks.

It was still gray and gusty, but good visibility under the cloud layer. I continued northward over the rugged mountain peaks on the west edge of the PDJ. We were too high to see the large stone jars on it, which were pretty much empty now, after centuries of grave robbers had ransacked them for gold and gems. Thirty-five minutes later we were at the northwest corner of the forbidden PDJ, where it was safe to start my right turn eastward towards LS218. It would be another twenty miles across uninhabited, gray-black ridges. I had seen LS218 many times before, but never landed there. It was as if the CIA had decided they didn't want to mess with it; a hundred miles from the nearest English-speaking person or village with a well. This morning would likely find these two gentlemen as far from civilization as they had ever been.

The general area was never safe; no CIA-trained Hmong even near here. Just three weeks ago Herb Clarke was making rice drops out of an old Curtiss C-46, when he took several incendiary rounds through his right wing—which burst into flames. He immediately turned towards an open area, hoping to make a successful forced landing, but it was only ten seconds before the wing folded right back over the fuselage. Before the aircraft inverted and spiraled in, one "kicker" bailed out; the rest went down with the aircraft. (Kickers—usually Laotian or Thai, but often ex-Special Forces guys or ex-smoke jumpers, were the crewmen who on parachute drops, kicked the loaded pallets out the back of the aircraft.) It was never safe enough to get a recovery team into Herb's crash site. The NVA would have been there in fifteen minutes, set up a ring of automatic weapons, planted mines in the area of the wreckage (even booby-trapped the crewmember's bodies)! Herb is still there. Another Air America guy rotting in Laotian soil.

Arriving LS 218

I overheaded the strip high, not wanting the villagers to know a plane was going to land. The village was at the bottom of the north side of the ridgeline. It was a mottled assortment of browns: dirt huts, faded materials, dried mud, bleached and dust covered boards, piles of straw—an absence of any color. Kids were wandering about, people were walking at a normal speed, dogs were playing, old women seated around some joint activity. As best I could tell, all indications were of an unconcerned village, not one that had been overrun the previous night or in danger of an impending attack.

On the south (PDJ) side of the village rose a high bony ridge upon which the inhabitants had hacked out a fifteen-foot wide, five-hundred foot long, almost straight, almost flat, rutted path that we called a runway. I'd be landing to the east—up an incline. You always land uphill, if you land downhill it's too hard to stop. I showed Ron and Mr. Christiansen how to use their hand-held radio, that they should leave it ON, and call me immediately if they suspected things were not right. (Watch the dogs, they'll know first.) Since after landing, I'd end my rollout at the top east end of the strip, I told them if trouble did break out they were to get back to that spot immediately. There was a long steeply uphill path from the village up to the runway. If they weren't leading the way up that path, the airplane might already be packed full when they got to it. *They had to be first if they wanted to get a seat.*

At a strip under imminent attack, I never shut down the engine for fear I wouldn't get it started in time, so I cautioned them about the engine being running: "For God's sake be careful of the spinning prop!" (We'd already killed dozens of Hmong who ran right into it, leaving the pilot to look through hair and pieces of flesh stuck on the wind screen.) They nodded they understood. I spiraled down onto a short final approach, pulled off the power and "*Kalunk-thud*!" Banged it on. Careened up the incline. Spun it around. Hit the brakes, leaned back in my seat, grabbed the door and slung it full open. They were out and waving (but certainly not looking all that confident). In less than a minute I was back in the sky. We'd surprised the villagers. Only a handful of them had time to make it up onto the runway (and fortunately stayed on the edges).

Starting My Overhead East West Shuttles
The weather held the same—gray and gusty, while I made my flights back and forth between my two strips and overhead LS218. I was in my own private layer of the world, between the ridges and the cloud bases, feeling a strange comfort in my own quiet compartment in an uncared-for corner of the world. No other planes. Not a sound on the radio. The cold air made the visibility great. I could see forever under the overcast. To the north I was looking into mainland China; a solid greenish-black canopy that appeared completely uninhabited. While a China border is marked on the map, there are absolutely no indications of it posted on the ground. The people there have no idea (nor do they care) what country they live in. I was able to peer down each time I flew by LS218, checking for any worrisome indication.

About ten-thirty, passing overhead it and staring down at the runway where I'd left my two guys: *a flash of fire and cloud of smoke on the south side of the ridgeline.* Almost certainly meant an attack was coming. The hamlet was on the other side of the ridge and neither my guys nor the villagers would have seen it, though they may have heard it. Uh-Oh, another impact! Since worrying about something like this since I was told we were going here, *something bad starting.* For me, no danger now. I was far removed from the action; high and above it, observing it from a safe distance. Although I knew I was soon going to have to put myself right in the middle of whatever was coming. Visually I could see the gray fire flashes, but from this altitude there was no sound. Grabbed the hand-held radio. "Ron, Ron! You hear me? Do you guys hear me?" They did. Surprisingly they responded loud and clear.

"You guys gotta start up to the strip right now! I'll turn onto final when you're almost to the top of the path. And when you get to the strip, run to the high end where I left you off!" I could see the activity in the village becoming chaotic. People were running in every direction—like a stream of RAID had been sprayed into a bunch of ants. Two more impacts, almost right in the village! After about 30 seconds I spied my guys, scrambling up the path and not far from the edge of the strip. Some villagers behind them, but they were first. I bent the Porter around, pulled off the power, wound down half flaps, and dove towards the touchdown end of the strip. Wilheim and Christiansen were now on the strip—running, aluminum cases banging off their knees, on their way towards the spot I had let them off. I wound down the rest of the flaps. Had to force her on, banging the struts hard and wrestling with a left swerve. The Porter lurched and bounded crazily up the inclining strip. Bunches of people were now appearing at the top of the path, clutching pots and bags, chattering and pointing. I threw it into reverse and blew a swirling cloud of sand in front of me, obscuring the spot where my two guys were waiting. *Whoa!* A deafening explosion somewhere real close behind the aircraft. But no sounds of ripping metal. Spun her around. Ron and Christiansen were right there. Slung the door open. The crowd of villagers was still a hundred feet away but coming fast.

A Brave Woman

My guys were in, but where did *she* come from? Out of nowhere, one hand grasping the door frame, the other covering a bleeding neck wound, was a Hmong woman—maybe thirty years of age, trying to board the aircraft. My two guys were dumbstruck, their eyes locked on this woman, her bare foot slipping on her own blood, dark eyes bolted on me, still trying to pull herself in. It looked like a piece of shrapnel had gone through her throat. More people closing on us fast. "Yank her in! Grab her! Up here! Push the door shut, just shove it! Yeah! Good! Got it!" Full power and we lurched ahead. Thank God no people still in the center of the runway. Some loud clunks as the rough runway pounded the hell out of the struts. *Hang in there gear!* More acceleration. Off the ground. In the air. Outta there! I climbed due west to avoid the PDJ. I'd skirt the north edge of it before turning south. Got to 6,000 ft. The overcast was lower now. We were about 3000 ft over the level of the PDJ, 1000 feet above the ridges, and 500 feet above the karst peaks. Safe—or as safe as we could be. My guys maneuvered the woman to a lying position. In a minute I could hear the gurgling as her lungs were filling. Got them to get her back upright where she could swallow the blood in her throat.

I twisted around to check my passengers, who were seated on the rear fold-down seat, their equipment sprawled at their feet. The woman was sitting on the side fold-down bench, six inches behind me. Her left hand was clutching the back of my seat (her fingers touching my left shoulder), her right hand still to her neck. Her gaze was fixed straight ahead—out the other side of the aircraft. This woman who had never seen a car, only witnessed electricity for a few hours each evening off the USAID generator, probably never in her life been more than ten miles from this village, had now just boarded this screaming, strange piece of silver machinery filled with strangers; opting to leave her only known existence. Looking over my shoulder at her I knew time was of the essence and decided to risk it— turn due south before I got to the west rim of the PDJ, *which now would have me cutting across it.* A dangerous route but one that would save at least ten minutes. We'd only be about five miles inside the PDJ, so if I took a critical hit I would be able to turn west and glide out of harm's way. (Out of harm's way from the enemy, but into aircraft-destroying terrain; an almost certain fatal crash.)

With course set, power set, we plowed with a constant, monotonous drone southward; no one speaking—overcome by the situation. The feeling of being alone was paramount. Miles from civilization or help, in our own private pearly layer of space between the enemy in the rippling green of the PDJ below and the wet gray clouds just above. The sound of the passing air and the steady drone of the engine were so constant, it seemed to have reduced itself to an atmosphere, rather than a sound. Ten— fifteen minutes now. Every other minute I would twist around and check my brave passenger. She was the same each time: left hand on the back of my seat, right hand to her throat, eyes fixed straight ahead across the cabin. Midway across, the somewhat safe terrain beyond the south edge of the PDJ was now visible. Still in dangerous isolation but soon to be out. No words. No movement. The constant hum never varying, as if the aircraft itself felt the urgency and realized its mission. I twisted around several more times to check my courageous passenger, who was hanging in there; not knowing to where she was bound or when she would arrive; only that she had seen the wounded leave in these loud crazy machines before.

Holy shit! The engine quit! My heart was in my throat! In terror I scanned the engine instruments, but they were okay! The engine was still running. But absolutely no question about it, I had definitely heard a sudden change in the sound of the engine, or change in the vibration level—*a marked decrease in sound! An input had quit.* Part of the hum had just suddenly gone quiet! Like when you're in the kitchen and the refrigerator compressor shuts off. You hadn't been aware that it was running, but suddenly you hear the new quietness when it stops. *Something had ceased to emit in this airplane!* I heard it. I whipped around. Her hand was off her throat. Her arms were at her side. Her head was hanging. She was dead. We were one soul less at that moment, *and I had heard it leave.*

Chapter Forty
THE EERIEST FLIGHT I EVER MADE

Flying in Far Northern Laos, and Further

In the classic Vietnam war movie "Apocalypse Now," Marlon Brando played a crazy colonel living in a cave. I don't know how the production company got the information, but there *was* such a guy! He was a real CIA case officer, named Tony Po, *and I was going to fly for him today!* Tony, his Hmong soldiers and Thai mercenaries were defending the area just inside the northern Laotian border. (The area known in drug circles as the "Golden Triangle" where Laos, Burma and Thailand touch, and produce most of the world's supply of Heroin.) Tony was not one to be fooled with. As an example, each time one of his soldiers killed an NVA soldier, *he had to cut off his right ear and bring it back to Tony.* One time inside Tony's cabin, along where all four walls meet the ceiling, I saw what looked like a continuous row of zip-loc bags containing dried apricots. (They weren't apricots.)

During my months of flying for Tony—out of the small village of Ban Houie Sai, it was mostly rice drops to Tony's troops at remote locations. In so doing, each time I opened the bomb-bay door and the burlap rice bags went out, the cockpit would swirl with thousands of miniscule jute fibers. After repeated breathings-in of these fibers I came down with terrible asthma. At 9 p.m. each night it was like an elephant was sitting on my chest. One day back in Vientiane I got a bottle of pills to stop the asthma. It did. Great, but I was still wide awake at three in the morning! Next trip to Vientiane I went to the same pharmacy and complained about the insomnia. He gave me another prescription to take care of the insomnia, which it did. I later learned the asthma pills were heavy duty amphetamines—*straight speed,* and the pills for the insomnia were Seconal, the strongest sleeping pill there was! *For a matter of months I was flying while unknowingly taking both "uppers" and "downers"!*

A Trip like No Other

But today no rice drops, something different—really different; a trip like no other I had while flying in Laos. Tony said he had some special cargo for me to take to a location an hour and a half north. *What? North?* We already were as far north in Laos as you could get without entering Burma; and if you did, twenty more minutes and you'd be in China! A couple Americans (I'd never seen before) loaded four unmarked crates onto my Porter. Tony called me inside his hooch where he gave me the exact coordinates of my destination: 23.50 north and 101.30 east; *well over a hundred miles into China!* The destination was so far north, it was only an inch below the top edge of my map. I had never heard another pilot even mention this strip, or that the Customer ever had any operations there.

None of we pilots would ever question Tony, but I think after I saw the coordinates, my glance up to him did not hide my wonderment. I was just smart enough not to ask any questions. I used my red pen to circle the coordinates on my map. He gave me the VHF frequency to use to establish contact when I got there, as well as an affirmation code. Since this strip wasn't in our Laos site book, I'd have no details about the strip (length, elevation, etc.). I'd have to get there and find it by comparing the actual topography to the features shown on the map. Making me feel even more on edge, it was *not* a pleasant day—no blue sky anywhere; a leaden gray overcast from horizon to horizon. Sort of a "You and Me Against the World" day; a weird, blustering, low pressure, not user-friendly day. Made you feel "antsy." I later heard that in Europe, these kinds of days are called "foehns." In Switzerland they discovered when this weather condition was present, the citizenry was more depressed and the suicide rate jumped way up. (In fact doctors there declined to perform critical surgeries when this weather condition existed.) On a map, concentric circular lines—called "contour lines," indicate rising elevation. The more and closer together the lines were, the higher and steeper the high ground was, and according to the contour lines around the coordinates Tony gave me, this strip was the top of an upside-down ice cream cone. On top of the world. At least it'll be easy to find.

The Flight

I drew a line from Houie Sai to the strip location, then custom-folded the map so as to display a one-mile expanse on each side of the intended route. Once in the cockpit I used a small alligator clamp to attach the map to the trouser on top of my right thigh. This way I could continually glance down at it to confirm that the terrain features I was passing over matched the ones on the map. On takeoff the boxes slid at least a foot rearward and could have put me out of the approved "center of gravity" limits. (Safe flight characteristics are *not* guaranteed if you are out of the CG limits.) As soon as I was airborne I felt that familiar and welcome jolt of newness and waiting adventure. I'd "slipped the surly bonds." And thankfully, in spite of the rearward cargo positioning, the aircraft handled normally.

Levelling off I opened the side windscreen porthole, wedged my hand into the buffeting air flow, and deflected a cold blast into my face. I was racing along at eight thousand feet, again just a couple hundred feet below the ragged gray stratus clouds—safe in my own aluminum capsule, in my own private, pewter-colored world, untracked by the rest of humanity. While I felt invigorated, I was also more apprehensive; never did this before (not sure any Air America pilot had*)*. Forty-five minutes north I was able to scan a thousand uncharted miles, virtually untouched since time began. No cities, no towns, no buildings, no roads, no power lines, no bridges, not the slightest indication of civilization—nothing! Just a million acres of dense canopy. Because of the overcast the landscape had lost its green and given way to a washed-out grayish brown; below me the shell of the oyster, above me the gray white of the pearl. Here I was in my modern flying machine, overhead a zillion never-seen nooks and crannies of daily use to some creatures, but perhaps never visited by Homo sapiens. I was out of radio contact with anyone, but it added to the mystique—to the exciting feeling of abandonment.

An hour. More than halfway there. I was on my own, almost in another age. If there were other people on the planet, other places, cities and such, there was no way to tell that, or ever suspect it from here. I felt as if I was in a time warp at this remote spot. (If a pterodactyl had flown by I wouldn't have been surprised.) No government regulated this area— national or local. Probably no one was here to care, or if so knew nothing of any international borders. From the air it continued to be a non-stop endless expanse of treetops. I worked for Air America, but the company wasn't involved now. No one was controlling me, no one watching or even having the slightest idea where I was: if I was dead or alive. I was my own boss and before long I would have every chance to see just how much in control I was. An hour and forty now—deep into Red China. Getting close. And one thing I did know: Not being a uniformed member of any branch of our country's military services, if I went down, the rules of the

Geneva Convention about the treatment of military prisoners would not apply to me. I'd be declared a mercenary and that's a war crime punishable by death.

Arriving, Landing, and Leaving (Quickly)

According to the map I was about 25 miles south of the strip; close enough to begin making radio calls and identify the terrain features that would lead me to the strip. The contour lines had indicated it would be the highest terrain within fifty miles, and it was! I now had it in sight. It was uniquely located—on the very top of a pinnacle that stretched upward at least 500 feet above the surrounding terrain. No one could possibly miss *this* strip. The peak it was on was so narrow, rose so steeply, and jutted up so high above any terrain in sight, it was as if the earth was "giving me the finger." I made calls on the frequency Tony had given me, but no answer. *Not good.* I overheaded the strip (still at a high altitude). Still no answer. It wasn't like so many other strips, hidden by brush, surrounded by trees, or overgrown with grass. This guy was standing tall—above the rest of the world, with his chest stuck out, damned proud of himself and his perhaps never-landed-on strip. (It did look recently made and no wheel tracks.) It was as if I was being dared to attempt a landing.

These kinds of strips always had a small village located alongside it, usually many hundreds of feet below it—at the base of one of the steep side slopes. Not only was there no village at the base of this mountain, there wasn't the tiniest hamlet anywhere in sight. In fact, not even a road or trail or any cultivated ground in sight. Hard to imagine there were any humans at all in this desolate area of the world. Nothing was moving on or around the strip. I scanned the length and breadth of it but didn't see a single person. It looked abandoned, or even never ever occupied. These wary observations and complete lack of activity would normally be all the signs I would need to get the hell out of there. However today, even without having made radio contact, based on my briefing and what I sensed to be critical cargo, I was reluctant to throw in the towel and just bring the boxes back. After orbiting for five minutes I had to make a decision. I didn't want to just keep circling around up here for any longer than necessary, though I doubt there was any Chinese radar coverage of this area—at least 200 miles from the nearest population center.

It's possible that the guys here to receive the cargo had heard my calls but their transmitter didn't work. Or they may have seen me overhead and were on their way (from somewhere) up to the strip. *Gotta do it.* Landed!

Minus the mood of the place—almost a defiant sanctity, it was not a difficult approach and landing, except for the strong gusty winds always encountered at these high elevation strips. Landed to the north which was slightly uphill, rolled out to the top end, spun the aircraft around (pointing it downhill for takeoff). I sat there motionless—minus the buffeting of the plane in the gusty winds. Besides the sound of the wind, all was silent—dead silent. This was the most removed from activity and humankind I had ever been. For 360 degrees the horizon was a dark enigma, holding its own secrets; sharing nothing.

As awed as I was by the forsaken surroundings, I left the engine running, jumped out and unloaded the crates. Hopefully a couple Americans would soon appear. No one did. I was in a hurry to get out of there but took a moment to have a better look. *The strip was the whole top of the mountain!* Just ten yards from the sides and both ends, the terrain dropped off precipitously. One would not be able to start down the sides without losing their footing and stumbling. I poured the coal to it, took off to the south, and had an uneventful (but still holding my breath) trip back. I found Tony and explained what had happened. He mumbled something and went to his radio. We Air America pilots are kept pretty much in the dark about the scope of these projects. It's not necessary that we understand the big picture. Although I later found out that as a result of a special request from the Department of Defense, I had brought up electronic equipment to be installed right on the top of that high peak; transmitting signals that our planes could use for more precise navigation on certain missions.

A Quick Trip to See the Family

Six months had passed, during which time and according to Sara's letters, everything was going just fine. It was not necessary for her to work, and she was able to be a full-time mom. Furthermore, she was now sure Hobe Sound was the best little town in the country. The kids had lots of friends and loved their school and were into surfing—at least Mark was. Sammantha was older but still bogey-boarding. I put in for two weeks leave and flew to the states, landing at the West Palm Beach airport, about 25 miles south. I got a room in a motel in Jupiter, just 10 miles south of Hobe Sound, and was able to do something with the kids every day. In Florida there are lots of theme parks, and we hit them all, making two trips to the Florida west coast, for the attractions and rides at Busch Gardens. I bought the kids a volleyball setup that they installed in the back yard. This thrilled the neighborhood kids and got lots of use. It was a week before summer vacation and I got approval from the school to sit in on several of the kids' classes. A weekend morning ritual became going to IHOP for one of those indulgent, whipped-cream-topped pancake breakfasts (Sara included).

And I have to admit, Sara was wonderful. She let me visit with the kids anytime I wanted, for as long as I wanted, and even take them away on several overnights. Each one of them had a hundred stories to update me with, and I was thrilled to listen to them. I hoped they felt the love and concern I had for them. When I left for the airport, I would have to say, "Mission Accomplished." Oh, one thing I picked up from the kids on this visit, Sara had met an Air Force Major, and they had started dating. I was happy for her, after her experience with me she deserved what could turn out to be a proper relationship.

Chapter Forty-One
ALMOST IN THE WORST POSSIBLE TROUBLE

Necessary Preamble

I worked for senior officers in the Corps, and other managers before hiring on with Air America, but I have to say, *none* were as respected or feared as Jim Ryan—the Laos "Manager of Flying." A few months ago one of my pilots was shot down just inside China. Jim piloted a plane to the area and dropped thousands of leaflets declaring a big reward for the return of my pilot. Sadly while doing so Jim's airplane took several hits, one of them going through his knee, shattering the bone and blowing the kneecap off. The kicker who had been throwing the leaflets out, used his belt as a tourniquet to keep Jim from bleeding to death. Jim spent quite a bit of time at the Stanford hospital and returned with a prosthetic lower left leg. (And he not only managed to keep his pilot's license, but still flew each type of aircraft we operated, and better than most of us!) There was not a pilot at Vientiane whose worst fear, was to get on the wrong side of Jim Ryan. *Boy did I come close.*

M.C.O.'s

The greatest perk we Air America pilots got, was the company issuing us a generous amount of "Miscellaneous Charge Orders." They were a sheaf of valuable documents *that could be used to pay for travel on the major airlines!* Some pilots stayed with the company just for these MCO's. The Boeing 747 had just come out and was making trips to Europe and the states—half empty. You could not only get a no-cost trip, but almost always find five empty seats in one row, flip the armrests up, lay across the seats, and sleep all the way from Bangkok to Paris.

A Slip Up With Airline Tickets

I planned a European vacation with the two kids, including stays at the Club Mediterranèe in Greece, Switzerland, and Tunisia! (In spite of my considerable efforts, it would include Danielle.) I purchased the tickets at the Vientiane Air France office, buying most of them using my company issued MCO's. I'm not sure I knew this, but: *we were only supposed to use MCO's for ourselves or blood relatives.* A civil service guy assigned to the US Army Criminal Investigation Command finds out I used some of my MCO's for Danielle's tickets and reports this violation to Jim Ryan! Jim calls me in and questions me. When he asked me how I paid for Danielle's tickets, without thinking of the problem I was creating—instead of saying "cash," I stupidly answered "With a check." (*A lie of course, and not a smart one.*)

Jim says "Good. When the cancelled check comes back, bring it in." I somehow responded, "Sure." But I can tell you, as soon as I did, a sick feeling overtook me. Now I'd really done it.

What Has to Happen?
I had said "With a check." That means I have to come up with a cancelled check. *But how in the hell am I going to come up with a check that doesn't exist.* I'll have to fabricate one; make an identical (counterfeit) one. I'd do anything to avoid going down in front of Jim Ryan. And terrifyingly, if the falsity of the check would be discovered, there would be even worse consequences than having used the MCO's; one of them for sure would be losing my job.

I examined some cancelled checks that had already been through the Paris and Hong Kong clearing houses and come back to me. I wasn't too worried about the front side; thought I could do that no sweat. But on the backside of each cancelled check there were two or three stamped logos of the banks that had cleared the checks. Each one was unique and a different color. I knew replicating them was going to take some innovation!

What I Thought to be the Easy Side First
The front side of the check shouldn't be a problem. I knew it would be written out to Air France, and I knew the date and the amount. I'd fill that in, sign it, and the front side would be done. I got a blank check and did just that. It looked fine. Half done. But wait. *What's that?* I saw something on the front side of one of my old cancelled checks that I had never noticed before: On the bottom of every blank check there are a series of numbers along the bottom edge, and—at some time during the clearing process, four new numbers are added! And I had no idea what those numbers related to. Did they signify something I didn't know about? And to make fabricating them more difficult, they were those geometric, abstract-looking IBM digital numbers. How in the hell am I ever going to *hand print* those series of *digitally printed* numbers? I could try, but they will be hard to replicate;

they're perfectly squared. It would be almost impossible to print them with the accuracy necessary to escape the scrutiny of Jim (plus who knows who at CID). Still, I made a trip downtown, bought a fine-point calligraphy pen, some black ink, came home and went to work.

I was ready to enter the series of numbers in the proper location. *But I couldn't figure out if there was a meaning to the numbers.* My hope was that Jim Ryan would also not be familiar with what those numbers meant. I had a whole book of blank checks, and with a spotlight clamped to the table, a clear plastic ruler and my new pen, I began trying to precisely draw each squared numeral. I had to discard a bunch of tries because the numbers I drew were too rounded, or crooked, or not perfectly even, and it would certainly be noticed. Finally—on about my twentieth try I had a set of numbers that were as good as I would be able to do.

And then—*disaster!* Looking at the series of numbers on the cancelled check, I realized that the last four numbers that had been put on during the clearing process of the series *weren't just any numbers*—they were the number of *that particular check!* On the one I had just done I had copied the last four numbers from *the old cancelled check I was using as a model.* Of course these numbers didn't match the numbers on the newly forged check—a dead giveaway. Aware now they had to be the last four numbers on the blank check I was forging, I had to start over. By supper time I had what would be the best I could ever hope to do.

The Back Side

There was one way I could replicate those bank logos stamped on the back, but it was going to require a trip to Taiwan and back. I remembered in Taipei, along the sidewalks there were various entrepreneurs: old women darning socks, kids selling cigarettes, and some old guys behind crude work benches, who made rubber stamps (usually return address stamps or "handle with care" stamps). I flew to Taipei. The old guys making stamps were still there, and I found a willing accomplice. He studied the impressions, figured out a price, and told me to come back about five the following evening. No one was more joyous than I when I picked up the stamps. He had a piece of paper with the imprint of each one, and they were perfect! God knows what kind of tools or dye he used to make such a perfect stamp. I also bought three different colored ink pads. Back in Vientiane I was shaking when I got ready to stamp the back of the check (knowing that if I screwed it up, I'd be two days drawing those numbers on the front again. I did all three and they looked perfect. *I was finished with my "get out of jail" card.*

The Day of Reckoning

Several days later (as boldly as I could) I told Jim I had gotten the cancelled check back. He replied "I'll be in the office tomorrow morning, bring it in." I don't know if I was ever more nervous than I was when I went into Jim's office carrying the check (which I had also creased twice, bent a corner, and made a couple stapler holes through it to make it look even more well-traveled). He held it up and looked up at it *without giving it more than a few seconds scrutiny;* looked back at me and said. "Great."

What I'm going to tell you now, I have thought about for the last 40 years. As I was walking out of his office, half—but only half-jokingly, Jim said, "And don't do it again." With his sarcastic wit, I'm not sure if he was joking, *or if he knew from the beginning, I would have to forge a check.*

Something I Evidently Didn't Do for Sara

I was off the next day and went to that dark old IT&T building to place a call to Sara. We talked a long time—not like the flawed, selfish man I was, but rather like a concerned and loving husband and father. I was pleased to hear that things couldn't have been going better. The kids had lots of new friends and a school they thoroughly enjoyed. Although Sara was disappointed I hadn't sent her the $200 she had asked for, to fly to New Jersey to attend her younger brother's wedding. I have absolutely no recollection of ever getting a letter requesting $200. In fact, I'd like to say I didn't get it. If I did get it, I can't imagine I wouldn't have sent the money. But even without doing so, I would have sent her $1,150 perhaps two weeks earlier, and another $1,150 would be coming in two weeks; $2,300 from which to find that $200. (And her younger brother could have sent her tickets.) But some good news, I was glad to hear that her older brother—also from Jersey, had visited Sara in Hobe Sound, loved it, and bought a house just down the street!

Chapter Forty-Two
YOU LANDED WHERE ?!

Something New in the War in Laos

In January 1972 the frequency and intensity of hostile activity seemed to be on the increase. In the mornings at Long Chien—almost every morning, right after we had arrived and parked our plane, a ten-minute siege of incoming artillery began raining down—*right on the ramp where our airplanes were parked*. Turns out the NVA troops had (God only knows how) been able to raise a 350-pound howitzer up an almost vertical incline, to the top of the ridge just a half mile north of Long Chien. Fortunately, at the edge of the ramp was a tall karst where we burrowed ourselves into its south-facing base.

We all wondered what the hell was happening. Well it wasn't until months later we found out what had been happening: The notorious military strategist for the North Vietnamese Army, General Vo Nguyen Giap had dispatched 27,000 regular troops into Laos, *with a specific goal to overrun and capture our CIA base here at Long Chien!* That information was not shared with us pilots. All we knew besides the rocketing of Long Chien—was we were taking much more small arms groundfire inflight, and that we couldn't land at many strips because they had been taken by NVA troops the night before. I actually flew days on end, personally loading my airplane with dead Hmong soldiers (one in the copilot's seat each trip) flying them back to their villages, returning them to their families. *A not-good few weeks.*

A Special Request From Hog

During this period I was approached by a CIA case officer—the right hand man of General Van Pao (the head of the Hmong army). His call sign was "Hog." His real name was Jerry Daniels, previously a smokejumper from Missoula, Montana, but now a combat-hardened expert in infantry tactics, and in charge of almost the whole northern Laos defensive action. His troops—numbering several thousand were comprised of Hmong soldiers and Thai mercenaries. I could see urgency in his eyes as he began to speak.

"Rog, I got something for you, if you want to do it. Won't be easy."

"Sure Jerry" (I said foolishly without having any idea what the mission was going to be.)

"We're going to have to go to a bad area. "No man's" land. Where we never fly; to a completely overgrown 1950's French strip. We've never landed at it and you might not be able to make it out from the air. One of my companies just finished a three-day firefight near there, with a column of North Vietnamese soldiers marching south. My troops had to retreat. They almost all got back except three: a captain, a lieutenant, and a staff sergeant. They are still pinned down there, and at least one of them is wounded. The last radio contact I had with them they were on their bellies in the high weeds right next to the top west end of the strip.

"All the troops know their officers are still there, and if I don't get em out I'm gonna lose the trust of the whole company. Now, I have to tell you, the location of the firefight was only about two miles from the strip. What's more, about five-hundred yards north of the strip, high up in a karst peak, the North Vietnamese have four fifty-caliber machine guns looking down right over it. So we're gonna have to be in and out of there real quick.

Geez, this might be the most dangerous assignment put to me since I was in Air America. I answered (surprising myself when I heard the words come out). "Sure Jerry. Let's do it!"

The Flight and Landing

Jerry and one other guy climbed on board. I taxied out and was airborne. After thirty minutes and about ten miles south of the strip Jerry told me he had radio contact with his officers and they were still in the weeds at the west end of the strip. This was good, because it was uphill to the west, and they were hiding only about fifty feet from where after my landing rollout, I'd spin it around for takeoff. I told Jerry to tell them we'd only be able to wait five seconds—about how long it would take for the four, fifty-caliber machine gun operators to zero-in on us. Several hundred rounds a minute would be going through the airplane (and our bodies)!

No way I could circle overhead and examine the strip, the NVA would see us and be on the strip when we landed. I snuck in at tree-top level in a deep valley alongside the strip (several hundred feet below the strip). Once past it I did a left, 180 degree turn to put myself on a final approach to the strip, but still below it. At the last minute I popped up to make a surprise landing. The strip had been so long abandoned my main concern was that after touchdown I might run into a log or a big rock, or some other thing that would tear off the wheels, collapsing the plane onto its belly, marooning us on the strip. Soon as I cleared the end I chopped the power and touched down. *Kheerist!* The grass must've been over six feet high. The prop hit it like blender blades and my whole windshield was covered with a green mash. I could just barely see enough to keep the aircraft on the runway. It was rough as hell and we bounded and careened the length of the runway. Don't know how the plane held together. Got to the high west end, hit the left brake and spun her around, pointed back the other way, ready for the downhill takeoff.

Jerry yanked open the door, and I began hollering out the seconds. I felt the aircraft shake as one body slammed into the cabin. And then my heart almost came out my mouth! Twenty feet away, several fully uniformed North Vietnam soldiers climbed up on the runway from a ditch alongside it. They were walking straight towards us carrying Russian AK-47 automatic weapons—levelled right at us. *This was it. We're all gonna be killed!* Just when things couldn't get worse, the quad-fifties up on the peak to the north, opened up on us! But for the moment—were missing us! They were using tracer ammunition, and fifteen feet in front of the aircraft, the air turned a bright fluorescent pink! The good news was, *the stream of gunfire hit one of the NVA soldiers, and caused the others to jump back over the side of the strip!*

I knew in a second the machine gunners would realize their sighting error, yank the guns back to the right, and the stream of bullets would go through the plane—front to back, killing us all (me first). And the gunners *did* yank the muzzle to the right, but in doing so must have accidentally jerked it upward, because (*thank you Lord*) the stream of bullets went *over* the plane—*above* it! I felt the plane shake as a second body landed in the cabin. I was ready for pain, knowing the gunners would yank the muzzle back to the left, and we'd all be hit, but this time from the rear of the plane forward. They did, but this time the muzzle must have been jerked downward, because all the rounds passed *under* the plane, coming out under the front side, without hitting the landing gear or a tire! I felt the third body hit in the plane, and with the door still open, rammed the throttle full forward and we were accelerating down the strip. Don't know where the 50-caliber fire was, but it must have been behind me, and the soldiers were still hiding below the south edge, afraid to raise their heads.

Upon Our Return, a Well-Done

After landing back at Long Chien, the head CIA guy for Laos—Dick Johnson, called me up to his office alongside the ramp. Evidently on the way back, Jerry had radioed him with exactly what had happened. Mr. Johnson told me somewhat sternly that we were paid to take "calculated" risks, but he wasn't sure what we had just done qualified as a calculated risk, *but I had his confidential thanks.*

Chapter Forty-Three
A FAUX-PAS AND MORE IN CAMBODIA

A Little Background

The U.S. Navy needed a special-mission, heavily armed aircraft for low-level monitoring of the narrow, winding rivers in South Vietnam. They gave the contract to a well-known US aircraft manufacturer. The aircraft—a Helio Stallion, was a large-engined jet-prop with a 900 round-per-minute machine gun installed in the open port side of the fuselage. And it was a tailwheel aircraft, just like my Porter. But a big political problem arose: the Navy had failed to issue an unrestricted bid and the other aircraft manufacturers who were left out, filed lawsuits. The project was buried and the planes were hidden in an area in the Arizona desert called the "Aviation Boneyard" (where thousands of WWII aircraft are still "moth-balled"). The Navy heard about further litigation coming and lobbied Congress to get the planes out of the country. They donated them to the fledgling Cambodian Air Force, just beginning their fight against the communist Khmer Rouge.

Never Knew I Was Specially Qualified for Anything

The Cambodian pilots who would fly these planes were going to need instruction (to be given in their native language of French). The Dept of Defense needed pilots who: (1) had experience in tailwheel aircraft, (2) had been rocket and bomb instructors, and (3) spoke French. In the whole US Air Force there was not a single pilot having all three qualifications, so they turned to the CIA, and guess what, there was one guy with all three qualifications: *Roger Yahnke!* (My nightly sessions studying French had emboldened me to list it as a "language spoken.") I accepted the assignment which would be administered from a secret airbase on the Cambodian border. To help me I chose one of my Porter pilots, a Louisiana Cajun named LJ Broussard who had spoken bastardized French from birth. The US Air Force was responsible for the project, so they assigned two of their colonels to the program; *to work for me!* I would be the "Project Manager."

LJ and I made the trip to Phnom Penh, met our new Air Force friends and attend a *really* posh meeting with the US Ambassador to Cambodia, the Cambodian Minister of Defense, the head of the Cambodian Air Force, and Major Sompai, the leader of the squadron we would be training.

What Can Happen When You Don't Know the Idioms

The meeting was held in the hundred-year-old historic Royal Cambodge Hotel; an edifice to view with wonder. It looked more like a German castle, being all made out of stone blocks with slate floors, fifteen-foot ceilings, and no glass or screens on the windows—just huge 8-foot high, wooden shutters. In the center of our meeting room was a long glistening mahogany table. In front of each chair was a place setting of a crystal goblet, a pewter ashtray, a quill pen, a tiny receptacle of ink, and a pad of linen paper. It was as sophisticated and urbane an event as I'd ever been a party to. The protocol was so thick you could have cut it with a knife. It took at least ten minutes to figure out how status would affect the seating arrangement. I was nervous because having learned all my French from books, while I could read and write it okay, when listening to the spoken word, I had to write the phonetics of what I had heard on a blackboard in my head, and then *read* it!

Halfway through the meeting, the head of the Cambodian Air Force comes up with an idea that could mean WWIII. A *terrible* idea. I felt like saying, "Holy shit, that's ridiculous!" But knowing the sophisticated nature of the meeting, there was no way I could say anything that crude. I quickly searched for some kinder words, some way I could discourage this idea without being rude. I thought of the stateside expression *"Well, I have my doubts"* and responded to his idea by saying *"Puis, j'ai mes dutes."* I was shocked at the reaction by almost everyone, one was furious, some obviously irritated, others chuckling. The US Ambassador recognized I'd said something wrong and chimed his water glass with a knife and declared a ten-minute coffee break.

I asked LJ what in the hell I had said. He answered that I had said "I have my doubts." And that as far as he knew I'd said it perfectly. Maybe so, but there had to be more to it than that. He suggested I ask Major Sompai who was having a cigarette in the hallway. I found him and asked him. He responded, "Well Cap'n Yonk, I never be to Paris, but here in Cambodia, we only hear that expression one time. When young girl misses second period and thinks she's pregnant, she says *'j'ai mes dutes.'* So you just told everyone that you were going to have a baby."

The Actual Training Program and Another Big Problem

It went surprisingly well minus one handicap we had to deal with throughout the syllabus, and particularly during landing training: the Cambodian pilots were all short and their feet barely reached the rudder pedals—something that could have caused us a serious landing accident. As an instructor, in spite of a possible landing accident, if you want your student to learn the landing technique, you have to let him go as far as possible towards actually touching down. Then if something's wrong, at the last second, you shout "Go Around," which means to abort the landing! Add power and pull the nose up. It is just a couple syllables and easy to get out quickly, so an instructor can let the student continue and wait till the last second before shouting "Go Around!" But in French, the landing abort callout is *"Representez vous pour l'atterissage!"* If you waited till the last second to try to get this mouthful out, you'd already be crashed. I held special ground school sessions to make sure all the Cambodian student pilots knew that *"Go Around"* was what they were going to hear instead of the longer French language phrase.

Chapter Forty-Four
A LANDING, BUT NO TAKEOFF

Two Things That Were Bound to Happen

The war in Laos was now getting not-good publicity. Recent United Nations resolutions favored a transfer of power from the existing ruling (US-friendly) family to communist-supported elements waiting in the wings. And perhaps it was the only way to end a twenty-year secret war. None of us knew what that might mean for Air America, but suspected it would spell the end of this long adventure.

I can't remember the Lima Site number, but I do remember the name of the village, because I was probably the last guy that ever went there (if not also the *first*). It was Muang Xon, almost on the same latitude as Hanoi and only about 40 miles west of the North Vietnamese border. *Not* a good place to be in early 73. You kept your ground time to the bare minimum never knowing when there'd be incoming artillery, or worse—an actual NVA ground attack. The Customer told me it would be just this once, sounding to me like they knew what was coming and were writing it off (which as far northeast as it was, was understandable).

At some strips the Customer had armed and minimally trained the old men to put up a fight if NVA troops tried to overrun their village when no Vang Pao Hmong soldiers were nearby to defend them. I hoped that was the case at Muang Xon. My cargo was medical supplies and plasma. *Plasma.* I knew that was a bad sign. Bringing in blood means transfusions are necessary, and that's because there are wounded soldiers at the strip or nearby; the result of recent, or worse—*currently* occurring firefights. Arriving just southwest of the strip I couldn't risk dallying overhead to check it out; that would draw too much attention (meaning ground fire). I made a 'straight-in' approach from the west, rolled out to the east end and spun her around for my hopefully soon-to-occur takeoff. The strip was between huts to the right, some others and small rice paddies to the left. No Americans were waiting for me. *Not a good sign.* (Let's hope they weren't currently leading a platoon of Hmong guerillas against some North Vietnamese soldiers a mile away.) As soon as the plane was stopped, a villager yanked open the sliding side door and began unloading the supplies. He was staying at the rear of the aircraft, away from the prop, so I did not shut down the engine; kept it running in anticipation of a quick departure.

Holy Shit!

I don't know how to best describe what happened next: the deafening explosion, the flash, the concussion, or the breath being sucked out of me. An artillery round hit somewhere behind the plane. *Parts of the guy doing the unloading flew into the airplane.* The force of the blast spun the tail a quarter turn to the left. Once motionless and sitting there in shock I realized I was now pointing north, crosswise to the runway *and the whole windscreen had been blown out.* While trying to gain control over my shaking body another round hit some distance to the left. I could hear the pings as dirt, rocks, and other debris hit the side of the fuselage. I was parked about fifty feet from some rising ground to my right. Looking in that direction I saw villagers running towards it, and more specifically—towards a barely visible cave-like opening at the base of the hill. I took this to be the entrance of a shelter from incoming artillery, or maybe even a hiding place that could go undiscovered if the NVA troops entered the village. Leaving the engine running I set the parking brake, leaped out and started running towards the opening. I am embarrassed to say this, but on my way there—about twenty feet in front of me a villager went feet over head when a third round hit nearby. I should've stooped and tried to gather him up on the way by, but I didn't. I ran right past him.

A Hiding Place

The entrance was so low and small, I had to drop to my knees to crawl in, sweeping aside the long grass that hung down across the opening—perhaps purposely left there to hide the opening. These side-of-the-hill shelters all had the same layout: the tunnel went in straight for about ten feet and then made a 90-degree turn. This was so people could get around the corner and not be hit if the enemy shot straight into the opening. I made it around the corner and found myself next to a woman whose whole heel was missing, and blood was pouring out of the gap. It was dark around the corner; had to strain to make things out. Above the desperate conversations and babies crying, I could hear lots of small arms fire outside. It could have been coming from either the village or from atop the hill—*right over us*. In fact

I could hear footsteps thudding on the ground above my head, causing me to wonder if any second a leg was going to come down through the dirt above me.

After ten or fifteen minutes I still heard voices shouting commands, and by the inflection—questions. I had no idea if they were from the villagers or the invading soldiers. I could hear the engine of my plane still running but am embarrassed to admit I was too scared to venture out and make a run for it. I looked at the people with me in the shelter; men, woman, children—about twenty of us. Some of them were soldiers who had probably done this before and would know when we could exit. It was quiet outside now, no shots, no voices. No one moved or spoke for at least twenty minutes; finally, judging by the gestures from a soldier further in, it was time to exit.

We emerged into a bright sunlit area; the aura of which was far removed from the actual situation. Quiet. Sunshine. Nothing moving. Looking straight ahead, not a villager in sight. No idea where they could have gone or be hiding. While standing half paralyzed, looking at my shiny silver and blue aluminum escape capsule, I heard a loud outburst of shouts from behind me. I turned and my heart almost came out my throat. On top of the hill (right over our shelter) were about a dozen of what I guessed to be NVA soldiers. They came stumbling down the hill screaming and looking at me with suspicion and emotions I could not interpret. The soldiers were not well-uniformed, in fact some were in ragged shorts and flip-flops, and no shirts, meaning they could be Pathet Lao (the Viet Cong of Laos) not a North Vietnamese Army platoon.

Leaving Muang Xon

After a short—well not so short (but heated) discussion, it was obvious that several of them were assigned to do something with me. One of them approached me, on the way swinging off his haversack and opening it. He took out a coil of rope. Not good (but better than a knife or handgun). He first tied my right wrist to my right ankle, and then my left wrist to my left ankle. After two hard shoves in the back and some hand gestures I realized they wanted me to start up the hill that our shelter was under. I did, but tied the way I was, I was halfway up the hill before I'd figured out how to coordinate my leg movements with my arm swings. *God knows how I'm going to walk far like this.* Over the hill and onto a path leading to the east and the North Vietnamese border (and possibly, eventually—*Hanoi)!* I was being escorted in a fearful direction. I was so concerned with my immediate situation, I didn't have time to dwell on the fact that I could end up in prison (the "Hanoi Hilton") with John McCain and that other Air America pilot, and what that would mean; couldn't think that far ahead.

We continued walking until we came to a small clearing where surprisingly, *these soldiers had left their wives and several kids.* After gathering them up, some bedding and cookware, we were on our way, me bringing up the rear. We continued walking until darkness made it tough to pick the best path. In case I could escape and would need to backtrack, I tried to determine and stay aware of our heading, which I figured to be a little north of east, maybe 070 degrees (meaning if I did escape) I'd have to head back the opposite direction: about 250 degrees. Wasn't sure if 070 degrees was a base course or if these guys were just taking the easiest route to wherever we were going. As you might imagine, tied the way I was, walking was not easy, especially through the waist high brush. I didn't say a word, trying to be as little trouble as possible, realizing that if I was too much of a burden they may give up on whatever the master plan was, and just shoot me here.

The First Part of the Trek

By the end of the first day I had determined that the ranking guy was named Bao. He issued all the orders and wasn't challenged. During the day they had assigned separate individuals to walk with me. Most ignored me, except one pissed-off guy who I was sure would shoot me if he had half a reason. That first night they started a fire, boiling some kind of broth, in an opened section of a hollow bamboo trunk (that even in the flames never caught fire). They also heated something in a charred gourd—some kind of stew. Everyone ate except me. After eating, the soldier they assigned to watch me, was skinny and young—maybe fifteen or sixteen; not one of the married soldiers. His apathy conveyed that he was just doing what he was told to do. I didn't have anything to lie on and the ground was damp, not to mention very likely crawling with vermin. I gathered some branches and fronds to keep me off it. When I had lain down I had time to conjecture on the likely end of this trek; with that on my mind I was surprised that I dozed off at all. I awoke some time later and several of the soldiers and their wives were still sitting around the fire, apparently having a reasonable time, not at all concerned about their prisoner. Woke up several times more.

I didn't go to the bathroom the first day and half the second day. And having nothing to eat for about 30 hours, didn't think I'd have to, but about noon I did! No way to communicate my problem to my captors. Finally realized I had no choice but to just step off the pathway in full view of the soldiers (and their wives), squat and pull down my pants (which wasn't easy). Succeeded, but of course without toilet paper, wondered what kind of problems this would soon bring about. We walked basically the same heading until about four and then took a hard jog to the right for about ten minutes, then back left for ten minutes, and then back on that basic 070 degrees. With a limited view of the sun, I was hoping my heading estimates were accurate, just in case I did get free and would have the right course to backtrack on. I was now thankful that I was wearing well-made high-top flying jodhpurs and thick socks.

That night I was included in supper. And I was hungry as hell. *But you should have seen supper.* A half-hour hunting venture netted several not-big birds. They did pull out most the feathers, but then on a flat piece of wood, using a cleaver-like knife, one of the women hacked these birds, scaly legs, claws, beaks, eyes, bones—everything, into small pieces, heated the mélange in that same gourd, and handed me a dirty metal plate containing a handful-sized portion. I knew that as distasteful as it would be, I needed the nourishment (and did not want to look ungrateful). Each swallow was a dreaded, pure mechanical act of necessity. I did not take one mouthful that I did not have to pick unknown things out of my mouth and sneakily flick them behind me in the dark.

After two days, having bragged about my jodhpurs earlier, I was getting blisters on the outsides of my small toes on both feet. Although I think it was sunny, the treetops were so enjoined and thick that at high noon it was like dusk, plus most of the time there was no trail. They just seemed to pick and choose their way, but steadily to the east/northeast. If we were making ten miles a day—which I wasn't sure we were, *we could be inside North Vietnam tomorrow evening!* We stopped at what was about noon (not sure what time it was, because I had forgotten to wind my watch and didn't notice till a half day later). I thought they were going to have lunch, even though by now it should have registered that they only ate twice a day, late morning and night. It was a 'siesta' break. They were going to take a nap.

While they're lying there, a couple of the kids—maybe just out of curiosity, came over to me—looking as if they wanted to be friends with this different-looking being. I gestured for them to come closer, so I could demonstrate a trick my father did. I held my two hands together, fingers cupped together, and then quickly moved them apart, *apparently pulling off the last joint of one thumb.* You should have seen the look in those kids' eyes and heard the shrieks as they jumped back. After a few seconds—knowing they'd been sufficiently shocked, I unfolded my hand and displayed the missing thumb still attached. One of them ran over to a nearby soldier—probably his father, and pulled him over to where I was. I knew he wanted me to do it for his dad and so I did. Had to do it several times for the at-first incredulous adult, who then brought the other soldiers over. I performed it again for them. I believe I had just made a breakthrough. And I was right, the soldiers and their wives seemed to begin almost treating me like a traveling companion rather than a prisoner.

That was the highpoint of the day. The low point was I had to 'go' but was unbelievably constipated; think I hemorrhoided myself in having some sort of movement. Though I couldn't smell myself, my sweat soaked clothes and dirty behind must have made me ripe; small thing—in fact nothing, *considering the possible outcome of this journey.* Surprisingly I had less bites and scratches than I would have thought after this time. The ropes around my wrists had gotten wet, dried, muddied, dried, and shrunk, and the skin on my wrists under them was chafed and sore. I had to be thinking of this every time before I moved my arms.

The next morning we stumbled onto a small hamlet, containing huge thirty-foot-across craters. (Undoubtedly from a B-52 bombing.) My captors exchanged greetings with those who came out to meet them. None of the villagers—after spying me, took their eyes off me. Some big guy from the hamlet approached Bao and they commenced a long discussion. The way they were negotiating, I think the hamlet chief *wanted to buy me!* For whatever reason (Thank God) Bao declined the offer. The mean guy in our group (the one who I said I had no doubt would shoot me if he could get away with it) whose name I picked up as Dinh, began shouting out his idea. The next thing I see is several villagers commencing some construction project with stalks of bamboo. Most of my captors showed no interest in the project—whatever it was. Both the women napped. I soon realized what the workers were doing. *They were building a cage!* (And I knew that when Ernie Brase was captured, that's how he spent most his time on the way to Hanoi.) Now, *talk about lucky:* at some point my captors must have realized that with me in the cage I couldn't walk, and I'd only be able to be kept in it at night, and they'd have to carry it in the day. This being the case, even though the project was half completed,

Bao goes up to the village chief, and pisses him off by declining the offer, relaying that we were going to continue on as is. *Thank God for small favors.*

A Second Breakthrough, and Guess What?

That afternoon, one of the kids—I'd say about five or six years old, approached me and held up his hand. *My conclusion was, he wants to walk with me.* I was not about to take his hand, thinking that could end up bad. I glanced up and his mom was looking in our direction with what I would describe as a not angry "wait and see" expression. She finally nodded, *so I took the kid's hand.* I suspected he would soon lose interest and it would be short-lived. But the kid held on for a long time. I had the feeling that this event even surpassed the thumb trick as humanizing me. And guess what, on the third day, by my very suspect calculations—real close or even inside the North Vietnam border, we stopped. There, the soldiers held several animated tête-a-têtes.

When it broke up, Bao comes over to me and starts trying to explain something. Though he must have spoken for five minutes, it was all in Vietnamese and I didn't understand a word. Then he takes out his knife and—with a level of care I appreciated, cuts the ropes on my wrists (leaving the lengths still hanging from my ankles). He then points at me, and then over my shoulder in the direction we had just come from, and then he makes the same two motions again. *Don't tell me he's saying I can go?!* If so, this was no time to dally. I was afraid to turn my back, so (carefully) began backing out of the clearing. After my first two or three steps Bao nodded approvingly. *My God. I can't believe it. They're letting me go!* Once I was sure they were in fact letting me go (and I can't believe this, I made a small wave-like gesture). I then turned and began walking quicker, on the reciprocal of the route we had just traversed; at least getting this first part directionally correct.

The Trek Back, Day One

I walked quickly for at least an hour—putting as much distance as I could between myself and my captors. (They may have a change of heart.) I wasn't too worried about being recaptured by other Pathet Lao or NVA soldiers, since excluding the one small hamlet we hadn't seen a single human being since we left Muang Xon. But being discovered was more than just a possibility, and the next people to capture me might not be so lenient. But it was true that Muang Xon—much further to the south had been attacked, and I was here—even closer to North Vietnam, there must be soldiers somewhere up here. And undoubtedly there would be 'unfriendlies' between where I was and where I hoped to go. I trudged doggedly ahead until dusk, not at all happy with my slow pace. (I'd untied one ankle attachment. The other one was too knotted.)

Under the strain of the last several days or the relief of being released, and finding myself completely on my own (still with a huge challenge), at the end of this first day free I just let myself sink to the ground, where the tears flowed. I stayed like that for a while, contemplating the perhaps undoable task that lay ahead of me. I began weighing my options; trying to come up with a plan. I knew the walk back was going to be much tougher because I would have to stay away from open areas where I could more easily be seen. I considered whether to better avoid a re-capture I should just walk at night, but quickly canned that idea. If I was going to stay on the back-tracking course of 250 degrees, I needed daylight. Not because I'd be using the sun, but because the only way I could stay on that heading without a compass, would be to pick and line up one landmark after the other—on that bearing. Holding this course, I would arrive at or pass nearby Muang Xon, which could now well be occupied by North Vietnamese soldiers. And while all this navigating stuff was important, I knew from my Marine Corps survival training that I was going to need water, and soon!

Day Two a Lucky Day on Two Counts

We never had any flights scheduled to this area so my chances of being spotted by another Air America plane were slim, and with the thick tree canopy over me they were reduced to zero. By now the company would have an "SAR" (Search and Rescue) operation for me (whatever good that would do). As I tried to navigate my way back, I reflected on having laughed at those Ex-Special Forces guys who wore a small compass on the underside of their watchband, or those Air America pilots who always checked out survival vests for their flights (which contained a compass, two flares and a signal mirror).

I would like to say that I found trails that went roughly 250 degrees, but I didn't. In fact I hadn't found a single trail, 250 degrees or otherwise. All I could do was pick a route that appeared to go through the least foreboding brush and adhere to a generally southwest bearing (that would take me to central Laos, and maybe some friendlies). Today, trying to stay on a course of 250 degrees was made impossible by bamboo thickets and swamps (without clean water). Late that afternoon I lucked out, the ground to my right was wet, and venturing further—became muddy, and then a big puddle (maybe an underground spring). It was still dirty so I had to hold each handful for thirty seconds until the sediment had sunk to the bottom, and then suck water from the top. Took a long time. I knew I would be lucky to find anything edible growing wild so was grateful when about noon I came upon a bush loaded with green berries. I plopped myself down alongside it and ate a ton of 'em (hoping they weren't toxic). Better energized I walked until dark. That evening I found a fallen tree with its center rotted out. After checking it for snakes or other vermin, I put in as many leaves as I could gather up, hoping to get my best night's sleep yet (which I wouldn't).

Never Thought of This

I was awakened sometime in the middle of the night by fearfully loud explosions and a violent trembling of the ground (and the log I was lying in). The retorts were coming just about every second were not only deafeningly loud, but a second or two later were accompanied by concussive waves that sucked the air out of my lungs. It lasted at least five minutes. Knew for sure what it was: another of our couple-times-a-week B-52 bombing raids (of this neutral country). As close as it sounded, it probably was five miles way. When we stayed overnight at Long Chien we often could hear them; three B-52's in formation, each with over one-hundred 750-pound bombs. I'm sure the Pentagon *thought* they had enemy positions, but to me the program could easily be called reckless, random "carpet bombing" of barely inhabited wilderness. When we flew over the areas of the previous night's "Rolling Thunder" bombings, the destruction was such that the ground was 75 % tan— *new dirt craters,* and only 25% green—*remaining jungle.* The bombings had annihilated many a small village like this, and the inhabitants were *not* keen on Americans. (Having been in one of these bombings may have been why that hamlet chief wanted to buy me.) One time the Air Force dropped cluster bombs on Long Chien, resulting in a case officer named Shep Johnson having most his left buttock blown off. (After that, the big joke was saying Shep was doing a "half-assed" job.)

Day Three

I was unsure of my position and not making good time; couldn't believe there was this much geography without any people. As serious as my situation was now and as discouraging as it was, I couldn't help but shiver with relief, when I speculated on *where I might have been right now.* And boy was I dirty. I'd walked through deep mud a dozen times. Also woke up last night when something bit me on my calf; jumped up and in the dark shook whatever it was out of my pants leg (or at least hoped I did). I was almost afraid to slide my hand up through the cuff and feel the area of the bite. In the morning I examined my calf which was one huge red lump, hot to the touch and hurt. Not very glamorous to relate, but I spent most of this day with the "runs." The berries may not have been toxic, but diarrhea hit me full force. I knew that would dehydrate me and I'd have to find water again soon. Still hadn't seen or heard another human being, which I guess was good.

Mostly Just Plodding Along

The next day I started early, but between the trees the dense scrub brush I couldn't make good progress. I'd be surprised if I couldn't make a hundred yards before having to settle for a detour. Mid-morning I came upon a small drainage creek (three feet across at the widest) and found an area in it where the water ran over rocks and looked clear. Again, just cupped my hand and drank about a hundred handfuls. I speculated that if I came upon an open area without any trees, I could lay out a distress signal and just wait there to be spotted. Rest, and hope some Air America pilot flying overhead would see it (though since we never flew up into this area, it would have to be one from the SAR). But laying out a signal wouldn't happen, I had no contrasting man-made materials. Search pilots look for something that is geometrically shaped or arranged—not otherwise found in nature. (A 4x8 piece of white drywall cut into four big triangles would be just fine.) The only thing I had and would be way too small, was my white undershirt. In the whole trek south, I hadn't come across a single piece of paper or cloth. I spent the day just trudging along, shoes ruined, trouser legs torn, aching, hungry, and tired by noon.

Maybe There is a God

What's that? A strange sound. Holy Shit, a river! Gotta be flowing south. (A possible project: make a raft and float to some 'friendlies.') *Hah.* Even if I could have made a raft, on one I'd be a sitting duck; real easy to be seen and shot. Even if I just walked on the hard sand bank I could make twice as much progress as I'm making now. But then again, have a much better chance of being spotted. Then, while debating what this river might mean for me, *what's that?* I realized what I was hearing was voices and quickly dropped down in the brush. I didn't see anyone. *Wait.* On the other side of the river there were a couple huts. A small village! This far north it was probably frequently visited by NVA soldiers, and the villagers would hand me over (at the least). I just crouched in the high grass and watched.

And miracle of miracles, *I heard a generator!* That would mean this place was being visited by personnel from the U.S Agency for Int'l Development, and therefore should contain mostly friendly villagers. *God! Was I lucky!* Still, I hid in the wooded area a while longer to be sure, observing the figures on the other side of the river. And then I saw an American! And I knew him! He was a longtime USAID volunteer named Pop Buell; an Indiana farmer who had been travelling all over Laos for the last 15 years—often to villages this far north, where he instructed the inhabitants how to better cultivate their land and plant and grow pest-free, nutritious crops. He was known and respected country-wide, even this far north, even by the inhabitants of "unfriendly villages." Unfortunately, before I could shout to him he disappeared back in the village. I ran down the bank to the river's edge but was afraid to try to wade across; didn't know how deep it was and the current was fast. I hollered and waved, gaining the ears of some villagers. They in turn started shouting back towards where Pop had disappeared. In a few minutes he was in view again, *waving at me!* He launched two guys in a small boat. Good thing I didn't try to swim, the guys in the boat kept the bow pointing 45 degrees to the north—upstream, against the current, getting to my location by riding a rapid drift downstream.

Pop Buell recognized me from the many times I had flown him to other remote locations, but he was not aware of my being the object of a Search and Rescue mission. He radioed back that I was there okay. A joyous night was had by all. The next day I found out this was the Nam Ou river—a major river in Laos, and that if I had continued to follow it south, in three more days, I would have arrived at the bustling city of Luang Prabang, the cultural and religious capital of Laos, frequented daily by Air America planes. I was bought back to Vientiane early the next morning, greeted well, and had—to this day, the best meal I've ever eaten: creamed beef on toast and a tall glass of tomato juice with a lemon in it! I was badgered to tell my story many times. And I didn't get home till late afternoon, where I sat in thought. It was sort of a wake-up call for me. *What affect would my death have on Sara and the kids?*

Chapter Forty-Five
KICKED OUT, BLACK OPS, AND A GOOD-BYE

The Move Across the River

After ten years of operating "in-country" covertly, Air America's tenure in Laos came to an end. In 1973 the communist elements in the Laotian government took over and we were immediately declared "persona non grata," meaning we had one week to get all our personnel and equipment out of Laos! The plan for operations (which would not cease immediately) was to relocate the whole Vientiane setup across the river into Thailand—to our sister station, the joint Thai/US Udorn air base. With no warning, this move had a negative impact on every employee; no way to transport even half our belongings; lose a year's advance rent, and for me, I didn't have time to find a buyer for my baby blue Fiat convertible so had to abandon it. Danielle was still living with me and this sudden expulsion was a problem (or an opportunity) since she had no Thai visa. In spite of its singular saving grace our coexistence had been so rocky I toyed with using this event as being a justifiable reason (excuse) for us to make the big break. But I failed to capitalize on it, I let her get a Thai visa and she accompanied me. Missed a big chance that would only delay an uncomfortable later experience.

Becoming a "Project Pilot"

The CIA was conducting a number of "Black Ops" operations, not just in northern Laos but actually *into* North Vietnam. Pilots involved in this type of hazardous work were called "Special Project" pilots. Shortly after my arrival in Udorn there was a vacancy for another Project pilot. I was humbled to hear I had been nominated by the pilots already in the program and approved by the head CIA guy himself—Buddy Rogers, who was willing to take a gamble on a guy he knew nothing about (for which I will always be indebted).

Air America pilots enjoyed a lofty regard, but as a Project pilot one had an even more elevated status (unfortunately—as well as the heightened danger). The present covert mission would be a 3 a.m. landing on a dike 13 miles outside of Hanoi, *tapping the phone lines to get strategic information.* Now, here in Thailand, instead of the couple dozen daily trips I used to make from Long Chien each day, now I was flying only at night— practicing landing, deep in the woods, on a 400-foot-long, 15-foot-wide dike, *without* using my landing lights until I was below 50 feet! I had to find the strip and make the landing using my newly issued (but outdated) night vision goggles. (They're amazing, but no substitute for daylight!)

During training—making those approaches, skimming the treetops, hitting and careening down the narrow, rutted landing area, scared me to death. I can't believe my wobbly control of the aircraft, last-second corrections, and to me—barely acceptable landings, weren't seen as such by the senior project pilots. As far as I was concerned, I wasn't up to the task. Usually riding in the right seat and evaluating my performance was the senior Project pilot, Pete Parker (who had been Wernher Von Braun's private pilot, and at 25 years of age piloted a B-26 in the Bay of Pigs Cuban invasion). Not on even one landing did I feel as if I had proper control of the aircraft!

My First Black Ops Mission

We finally got the go-ahead for the mission, and though I cannot think of any reason they would have chosen me, I was scheduled for it. I was going with Pete (a pilot's pilot, like Jim Ryan—the "best of the best"). I assumed I'd just ride in the copilot seat. We had no maps for the terrain once inside North Vietnam, and even if there were, since it would be pitch black, we couldn't use them. *So how did we navigate there?* Installed in the aircraft was something called "Terrain Avoidance Radar." It was there for us to study the "ground return" on the scope and keep ourselves centered in the valleys that led to Hanoi. The goal was to make this whole trip not higher than 50 feet above the rocks or treetops. Interpreting the returns on the scope and choosing the proper headings was an art—a real scary art, because without immediate interpretation of what you were seeing on the radar scope, and a quick turn, you could easily fly into suddenly rising terrain (which more than one Air America pilot had done).

About one in the morning Pete and I were driven to the ramp where we met our two Thai mercenaries. These two guys had been selected after a dozen of them with gaff-hooks strapped to their ankles, competed to see who could dig them in and get up a simulated telephone pole the quickest (where they would then do their handiwork on the crossbars). At the aircraft I got a real surprise: *Pete was going to ride in the right seat and let me pilot the aircraft*. But I guess that made sense, since the biggest danger was flying into the side of a hill, Pete may have concluded the safest thing he could do was not be occupied controlling the aircraft but rather sit in the right seat interpreting the ground radar returns and giving me headings to fly to keep us from impacting rising terrain.

We were airborne at one-thirty and headed north. The first hour and a half was no problem. Approaching the North Vietnamese border we started paying particular attention to the "Holy Shit" gauge. Oh, I hadn't mentioned that gauge yet. The anti-aircraft weapon we feared the most was the SAM-7 missile, which could be carried by a single individual. It had an infra-red homing device in its nose, and not only traveled in excess of the speed of sound but could make sharper turns than the aircraft! While it was in "Search" mode and hadn't locked onto us, our gauge was blank and quiet. As soon as the missile system locked onto us, a beeping tone would begin. When the missile was actually fired, the beeping tone would change to a shrill, steady tone, and your fate was just about sealed. That's why it was called the "Holy Shit" gauge.

How did we navigate the last five miles to the dike? We used what we called the "Skippy Peanut Butter" jar system. Earlier in the day of our arrival an empty peanut butter jar with a small radio beacon inside it, was dropped from a small, specially sound-attenuated helicopter—hopefully hitting right on the dike. Upon hitting the ground the jar shatters, allowing the beacon inside it to be freed, and its spring-loaded lever (like on a grenade) pops open and activates the beacon (for us to home in that night). It was a low-powered beacon with a battery life of only 24 hours (so the North Vietnamese would have less chance of picking it up). Today they must have missed the dike, since when I over-headed the beacon, even with my night-vision goggles, we weren't near any dike.

I didn't want to but had to climb to a hundred feet of altitude to visually spot the dike. Great. Spotted it. I flew ten seconds west, made a quick 180-degree turn, and started in for the landing, heading due east— the dike orientation. And like in practice—with the aircraft landing lights out. Reduced the power and began my descent. Whoa, can't pick out the end. Think that's it. It is! Bank left! Line up! This should do it! Was going through 50 feet above the ground; night vision goggles off and landing lights on! Hit hard, but centered on the dike and not too far down it. Threw the engines into full reverse! Couldn't see anything left or right, just kept the nose pointed directly down the center of the dike (don't want to go over the side and into the canal). Suddenly the end of the dike was right in front of me. Full pressure on the brakes! Skidding! But mercifully, got it stopped (without going off the end). Landing lights off.

The Thai guys jumped out with their gear and the gaff-hooks already strapped to their ankles. I looked down at the narrow width of the patch of raised ground I was on. It was going to be real tight turning the aircraft around to point it back for takeoff, in fact *maybe not possible!* One wheel might go over the side, and then we'd be stuck here and captured for sure! Pete knew what I was thinking and jumped out. He shined his flashlight on the edge of the raised dike and motioned me to continue my turn, with full left brake (and a bit of reverse on the left engine to back that wheel up). Thank God for small miracles: the right wheel stayed clear of the edge. We were pointed back down the dike—ready for takeoff. While waiting—in spite of the noise I left the engine running, since we might have to make a hurried departure. Pete joined me in the cockpit. (One hundred yards away there was a road paralleling the dike with a passing car every thirty seconds!)

I didn't know how long it would take our guys to accomplish what they had to do: first—get up the pole; second—unscrew the ceramic insulators on the cross-bar that supported the wires; third—when the cross bar was clean, overlay it with a solar strip (to power what we were about to install); fourth—screw the ceramic insulators back in, including one bogus insulator that was actually a tap, *that would transmit the telephone conversations carried on this line.* These transmitting insulators only sent out a narrow signal, and the Thai guys would position it so the signal went southwesterly (so it wouldn't be picked up to the northeast—in Hanoi).

The power of these insulator/transmitters was so weak the signal only went out about thirty miles, so we were going to have to place another receiver/transmitter in the top of a tree, every 30 miles for 150 miles—to get it to a final listening post. These re-transmitters were ten-foot-wide artificial treetops: a network of thousands of metal leaves. The experts in the home office at Langley told us which precise, exact, tree to drop this re-transmitter over, (You can imagine as hard as it was to find one tree amongst a thousand, and at night, we just draped it over any tree in the area.) 30 miles south of the last re-transmitter—in a shack in a safe area, we had captured NVA soldiers in headsets, listening 24/7. Each time they heard a high-level conversation they would record and translate it. The English translation was coded and sent to the Joint US Military Advisory

Group in Bangkok, who immediately sent it to Henry Kissinger in France, at the "Paris Peace Talks."

I sat there a bundle of nerves, imagining persons in nearby neighborhoods hearing the engine, and coming to investigate. (I was just outside a suburb thirteen miles from city center!) *Please God, give us another five minutes.* It was less than that when I heard the Thai guys jumping back into the airplane. They hollered that it was done and we could leave. I jammed the power levers forward and we were accelerating down the dike. Shortly after takeoff one of the Thai guys comes up to the cockpit, apparently well satisfied with his work. We asked him how it went. He said, no problem, except his gaff-hooks weren't much help, *the telephone pole was concrete!*

Udorn Just Before Dawn

Back in Udorn, having just parked on the ramp, as Pete was exiting the right-side cockpit door (about eight feet up), his foot slipped off the exterior step and he began falling backward. Instinctively he reached up to grab something to arrest his fall and got the sill of the door opening. This abrupt stop snapped his head back. When I got around to that side of the airplane Pete said he was okay but was turning his head from side to side (indicating to me he wasn't really sure about his neck). We attended a short debriefing and then went to the Air America cafeteria, feeling euphoric at having successfully completed our mission and being back—safe! The cafeteria had stayed open just for us (as well as Pete's wife "Smiles" and Jim Ryan).

I could see something was bothering Pete. He was only taking an occasional bite. He soon stopped eating altogether and leaned back in his chair, silent. After a minute he said "God, I feel terrible." With that he pushed back his chair, stood up (but not steadily) and then just laid down on the floor. For him (or anyone) to do that, it was obvious something was bad wrong. We called the Udorn Air Base hospital and in five minutes an ambulance arrived. The next morning Pete was flown to the Stanford University Medical Center in California. Not sure they would have done that for any of us, since most of us were just "contract" employees with the Agency (big bucks but no government sponsorship or retirement) whereas Pete was actual CIA. He was gone three months getting treatment for varying stages of lower body paralysis. When he returned he had no paralysis, but had no feeling in his right leg. He wouldn't know it if you held a lit cigarette against his leg. He was obviously off the flight schedule.

Perhaps the Most Beautiful Words a Husband Ever Said

After he was back in Udorn recuperating I would often stop over to check on him. One afternoon, approaching his house on the incoming stone walk and just before passing the open window (which I knew was right over Pete's couch) I heard Pete talking to one of his sons. He had four boys— no girls. He had no idea anyone was coming. Evidently one of the boys was pulling that famous ploy of playing something the father said, against something the mother said. Approaching the open window, from inside I heard Pete's voice: *"Danny, I was in love with your mother long before you came along, and I'm going to be in love with her long after you're gone, so don't ever try to come between me and my wife again."* (How many wives would be thrilled to hear their husband make a statement like that!) For me to be nostalgic for a moment, Pete died of esophagus cancer not long ago, and his beautiful smiling wife is in an assisted living home with dementia. I still see Danny from time to time.

Finally, Making the Big Decision

May of '74. I did several more Black Ops trips, but I and the others knew we'd lost the war in Vietnam, and even operating out of Udorn, conducting operations in Laos was all but over. The NVA forces were driving the lesser trained and armed Hmong soldiers backward ten miles a day. I feared it could only be a matter of months before Air America shut down. Should I struggle along to the bitter end or just quit now? I'd spent nine and a half years in Southeast Asia. I was going to have to go back to the states (or somewhere) sometime. Of course I had no idea what I'd do (especially with a one-eyed pilot's license). Still, the glow was sufficiently off the operation that I made the decision to quit *but cannot adequately relay the array of confused thoughts and strange emotions that plagued me after this parting decision.*

Danielle Now, and That Yet Not-Met Woman

As I said before, two people could hardly have been less like-minded than Danielle and me. The sole benefaction—sustaining the relationship was the merciful relief I found in being able to at least consummate the act with her. That was enough to confirm my thoughts about that chemistry thing: *Danielle had some of it, and that one woman who had it all, was still out there waiting for me to find her!* But stuck in this relationship I would not have the opportunity to find her. I tried to make the break when we were kicked out of Laos but didn't. Now quitting Air America was another chance, but I still wasn't able to do it—at least not "cold turkey." But I did have a cowardly plan to bring it about. Danielle was returning to Paris, where I told her I'd meet her in June. She accepted this, knowing I had an appointment with Barraquer then, and would be flying through Paris on my way to Barcelona. She gave me her brother's phone number and told me to call him when I arrived. Although, while relaying these plans aloud, *in my heart I knew there was every chance this Paris meetup would not come about.* Danielle and I made the trip to Bangkok. No promises or more definitive plans. After a couple days there I waved her goodbye as she boarded the Air France flight to Paris. A few days later, back up in Udorn the guys threw a really great party for me. The next day I was no longer an Air America pilot, and off for the States.

Chapter Forty-Six
BACK IN THE USA AND ELSEWHERE

Going to Need a Job and Soon

Won't tell you how little money I had saved after nine years with Air America. For this reason and with no idea where I would find work and locate, I initially bedded down in my folks' guest room in Fort Myers on the west coast of Florida. Staying there made it easy to accomplish the first thing: reunions with the kids. (Just a three-hour drive across the state.) It seemed each of them had some sporting device, article of clothing or other need that I was more than glad to purchase for them. And Sara was friendly and more than accommodating. She even introduced me to her Air Force Major; a really nice guy. The kids and I again went just about everywhere Florida had to offer: Disneyworld, Busch Gardens, Sea World, and one Rock concert. When not on a special event we were on the beach.

As far as my job search, besides my one-eyed license I was too old for everyone's first choice: the airlines. And another problem: I had been out of the states so long I had no contacts with anyone in stateside aviation. No chance for networking. I designed the best résumé I could (having flown uncommon aircraft) and sent out a bunch of them. I even took out "Position Wanted" ads in *Trade-A-Plane* and *Flying* magazine. But there was a deep recession in 1974. No flight departments were hiring (in fact there were layoffs). My résumés garnered a handful of offers, but they were not desirable: ones to fly old and poorly maintained aircraft, out of rusted hangars on rundown airports in rundown cities with brutal winters—for almost no pay. (Made it clear to me why aircraft from these organizations are always crashing; only the least-experienced pilots would accept positions there.)

An Old Friend Comes to the Rescue

After almost two months with no luck, I was contacted by Mr. Earl Richman who had been a VP with Air America and was familiar with my reputation. He was managing an aviation operation at the old Stewart Air Force Base in Newburg, NY, and offered me the position of Director of Operations at his company. Earl said Stewart—only sixty miles north of the Big Apple, would soon be designated the alternate for aircraft that couldn't get into LaGuardia or JFK. By all rights this would guarantee a bright future for his operation. The pay was okay and it was a reasonably respected position, but the idea of working a thousand miles from my kids and in knee-deep snow was *not* my first choice. Plus, his company operated small, puddle-jumper aircraft that I had little experience in.

Leaving Florida, I stalled as long as I could alongside my loaded Mustang and U-Haul trailer, before waving goodbye to the folks and starting on the two-day trip. I had no conviction that this was the right move but made the trip. Upon arriving Earl was thrilled to see me and could not have been more obliging. He came from a blue-blooded family. (In his hallway was a photo of him sitting in a chair with his father and grandfather standing behind him—all three in their Yale sweaters.) Earl said his new company—Banner Flight, was growing fast. However I didn't know how. It was apparent the recession had hit hard here (the Ford dealer had closed or at least moved). Going to the local Kmart I was shocked to see all the rusted, banged up cars in the parking lot, and the unkempt, slovenly dressed shoppers inside (compared to what I had seen on the Haufbahnstrasse in Zurich). And again—to me, Earl's company appeared to be, at best just making it.

I struggled in the job, never being able to come up with significant revenue-producing ideas. Fortunately, I appeared to be the only one worried. The existing chief pilot was a solid, 100% guy—Stu Carlton. He kept me out of trouble more than once, and as you'll read later, continued to look out for me years later. One day I told him that we had become such good friends, I would venture to make a suggestion: "When someone asks you a question, you put your fist up to your mouth and clear your throat before answering. Anyone seeing this would recognize that you were just stalling to assemble your thoughts."

He responded that since we were such good friends, he'd share something with me: Had I ever noticed, that just before I began to talk to someone, including our secretary, I would put a hand in my pocket, find the elastic in my jockey shorts, pull it away from my leg, and jiggle my hips to let my balls hang free.

Earl scheduled weekly departmental meetings during which the marketing guys got their chance to make exciting pitches about huge contracts that were coming—not just in New York, but across the country (including leasing California helicopters with earth-penetrating sonar, to discover underground oil reserves). I listened but didn't understand how it was all going to come about. I left each meeting feeling I wasn't even qualified to be attending it. I just had no business acumen. Nothing seemed to be adding up. After two more meetings of glad-handing and high-fives, I concluded I just wasn't cut out to understand the business world. The following month Earl announced we were declaring bankruptcy and shutting down the operation.

Sometimes You Have to Consider Every Offer

The owner of a small company in Wichita, Kansas sent me tickets to fly out for an interview. I did. His company had contracts with Beechcraft, a Wichita aircraft manufacturer who made a fast, small, single-engine plane (often purchased by doctors and lawyers) called the Bonanza. Beechcraft had just secured a contract with the Iranian government to modify them into planes that could fire rockets and drop bombs, and deliver them to the Iranian Air Force. (This purchase was back when the Shah was in charge, and just doing whatever our corporations wanted.) If I hired on I might have to move to Wichita. To enhance its appeal the owner planned a barbeque at his house that night, so we stopped to buy a couple steaks. While walking through the store, Dave—in attempting to point out the good things about Wichita, was actually stumped. By chance, in the next aisle we bumped into his business partner. Dave tells *him* to tell me what's good about Wichita. The partner thinks for longer than necessary then responds, "Well there's not much bad about Wichita."

A Little Bit About My New Job

If you needed any further indication as to how little I consider the details and consequences of what I am about to do, I agreed to hire on, *to fly single-engine, slow, propeller-driven aircraft, alone, sitting on an aluminum gas tank instead of a seat—for ten hours across the icy Atlantic.* And it didn't matter if it was icy or not, it's a big ocean and you'd never be found. (If the water *was* icy, you'd die of exposure in fifteen minutes.) First I had to go to Moncton, Ontario, where the Canadian Civil Aviation Authority made me watch videos of Canadian Air Force pilots bailing out into the Saint Lawrence Seaway, and freezing to death in the first minute. The CCAA doesn't allow any pilot to fly a single-engine aircraft from their country, across the Atlantic, until he had attended this seminar and passed a written test. (I later discovered that I was one of only nine pilots that had been approved.)

My first trip: Picked up my plane at the factory (painted a camouflage design) and flew it to Gander, Newfoundland. After a restless night, I got up at three a.m. and by five, was airborne heading east to Shannon, Ireland, across the soon to be sun-streaked glassy Atlantic. What made this trip even more difficult was these aircraft did not have any navigational aids. Airborne out of Gander I would just "aim" at Shannon, and hope that for the next 1,702 miles the winds would be as predicted; that I wouldn't drift too far, and would be able to orient myself when the west coast of Ireland came into view—a lot of if's. (Some guys missed Ireland altogether, arriving at the Scottish coast to the north or the southwest tip of England to the south.)

After arriving in Europe the rest of the trip to Iran took me over a southerly route, which had me passing over the northern edge of Syria (violating their airspace). As small as the plane was, I was surprised their radar picked me up. Doing so Air Traffic Control demands my "Overflight Permit Number," and says if I don't have one, *they're going to launch fighters and shoot me down!* I didn't have one, but spouted out a series of made-up numbers for them to look for, repeatedly insisting they had to be able to find it, because that was the one I was issued. My hope was—and it happened, I was able to exit their airspace before they realized I was bull-shitting them. This kind of thinking and my arrival in record time impressed Dave and his partners, and from now on I would be leading two other guys over each time.

An Embarrassing Anecdote

After the ten-hour crossing of the Atlantic to Ireland, and then to Le Bourget, France, we now had a short five-hour leg to Malta, but still one that could exceed our bladder capability. I couldn't find an empty jug but assumed I'd have no problem holding it for a flight of only five hours. Crossing the south coast of France and venturing out over the pitch-black nighttime Mediterranean Sea, my teeth started tickling. I bore it for as long as humanly possible, but it got so bad I feared internal damage and knew I was going to have to relieve myself. *But into what? My flashlight!* I screwed off the lens end and dumped the batteries out. Being seated, I wouldn't be able to angle the flashlight down enough to keep the pee from running back out. I would somehow have to raise myself enough to allow me to angle the flashlight down.

I stood up until my head hit the ceiling, then bent over 90 degrees at the waist, which allowed me to raise my hips a bit. However to do this required that I wedge my head forward across the top of the instrument panel—all the way to the windshield, *in which case I couldn't see the instruments or manipulate the controls!*

I knew I had to avoid over-filling the flashlight. I'd have to stop before the pee rose to the level of the opening. Since I couldn't see the flashlight, I held it with my index finger a half inch down inside the opening. As soon as I felt the warm liquid hit my finger I would stop peeing. I peed, and peed, and peed some more. There were tears in my eyes and warm shivers went through me. I continued, a*nd the good news was the tip of my index finger was staying dry!* In fact I was able to complete the whole urination, or so I thought. That was before I realized the screw in the other end of the flashlight was missing, and my pee was running right through the screw hole and puddling on the seat I would have to sit in the rest of the trip!

A UFO Encounter (or Inexplicable Airborne Sighting) Over the Caspian Sea

The last leg—from Ankara to Teheran, was usually flown from midnight to just about dawn. On this leg we had to climb to 13,500 feet to clear the high mountains in eastern Turkey. Pilots are not allowed to fly above 10,000 feet without oxygen, and we didn't have oxygen in these airplanes, so we had to be on guard that we weren't succumbing to hypoxia, which at the least makes you slow-witted if not pass out completely! It was about 2 a.m. We were north of Syria and south of the old Soviet state of Georgia. The Caspian Sea would be coming up off our left wing in just a few minutes. When it did, we would then be able the make our right turn southeast, and soon cross the Iranian border towards Teheran.

We were not being monitored by any air traffic control; absolutely alone, droning eastward in the pitch-black night. Even listening to the airline "gossip" frequency (VHF 123.45) for the last couple hours we hadn't heard a single wise crack. Just three straight hours of eerie silence. Our only friends were the stars. And then it happened: crossing over southern Armenia I glanced to the north, and saw what seemed like—about a yard outside of my left wingtip, *a luminescent lime green golf ball!* This was sufficiently incredulous that I was afraid the lack of oxygen was getting to me. Then I thought it might be a reflection of the cockpit lighting. I turned all the aircraft lights out. No luck, still there. Hard as I tried I couldn't tell if it was something the size of a golf ball a couple yards off my wingtip, or something the size of a beach ball fifty feet off my wing. I strained to determine the distance. (It could even have been something fifty miles away and a thousand feet across!) As hard as I was trying, I just couldn't tell. Just then (and making me feel a lot better) the pilot flying the second airplane, keyed the mike and said, "Is anybody seeing what I'm seeing?" At least I wasn't going crazy.

In five minutes my golf ball had turned into a beach ball. In ten minutes it was twenty feet across, and in fifteen minutes it had increased so much in size, that it occupied a third of the northern sky! I considered that it might be a cloud from a nuclear explosion in Russia, but that would be gaseous, and being gaseous the differing atmospheric pressure would misshape it. But this ball was perfectly round—like a dinner plate. We were never sure if it was something at a fixed distance growing in size, or worse—something of a fixed size rushing at us, making it appear to grow larger! *Maybe it was another planet on a collision course with us. The end of our earth!* We were jointly becoming more concerned. And sufficiently so that the pilot flying the third plane turned right—to the south, added full power and attempted to outrun it. When Eddie and I called him back he didn't even answer. As the ball had increased so dramatically in size, it lost some of its brightness (whatever that would indicate). A few minutes later it suddenly disappeared. It didn't shrink or sink or fade, it just did away with itself. Zap!

Planes Delivered, Back to the States, and No More Deliveries
We landed at Teheran about dawn, gathered up the life rafts and vests, and hailed a cab to town. At this time in the morning there was not a hotel in town with a vacant room. While waiting we tried to find an English language paper that might have an article on what we had seen. As big and bright as it was, it should have been seen by tens of thousands of people on the ground. However, looking for two days we could find no reports of what we had seen. Never got a room; slept both nights on the floor in a hotel's unused banquet room (with all our junk). The commercial flight back was uneventful.

A week later at my folks' house I got word that Dave's company was no more—finished! A group of investors sued him, claiming Dave was rifling through the profits to enhance his lifestyle. (And from what I had observed—the Porsche and private club memberships, could well be true.) So here I was again, back in search of a sufficiently revenue-producing, and hopefully more orthodox aviation position. Especially one that might have a future, and my real hope: a retirement!

Chapter Forty-Seven
STUNNED LIKE NEVER BEFORE

The World is NOT the Same and Never Will Be

I had been resting up at my folks' house for a little over a week, at a loss for what work I would find next, when a letter arrived from Angie, June's sister in the UK. It produced the greatest confoundment and disbelief I had yet experienced in my life—causing me to stagger backward to a chair and with the help of its arms, lower myself into it. It was the most unexpected, unjust and unfathomable thing I had ever been apprised of: For unknown reasons June suddenly became so weak she was hospitalized, but they could come up with no diagnosis as to what had beset her. *She seemed to be gaining strength but died in her sleep the fourth night.* My June. Good, brave June. The only person I had ever met who had the world right and was without fault. The only woman I may have been able to at least say I loved. My head was in my hands except for the times I would slide them away and reread Angie's words. I would have given anything—*anything,* to have been at her bedside.

Gratefully, the letter got to the states in four days and left me time: Her Celebration of Life was not going to be for a week. I phoned Angie and asked her. She said yes. I flew to England and attended the service—which June herself had written some years ago. The service included a letter of joy and satisfaction from June, read by her sister. Throughout the service, songs from hit Broadway musicals continued to play, ending with "The Show Must Go On." In attendance were many of the dancers that I knew from Spain, who had also flown in from all over the world. I wept as her coffin withdrew through the curtains, and I was pretty sure neither I nor the world would ever be the same; without this other person moving about somewhere—anywhere.

Chapter Forty-Eight
HALFWAY AROUND THE WORLD

Another Temporary Job

I told you about an Air America pilot who had landed at a strip in Laos, not knowing the North Vietnamese had overrun it the night before; was captured and marched to the "Hanoi Hilton" where he was imprisoned for 7 years with John McCain. Well I get a call from him! His Washington State company had just gotten a contract with the Organisation Mondiale de Sante (the WHO). For it they needed an aircraft with the best slow flight capabilities, so they bought an Air America Porter now owned by the Thai police. Now they needed a Porter pilot with transcontinental experience and who spoke French, to deliver it. Ernie offers me the job: fly commercially to Bangkok, pick up the Porter, and fly it to the city of Ouagadougou in the French colony of Haute Volta in West Africa. In view of the challenges this would entail (transiting a host of primitive third-world countries and a low-level crossing of the Sahara) I asked him to give me a week to think it over.

President Trump referred to some African countries as "shithole" countries and received a lot of criticism. But my experiences had also led me to believe the most dangerous and corrupt countries of any continent were in Africa. Your safety is not guaranteed more than a hundred yards from a five-star hotel. And, with no auxiliary gas tank, the Porter would be limited to 800 miles, meaning I'd have to make many refueling stops. The route would overfly Thailand, Burma (now Myanmar), East Pakistan (now Bangladesh), India, West Pakistan (now just Pakistan), Iran, Saudi Arabia, the Red Sea, Sudan, Chad, and Niger, before arriving in Haute Volta (now Burkina Faso). That's a lot of countries for something to go wrong in, and with no U.S. government sponsorship. When Ernie called a week later, I responded I'd do it (but with a marked lack of enthusiasm). Since bribes and credit card refusals were the "fait du jour" in those countries I told him how much cash I would need to start the delivery. I ordered all the maps and aviation info I'd need for a trip a third of the way around the globe.

Arriving in Bangkok, the Thai police representative acted like he wasn't sure I was qualified, and worse—like the Porter was still his. I was finally acknowledged as the new owner and released to commence my journey. Pilots nowadays don't get their own overflight permits; specialty companies take care of this. In the 70's the pilot had to do it on his own, and for international flights it required the use of a now forsaken communication method known as teletype. They were typewriter-like machines connected through international telephone lines, that when successful spit out a half-inch-wide, long ribbon of paper containing individual letters that spelled out the answer to your request. In third-world countries the teletype offices were often not manned, or when they were, the operators had extended cigarette breaks, coffee breaks, or prayer times, and often to save electricity—had *turned off* their teletype machines. The flaws in this procedure (especially in Africa) usually caused me to skip applying for approval and just make the flight in the middle of the night when there was no radar following, and only the most non-caring junior ramp workers met me at my landing site.

Rangoon, Burma

At 7 a.m. I launched for Rangoon (now Yangon), Burma (now Myanmar), with no flight plan, no overflight permits, and Burma not apprised of my arrival. The flight would be a little over 500 miles due north. When I had the Rangoon airport in sight I called for landing clearance but could not raise anyone on the radio. In no way did this aerodrome look like an international airport. There was only one runway and it had rows of grass sprouting up through the cracks between the concrete slabs, and herds of cattle were milling about in the high weeds alongside the runway. The terminal was a one-story building in major disrepair and apparently deserted. I taxied to the ramp in front of it and shut down. A single attendant came to the aircraft. I pulled off the gas cap, pointed inside the opening and showed him my Shell credit card. I then walked over to a nearby JP4 fuel truck and pointed to it. (The Porter had a *jet* engine, but also had a *propeller*, causing many refuelers to think it took the type of gas used by propeller aircraft. If that happened, all your tanks had to be drained.)

Next I had to hand in the Passenger Manifests (never mind I had no passengers), pay for the fuel, and file my flight plan to East Pakistan. The office to do this was in the top of the control tower. I had to take a none-too-sturdy, rusting bolts, exterior staircase up the outside of the building. Of the four large windows in the control tower, all but one had the glass completely broken out. Inside, the operator on duty was asleep in a cloth hammock strung between two opposing widow frames. Scratchy music was coming from a radio whose plastic case had long since departed, and whose antenna was now a bent hanger-wire. I waved the required form in front of him. He sleepily pointed at them, gave me a "thumbs-up," and appeared to doze off. I filled in all the blanks with at least some information, whether or not it applied or was accurate.

Done, I woke him and handed them to him. He took them but held up two fingers, which I assumed meant he needed another. I went through the process again, trying to repeat the same lies as on the first one. When finished I gave him the second one and a flight plan which normally requires a copy of the landing approval at the other end—which I didn't have *and he didn't ask for it.* The next step: give him about fifty dollars to call the proper authorities with my flight plan (which call I knew would not be made and was just as happy). Back in the aircraft and the fuel level visually checked, I started the engine and playing by the rules, called for taxi clearance. On the radio he tells me before he can release me, he needs one more copy of the passenger manifest. Let him try to stop me.

Calcutta, India

I could stay over land by flying up to East Pakistan (now Bangladesh), or fly directly across the Bay of Bengal to Calcutta (now Kolkata), India. The latter route would be about 80 miles further, but still just within the aircraft's fuel range. This would save me the hassle of customs and fueling in East Pakistan. (If I lose an engine I'll just drown quietly.) I did it; crossed the bay and landed in Calcutta. At the airport the workers were organized and spoke perfect English. Of course this made sense, India having been a British colony for over a hundred years. At 6 p.m. I grabbed a cab and told the driver to take me to a four-star hotel. On the way, mile after mile of cardboard tents—thousands of them, trash, garbage, waste ditches and impoverished destitution; emaciated figures as far as the eye could see. Arriving downtown, only two blocks from the hotel, we were still on an unpaved street, in deep, wet, rust-colored mud. I got a fourth-floor room and once high up and inside it, felt somewhat normal and safe.

In the morning, viewing the activity below, in the middle of that same nearby rust-colored mud street was a large cart being drawn be two white oxen, performing a shocking mission. The sidewalks on each side of this apparently busy commercial street, were wooden—a series of warped, sun-bleached boards. On them were rows (side by side) of lying, still-sleeping figures, wrapped in their native white swathing. Workers *were picking up the ones that had died during the night and throwing them into the oxcart.* I guess it was a morning hygienic ritual—just two blocks from a four-star hotel! Checking out I asked the concierge about what I had seen. He said, "Too bad you're in a hurry, or you could see the disposition of those whose family had more means." He went on to describe a huge steel-grilled 'hibachi pot' mounted on top of a 100-foot wide circular cement base. Onto it, family members placed the bodies of their deceased relatives. Carnivorous birds would then set about eating their fill—de-fleshing them, until all that remained were bones that fell through the grillwork to a pit below.

Somewhere Near Agra, India

Crossing India I'd have to find a midway refueling stop. I chose a rural airport near Agra, which my aerodrome book described as "reasonably" well-used. Upon arrival I saw no airport at all; not even a nearby town that might have one. After twenty minutes of circling over barren dirt acreage and scrub brush wasteland, I was able to make out what could be a dirt strip. I had no other choice but to land and hope. There was not a single building on the airport; not even a shack on or near it. A gathering of shabbily dressed onlookers were excited to see me—as if some anticipated cargo might be aboard my aircraft. I was in luck. I spied a giant Shell Oil billboard. A better dressed English-speaking individual arrived and offered assistance. I told him I was just stopping for gas and would be taking off as soon as I was refueled. After that was done (all of which I did myself), I was told I had to sign some forms and pay a landing fee.

The new arrival gestured me to join him in an old Land Rover. We bounced about a mile across flat fields without a single tree as far as the eye could see, to an unoccupied two-story house; the only structure in sight across the entire horizon. In his office was a safe containing the required forms and monies paid by previous pilots, but my new friend could not get it unlocked. He tried the combination a dozen times, becoming more apologetic and more frustrated with each try. *But couldn't I just leave the money with him?* A frantic shaking of his head indicated to me that my suggestions were unthinkable. I even tried to bribe him (which rarely fails). He held up his hand as if to stop the words coming out of my mouth. He made a phone call and the expression on his face gave me a glimmer of hope. It was more than an hour before the guy arrived with the proper combination, and it was four in the afternoon before I was able to take off.

Karachi, Pakistan

The next leg would be about 700 miles—six hours, to Karachi. I arrived there about 10 p.m. In so doing, I learned that Pakistan and India have had an adversarial relationship for centuries. Me arriving there from India was like going to a NY Yankee baseball game wearing a Boston Red Sox shirt. I was about to have my aircraft extra-thoroughly inspected for contraband. When you first fly into a country you have to declare what is in your cargo compartment. Because I had the audacity to come here from India, they wanted to see everything in the airplane—anywhere in the airplane! They declared that the oil inside the engine was being carried into their country and had to be inspected. *I actually had to drain all the oil out of the engine and show them!* Once this is done, that oil is not supposed to go back in the engine. But I was going to have to do so. I found a reasonably clean pail, something that would work as a funnel, scrubbed them both good and used them. I locked the plane and got a cab to town.

Dhahran, Saudi Arabia

Due to more forms and regulations, my departure to Dhahran was delayed till almost noon. This leg was over 800 miles and was going to be a stretch. Meteorology swore that I could expect a tailwind the whole way, which would make it "doable." The most memorable part of this leg was flying over the Gulf of Oman, just off the south coast of Iran. The Iranian topography inland from its southern coast displays the results of a perhaps catastrophic prehistoric event. I had never read of it, but now viewed it aghast: a hundred-mile-wide area of what looked like dried and hardened, weathered, dark gray molten lava, with bubbles and caverns. (If we ever wanted to fake a moon landing, this would be the place to do it!) It was completely absent of any type of any roads or structures; in fact any sign of life at all.

I landed in Dhahran which is more westernized than most places in Saudi Arabia. About a thousand American petroleum engineers employed by Aramco were living there. Since the Saudis didn't know I was coming, I was ready for a fair amount of mistreatment, which did ensue. Having been told to expect this in Saudi Arabia, I had been advised to bring something with me that would work miracles: a case of the stateside cookie product *Fig Newtons*. With this offering, I was able to smooth things over, get dinner (without alcohol) and lodging for the night.

Jeddah, Saudi Arabia

Was airborne early on the 750-mile leg to Jeddah—the large cosmopolitan city on the Saudi west coast, right on the Red Sea. Landing there wasn't a problem since I had already been stamped into the country. The only problem: they wouldn't let me take off until I had gotten a teletype approval for landing at my destination—Khartoum, Sudan; something that would take at least a couple hours. I decided to put the time to good use: *find my old Vientiane Air America boss—Jim Ryan.* I knew he was here in Jeddah on some project for the CIA. I asked every American I spied, describing Jim: over six foot tall, a crew cut, *and a wooden leg!* (Remember? His lower leg had been shot off in Laos when he was dropping leaflets to rescue one of my pilots.) The third guy I asked knew him and drew me a map to get to his apartment. I hailed a cab and sped there. Wrong address, but fortunately that guy *did* know where Jim lived, and drew me another map. Back in the cab and to the new address. Knocked on the door, and *Bingo!* I heard the clump, clump of someone with a prosthetic leg approaching the door. I was excited knowing how thrilled he would be that I took the trouble to look him up. The door swung open, and there was a six foot guy with a crew cut and an artificial leg, and it wasn't Jim! *There were two Americans with wooden legs flying in Jeddah!* (This guy did know Jim and directed me to the correct domicile. I went there and Jim and I had a short but good reunion.)

Khartoum, Sudan

It took all my Fig Newtons, but at 4 p.m. I was cleared to depart—across the Red Sea to Khartoum. Landed about 9 p.m. Went through all the rigmarole as other arrivals and got a cab to town. I told the driver to just take me any hotel. If we went to one, we went to ten; from four-star to no-stars; from main roads to less travelled roads; to lanes where the brush scraped each side of the car. *Nothing.* Then an idea evidently hit him and we went even further out of town into an even more remote area. I was beginning to worry for my own safety. We finally emerged into a clearing with a wide, three-story, old wooden-sided building (with nothing indicating what it might be). He stopped the car, jumped out and urged me to follow him up the steps. Since he led me to a registration counter, I guessed we'd finally found my lodgings for the night. He accepted his fare and left. Registration completed the attendant motioned me to follow him. He led me up to the second floor, and then—slowly walked the entire length of it. And what was more strange (by a lot), all the rooms were brightly lit and had glass-paned double-doors, so you could look right into them! And each time I did, I was not only looking directly at the bed, *but usually with one or two men sitting on it!* (I can only guess the object of my tour of the second floor.) We mounted the stairs at the far end and started down the third floor. Halfway down this third floor he gestured into an empty room, the glass doors wide open. I went in, closed them, locked them, and went to sleep (a restless, worried sleep).

Geneina, Sudan

Couldn't complete my next intended leg (to Fort Lamy in Chad) without another refueling stop in Sudan. And in sub-Sahara Africa there aren't many refueling locations. I chose El Geneina—a village on the western border of Sudan that supposedly had jet gas. Once again, with no electronic guidance I had to navigate by topographical symbols on my maps. I could have thrown them away and just clipped a brown paper bag to my leg. The whole way—as far as I could see, ahead, left or right, there was nothing but flat barren sand beneath me; no towns, no railroads, no rivers, not a single terrain feature worthy of being marked on a map; a 500 mile leg with no landmarks and unknown winds.

Uh Oh! Geneina didn't show up when my flight time was up. And this was serious, because I was low on fuel—*very* low. After twenty minutes of looking for it, I considered that it might be safer—while I still had fuel and an engine, to make a controlled, power-on landing in some flat area. At least I'd climb out of the aircraft alive. With the gauge on Empty (after performing a 1940's "square search") I found it and landed. Besides a herd of goats to meet me there was a group of tall natives with eight-foot spears, dressed in skins (and standing on one leg). The fuel was in 55-gallon drums and I had to use a hand pump and hose arrangement to refuel the aircraft. Since no one of any importance arrived at the strip, I was airborne again having filled out no forms or paying any fees.

Fort Lamy, the Original Headquarters of the French Foreign Legion!

I was excited about this next to last leg into Chad, to Fort Lamy; the original headquarters of the first French Foreign Legion! In 1973 Fort Lamy became N'Djamena, but still kept most its French population and all its flavor. At Fort Lamy I filled out the required paperwork, refueled the aircraft and hopped a cab to a hotel on the outskirts of town; a spreading two-story white wood building that I think was the only hotel utilized by European travelers. Even so, most the front lawn was covered by natives' blankets, displaying a wide assortment of handicrafts for sale, including a fake watch artfully carved out of a solid block of silver (that I could not resist buying).

Ouagadougou, Haute Volta—My Final Destination

Arrived at Ouagadougou about 5 p.m. Many chapters ago I described the ambiance and charming cosmopolitan nature of Vientiane in Southeast Asia—a truly French-provincial town (where you felt safe). Ouagadougou, while still a French colonial town was *not* of this ilk. Even more than the remote locations I had just transited, it oozed being isolated. It was a small enclave surrounded on all sides by a wall of ever-stretching dark wilderness. I sensed this small French community considered itself lucky to have thus far gotten by without a horrendous occurrence. There was an aura of mild apprehension even inside the white-linen dining room of the best hotel; a feeling that you were little more than prey to something lurking behind the tree line. The following day, after the WHO rep signed for the aircraft, I took a vintage and thread-bare African airliner to Dakar, Senegal, to wait for the once-a-week Pan Am flight back to New York (the only way to get back to the States from West Africa).

The Next Chapter! What You've Waited For!

Dear reader, thank you so much for having waded through all the foregoing, your kind patience will be finally rewarded as the next chapter unfolds....

Chapter Forty-Nine
DAKAR SENEGAL, AND EUREKA SHE EXISTS!

Arriving in Dakar

I checked into one of three surprisingly plush oceanfront hotels—perhaps recently built for the burgeoning French tourist business. Three days to enjoy it while awaiting the once-a-week flight to New York. Checking in, the lobby had been bustling with activity, so after showering and putting on a new outfit I decided to give it a roam-through before dinner. Viewing it a second time I had to admit, it *was* first class, still replete with French tourists checking brochures and discussing the next day's activities (with sufficient drama). Right next to this hotel was an even more impressive (and likely more expensive) lodging I had passed up. I wandered over to it and if I thought mine was first class this one was really top-of-the-line! Elegant furniture, tall figurine statues, polished marble floors, and immaculately uniformed and attentive bellmen. There was a display of artwork on a balcony above the foyer that I chose to view more closely.

Something (Someone) Special, Very Special

While in the balcony an impressive entourage entered the hotel, striding erect and quickly across the lobby; almost as if they were royalty. They were led by a tall honey-haired blonde in high heels and a floor length fur coat. I wasn't sure if she was a super-model or just a super-rich tourist, but either way, it was clear she was not accustomed to encountering the type of obstacles we mortals dealt with. Her hair was pulled straight back, tied in a ponytail that hung down to the small of her back and bounced with each strutting step. I realized it wasn't just me, no one could take their eyes off her. She wasn't cute or pretty like Debbie Reynolds, *she was sultry mean like Greta Garbo or Lauren Bacall.* Her eyes were steely-gray and fortunately she stayed looking straight ahead, because you knew it would not be comfortable to be caught in her razor gaze. She was closely followed by a well-dressed couple and one lone woman. Wow. Enough of subjecting myself to this belittling comparison, I'll return to my safe hotel and have dinner.

The Early Part of the Evening

After eating I took a stroll behind the hotel. There was a light breeze and the temperature was balmy perfect. You could easily feel good about yourself and the world on a night like this, and in a place like this, or maybe I was feeling good knowing I had successfully accomplished a not-easy mission and was on the way home. Just in case this would be the night that special woman would appear, I had put on an avant-garde pre-washed ("de-lave" in French) shirt and trousers I had bought in Athens (accented by a puka shell necklace Sean Flynn had given me). Hearing some high energy music coming from the beach, I headed that way. After rounding a large clump of tall kenkiliba bushes I spied the hotel's main draw for nighttime activity: a large thatch-roof-covered cement slab. In it were a bunch of guests dancing their booties off. Those not dancing were reclining on over-stuffed furniture located around the perimeter of the dance floor. Not feeling bold enough to just walk into the middle of all those laughing and chic French tourists, I made my way to a stool at an adjoining outdoor bar.

After one stiff drink I wagered I was as ready as ever to check out the crowd in the hut. Just inside the entryway—at the edge of the dance floor, sprawled on a large floral-print love seat was the imposing and privileged-looking group I had seen cross the lobby in the hotel next to mine (including the fearsome blonde). They of course were speaking French (in the same elevated, careless and superior manner so common among *la crème francais de la crème*). Being at best an average American with only a rudimentary French capability, it was a group I should not even consider approaching. But while in the midst of these thoughts, one of the women in the group—a thin brunette, pops up, comes over, grasps my hand and pulls me out onto the dance floor! It was a slow dance and she shocked me by immediately pressing the length of her body firmly against me. And more, her right hand above my collar—she was moving her fingertips across the back of my neck. I was startled at this likely purposeful intent to arouse me.

After the dance I unsurely escorted her back to the group, who did not take exceptional notice of us. Starting to leave I was surprised when my dance partner gestured for me to take a seat. At a loss for what else to do, I did. But *boy*, was I out of my element! While sitting there feigning to understand what was being said, the man to my left leaned over and whispered a few French words into my ear: After repetitions and laborious translation, I understood he was telling me the brunette I was dancing with was the wife of the guy sitting to my right! Then he added in French what I worked out to mean *the blonde was available.* Could such a thing be right!?

Mostly because I was afraid to make eye contact I had not yet looked her way. From this afternoon's procession I was sure she was the ranking member of the group; the one to whom homage was due. In observing her now I came to the same conclusions as this afternoon. A man—any man, desirous of approaching her would think twice before doing so. She was no kitten to be picked up and petted—not by a long shot! While her features: forehead, nose, mouth, jaw (and 30-inch-long ponytail) were perfection and hard to look away from, *her eyes were cold and filled with distrust.* It appeared the group had no objection to my lingering presence. While my months of bedtime French lessons had gotten me to where I could (given the time) write and read a phrase or two, when listening—the spoken word escaped me. I added just enough short responses to lead them to think I was understanding half of what they were talking about. While from time to time the others threw out an English expression, I gathered the blonde spoke no English at all, never having uttered a single word in English (or for that matter—in French).

The Evening Continues in an Unexpected Fashion

After about an hour (me listening to the music and all of them smoking), it was apparent they were leaving, and to my great surprise motioning me come along with them. Strolling as a group—when we got to the narrow walk I found myself walking alongside the blonde (keeping a safe distance). Her name was Mireille. We made our way back to their hotel and up to one of their rooms. There, after another hour of light-hearted conversation (of which at best I may have understood a quarter) and a couple snifters of brandy, I hazarded to believe the suspicion radiating from Mireille's eyes had softened, perhaps even to a mild trust—at least of those in this room. Throughout the evening and even here, she had barely added a word; her silence amplifying her mystique. And I was taken aback because when she did voice her thoughts they were in striking contrast to her stern appearance! *The words came out as if from an unsure and innocent pre-teen schoolgirl!* That frightened tone, so differing from her self-assured presence, had the effect of causing me to feel a new concern for her—to want to be protective of her and reassure her she need not be afraid. (What? *Me?* I must be crazy.)

During the whole time in the hotel room she just sat on the end of a bed, and I think or imagined, from time to time looking up at me; almost as if something (God knows what—perhaps being an American, or my humble ineptitude) had struck a vein of curiosity within her. A cautious trembling excitement overcame me. She and I were the only two unaccompanied people in the group. *Could it possibly be we might end the evening together?* (The guy did say she was available, whatever that might mean.) I could think of nothing further from reality than that scenario— she and I, which should it wondrously occur would be the most miraculous thing I'd ever been gifted with. But on the other hand, in view of my almost incessant failures, this particular attempt could also bring me the worst embarrassment and disappointment I would have ever suffered! No idea how I mustered the courage, but with respectful hesitancy somehow communicated to her I was open to us ending the evening together. It was all I could do to keep my balance when her response was a warm smile and a nod.

Please God, Just This Once!

The walk to my hotel was without conversation. Even if we spoke the same language I doubt in my state of mind I could have said anything meaningful. I was barely able to put one foot in front of the other. Into my hotel and into the elevator, where my heart was lifted when I saw an unearned but trusting smile on her face (that caused me to pray to the gods of lovemaking even more earnestly). *Please, even if never again, bestow me with what I will need.* Walking down the hallway I was already thinking of what excuses I could come up with. If I would not have had my jaws clamped shut, my teeth would have been chattering. I had never been more apprehensive, poised for what any man would have killed for. Into the room—still without speaking. On entering she glanced up at the fifteen-foot-high ceiling—which allowed the right half of the room to be an eight-foot-high loft with the bed and nightstands—arrived at by a ladder (as opposed to stairs). The room's left side faced the ocean, it's curtains from the still-open windows billowing in, with the sounds of the waves below. I used the bathroom first then climbed the ladder to the bedroom loft to await her arrival (feeling cold and trembling).

When her head appeared at the top of the steps she was—shockingly to me, still with that warm and trusting smile. I noted that while she would have been considered slender, she was supermodel thin. I raised the sheet offering her a place next to me. As soon as our bodies touched, *it happened*—like never before; an arousal that I had never dared to imagine; one that would be more than up to the task! In my life I had never been even remotely so endowed, so surprised, so gratified—this euphoric. In possession of this hardened tool, natural quests took over. I was taken aback at my own physicality. It rose to a ritual of passion that caused me to feel the possessor of this woman. In response she clung to me and kissed me with an almost desperate desire. Between the deepest exclamations of fulfillment I heard her breath coming in quicker and deeper gasps. I finally experienced something for the first time, the feeling of a woman taking her pleasure with me inside her. I now knew—after twenty years of deprivation, what every other man regularly experiences and never questions. It took the belief, and years of searching, but I finally had found *that* woman! When her movements slowed and then subsided, she forced me over onto my back and just lay atop me, arms around me, speaking to me (in French) with what I interpreted as being the most loving utterances, while her tears ran down my neck. *At last, my entire view of the world had changed; changed into one that allowed me to be a part of it, to at last talk and joke with other men as one of them!*

The Next Three Days

It wasn't over. It had just been the beginning. There was not a moment the following two days that she was not at my side, holding my hand with one (or both) of hers. I never looked at her that she was not looking into my eyes with the most loving and trusting expression (which just upon observing it provoked that same newly experienced heat and fullness). I was in a state of mystification and a never-before-experienced capability; now sure it *was* that chemistry thing I'd hung my hat on for twenty years. The day before my scheduled Pan Am flight, I got another gait-altering surprise: "*Je veux que tu viennes avec moi en France.*" My translation staggered me and I asked her to repeat herself. She did and my heart stopped; Mireille was asking me to return with her to France! Now at last with a *meaning* to my life; having never known the exhilaration and gratification—such pride and power. In spite of no idea about what the future would hold, I knew I would follow her to the ends of the earth—sacrifice anything, *and I agreed to cancel the New York flight and accompany her to France!*

Chapter Fifty
JULY '74 VIVE LA FRANCE

Dakar to Paris

The drive to the airport found me pretty much unable to voice anything; silent, numb—hardly able to believe what I was embarking upon. The effects of the last few days had eclipsed all else: my concern for my family, a possible flying job in the States; in fact any plausible future— *everything.* Since I had not yet been scheduled for another aircraft delivery, and with no idea what this stay in France would bring about, I did not make reservations for my flight back to the states. For sure this first trip would not be permanent, and if it evolved that to make it permanent, I would have to return and find work in her country, I was in big trouble. Although I suspected for her, finances were not an issue, I would at least need a token job. And speculating on the circles within which she traveled, it would have to be a respected professional position—next to impossible in France. My resume showed no more than three little-sought-after skills: fighter pilot, bush pilot, and transatlantic aircraft delivery pilot; no technical specialty or business experience (not to mention not speaking the language). Even if I could get a work visa, working in France was just about out of the question.

Glancing at Mireille's face afforded me momentary reassurance. Her eyes were still glued on me and fortunately seemed to indicate she had no doubt about having done the right thing. Awaiting our boarding call I couldn't avoid shaking my head in wonderment. This whole group *knew* what they were doing: going home! They were anxious and upbeat— nothing but smiles and idle conversation. Me? The boldest, riskiest thing I'd ever done, and with absolutely no plan. I had no idea how my accompanying her back to France would work out.

From Paris to an Historic Hamlet

We arrived in Paris about 3 p.m., picked up our luggage, walked to Jacque's car, and were soon on A6 bound for the Lyon airport (where Mireille had left her car when she flew to Paris to join the group). Jacques must have had a death wish: for the last 45 minutes the speedometer was locked on 160 km an hour, and our front bumper was just two meters behind the rear bumper of the car in front of us! Luckily that car's driver never felt it necessary to tap his brakes. It was a three-hour drive to Lyon. There, we found Mireille's BMW, transferred her luggage into it, and exchanged our goodbye hugs and kisses with Jacques and his wife.

In a matter of minutes Mireille and I were out of the parking area, and on our way. My nervousness was lessened a bit now being alone with her. It was an interesting drive, winding our way through tiny villages with streets of uneven pavers, and so narrow they all but excluded two-way traffic. We passed by century-old facades just a few yards away on each side; their parched stucco, brightly painted window shutters and flower boxes were the things of postcards. In the declining light, everything I was taking in—on all sides, was new and appealing to me. Through the last town and after fifteen minutes on a deserted unlit road, we came upon a scattering of small residences. As best I could translate Mireille was telling me we'd arrived in her town of St-Martin-du-lac. While she was speaking I heard the French words *maison, mere,* and *mes enfants* (all of which having been in my first few French lessons, were part of my limited vocabulary). I concluded that instead of going directly to her house, we were going to her parent's home, where likely her children were being watched by her parents. Up till now, other than knowing she was single, the nature of her previous marital status had not been explored, and I of course was very interested.

A Welcomed Evening

We arrived in a remarkably preserved village. She stopped in front of a small "mom and pop" hardware store and pointed above it to a second-floor balcony. I think indicating that was where her parents lived. I later learned they owned the building and the hardware store. I don't know what kind of residence I was anticipating but this was not what I would have expected. Her parents must have heard the car. Before we had a chance to ring they were coming out the side door with open arms and great enthusiasm. (Their welcoming of me caused me to conclude my arriving was not a surprise.) Inside the store in improved light I was surprised to see her father's eyebrows just like Mireille's—that same sweeping high outward arc (that cover-models create by tattooing). And the reason we were here was affirmed: Mireille's parents had been baby-sitting her two young children—who were now asleep. We were stopping here first to pick them up.

It would not be a quick stop. Upstairs, in confirmation of the most appetite-inspiring aromas from the kitchen, was a well-set table boasting two bottles Bordeaux. A likely delicious dinner was going to be had. Mireille's mother had prepared the ultimate French beef treat of *Chateau Briande*. It was absolutely delicious, melting in my mouth and then being washed down with the hearty wine. While I understood only short phrases, I was gratified that when her parents appeared to be referring to me it was accompanied by an approving smile. (And I can tell you, about now this reassurance was sorely needed.) This was the best I had felt since Dakar. To this day I can visualize the candle-lit table in a warm corner of the room, the softness, the special ambiance of the occasion. Once again I was far from anyone I knew, at a location unknown to anyone, poised as I had been before (like the airport in Bulgaria) unaware of what lay ahead. I was on the brink of something that could hold a fulfillment and happiness like never before imagined, or the possibility of for some reasons not working out and leaving me distraught. The meal finished and ready to leave, a discussion ensued between Mireille and her parents. They were offering something she seemed reluctant to accept: that we return to her house alone—just the two of us; come back in the morning to pick up the kids.

Home at Mireille's

We exited the village, went through a sparsely populated area, and then onto a country road; paved but unlit and deserted. The drive was pretty much without conversation, which was just as good. We both were tired and it probably would have been fraught with translation efforts. After about fifteen minutes Mireille evidently came upon what she was looking for, turning the car sharply left into a mostly hidden break in the foliage, which I assumed was the entrance to her property. We wound our way steadily uphill—quite a distance, low brush on both sides at first, and then—best I could tell (which was pretty good under a full moon) on the other side of a well-maintained white fence, an open meadow stretching as far as I could see. We topped a final rise where ahead and to the left I spied two large stone pillars with a wrought iron gate between them. Mireille touched a button on the dash panel and the gate swung open. What I next saw, from what little exposure I had to Mireille, was exactly what I would have imagined to be her home.

Inside the gate was what appeared to be a thatch-roofed Shakespearean-era stone cottage. A *large* stone cottage. She parked alongside it and opened the trunk. I leapt out and grabbed our baggage, ready to follow her into the home. As I got closer to it I was further impressed by the exterior walls which had obviously been fashioned by a skilled stone mason; large, odd-shaped rocks carefully fit together and mortared. Inside, after passing through an old farm-style kitchen, I was surprised to see a contrasting ultra-modern interior décor. Most walls held large and brightly colored works of abstract art. The partitions to a couple small rooms (even the bathroom) were see-through, only slightly tinted thick acrylic. For sure I was in a uniquely designed, one-of-a-kind domicile.

After stowing the luggage we (for some reason) returned to the kitchen. There, standing in the middle of the room, Mireille pressed herself against me and slid her arms around my waist. Because of a kitchen skylight, her face was well illuminated by the moonlight flooding down through it. She was looking up into my eyes with the most loving and contented look I was ever gifted to receive, and said a few words which I was startled to realize, in English were: *I think we should get married!* While I had dared to consider this eventuality, I had not dared to imagine *she* might have also considered it. My knees went weak and my heart was racing as I digested these now-spoken words. When I had my breath I exclaimed (in the best French I could) *"What will your parents think?"*

Still, without breaking her loving look, she replied in French "I already told them." I was speechless (and thoughtless). *She already told them— before she told me?!* I was stunned but also grateful for her seemingly entirely confident, doubtless position on the subject. I hoped she had considered all the obstacles in bringing that about, but was quite sure she had not. I again realized Mireille was a dichotomy; living inside that outwardly assured and intimidating exterior was an unsure but hopeful little girl.

As long a day as we had endured; as much that we had encountered, and the doubt and lack of any certainty I felt, we still made love—I'm sure what would be described as ultimately rewarding. Even before Mireille's warm naked body was next to me, I was once again immediately aroused and in possession of a force and capability never experienced before my first night with her in Dakar; and what transpired was another in an unbroken row of tearful "bests." I was humbled, and hugely gratified at Mireille's unrestrained expressions of pleasure and satisfaction, gasps, cries, and for some time afterward—her emotional, thankful and tearfully loving utterances. I was at a loss to understand how I—me, could possibly be responsible for her bliss-filled reactions.

Our First Morning Together

The morning met us with a golden sun flooding into the kitchen. Mireille had made a delicious breakfast (even though I never eat my eggs "sunny side up"). For fruit it started with a quarter of cantaloupe topped with a thin slice of smoked ham. Once again I was dismayed that even after ample time to demonstrate my mediocrity, she seemed to never stop treating me with affection and respect. I can even say an apparent "gratefulness;" an appreciation for my just being with her. I was honored. Although we had few conversations relating to our life views, what comments she did make about her social engagements and business experiences, were very surprising to me. They always portrayed a striking lack of confidence and a feeling of vulnerability; in every case containing fearful premonitions of hurtful outcomes. This frightful mindset was in striking contrast to her commanding presence and caused me to feel a want—even a need, to be protective of her; provide her assurance at that moment and henceforth. After breakfast she took me outside the house where we sat on a wooden swing on a flagstone patio, observing the whole downward sloping, grassy meadow to the west of her house. It was beautiful, descending several hundred yards, with a small trickling stream in the center. And not only that, at least a dozen large and healthy cows were wandering on the meadow. On the other side of the house, when arriving I'd seen a thick tree line marking the edge of a likely rarely entered woodland.

The Village and Her Kids

Shortly before noon we made the drive to her parent's house, which included a tour of the town in daylight. It was a seventeenth century village, immaculately preserved; most buildings at least 200 years old, and not a broken window in one of them! She made a point of taking me to the city hall, which was fully functional, every room occupied and busy with people streaming in and out. She pointed at the four large numbers etched in the stone over the front entrance: 1692! (I remember it exactly—being two hundred years after the date of Columbus's discovery of America). The town was immaculate, not a single item of trash anywhere. I felt warmly towards a citizenry that would in such a practical way respect the efforts of those who had lived there long before them. Arriving at her parent's house, after a very warm exchange of pleasantries we picked up her two children—both boys: Paul and Pierre. They greeted me dutifully and with no suspicion that I could discern. I don't know what Mireille had told her parents before introducing me, but once again they seemed to regard me with approval, and even affection. (Perhaps they had not yet considered I might be leaving France with their daughter.) Back at Mireille's I attempted to make some points by tussling with the kids—fake wrestling and then traipsing ape-like around the room on all fours carrying them on my back—both at once. They seemed to be enjoying the activity. I wondered if they had sampled this effort by other gentlemen callers, or might I be the first.

Me and My Big Mouth

During the afternoon while the kids napped, Mireille was intent on learning more about me. Sadly (and deservedly) I was at a loss for what I could say and be truthful. I had made a big mistake in Dakar: I admitted to Jacques I was a pilot, but instead of owning up to flying small puddle-jumper aircraft, when asked what I flew, I said a *"sept-deux-sept." (A 727!)* He of course relayed to Mireille that I was an *airline* captain. And worse, not only was I not an airline captain, at the moment I didn't even have a permanent job. And in addition to living off sporadic cash payments (and not knowing when the next one was coming) I was legally separated from a wife and had two kids. Here now, I was paying the price of a life of not planning. I managed to—as best I could, massage or minimize each of those misspeaks, harboring hopes (but no real ideas) of at some future time correcting them.

Our Activities

We spent the next few days carrying out just about the same routine, including taking at least one trip a day to some local natural attraction. (Not at all the same, but experiencing this activity with Mireille I couldn't help reflecting on my times with brave June.) One day—because of some not-clear business Mireille had to take care of, we drove back down to Lyon. She was dressed to the nines, wearing a wide-brimmed hat tipped low over her face, making her presence even more striking (and intimidating). Her business would not only be conducted in the city hall, but with the mayor himself! As soon as we entered his office he was up from behind his desk, around it, and giving Mireille an enthusiastic embrace while proclaiming his pleasure in seeing her again. This meeting resulted in the mayor inviting us to lunch—which was a two-hour (not comfortable) affair. While in Lyon, knowing my first sojourn in France might be best to not be too long, I made reservations for my flight back to the States.

One day Mireille drove to one of her friend's houses, to introduce me. The woman offered me a piece of peach pie. Thinking we were only stopping in for a few minutes, when the host asked me if I would like her to wrap it for me, I replied in French—as best I could, that doing so would be just fine. In the car Mireille let me know that in France it's very rude not to eat an offering of food when it is made—right then; never take it home. That incident was the sole occurrence the whole visit in which Mireille showed any disappointment with me (and of course you can imagine I hated myself for it). Our nights continued beyond my wildest dreams, and even our days (me having left a knee-abraded blood smudge on her living room rug).

One Thing I Guess I'll Have to Get Used To

Something happened more than once while walking the streets in Lyon: a tall and handsome, obviously well-placed guy would pass us on the street, and after he passed, if I snuck a look back, in every case he was turned round, his eyes fixed on Mireille. I recognized this was something I would likely have to be prepared for, as unsettling as it was.

At Last, Hearing About Mireille

In the days that followed while continually asking her to repeat a French word (and then referencing my pocket dictionary) I learned more about her. I assumed she must have been very attractive and popular from an early age. Surprisingly she said she was not so, and not happy growing up, and that her schooling was not memorable or rewarding. And then she said as best I could translate it: *It wasn't until I met my husband did my life begin.* Hearing such a touching and loving comment by her I was wondering why she was no longer married to him, and where he was now. She went on as I labored to translate her explanations. He had been from the southeast of France; from a family of Italian lineage. She went to a cabinet and returned with a photo of her husband, who was not that handsome and the same height as me. Her respect for him was obvious and deep-seated. He was college-educated and skilled as both an engineer and businessman, becoming a Vice President at Peugeot (one of the largest car manufacturers in France). As best I could translate—several times asking her to speak even more slowly, she told me her husband was diagnosed with brain cancer almost two years ago, and a year ago—while descending that winding, precipitous road leading down to Monte Carlo, he had gone off it and *was killed in the crash.* The insurance company couldn't prove whether it was because he had a seizure, or because he knew he was terminal and had committed suicide. Mireille was the recipient of a very large settlement (though she didn't say how much in Francs). Not sure if this was their house together, or she used some of the insurance money to build it.

Taking Stock of Our Situation

It was the night before my departure. All had gone as well, or maybe even better than I could have anticipated. As probably could have been expected, we failed to reach any definitive plans for our future (not that this wasn't greatly on my mind). I assured her I would be back soon; as soon as I had taken care of a few things in the States. (*What* few things I had no idea.) I had not yet asked her if she would consider leaving France to live with me in the States. Based on what I had seen here: the beautiful countryside, her historic town, her home, her closeness to her parents, her circle of affluent and sophisticated friends, I didn't have the nerve to even suggest it. While my chances of obtaining a respected position in the states were small, here they would likely be impossible. If I was lucky enough to secure a position in Florida and she agreed to come, the absence of any elevation (even the slightest hilly area), certainly no historic villages, and the unanimous aging population (nothing but silver-hairs and aluminum walkers) she could undergo a cultural shock that could be fatal to our relationship. I could not envision her feeling comfortable with this and the tropical climate—either hot or sweltering hot. That night, my mind tired—in fact worn raw from considering "what ifs" I escorted Mireille to the bedroom for a now consistent occurrence.

Leaving France

The flight would depart from Lyon at 1 p.m. The drive was only about thirty minutes, so we weren't in a rush and had a family breakfast outdoors—on a picnic table on that same flagstone patio. No matter where in France you take the morning meal, the coffee and bread—any kind of bread, is the best in the world. Mireille had bought croissants that we ate, warmed and with cold butter and black cherry preserves. (I learned a new word for jam—*confiture.*) We were in the car about 11, dropped the boys off at her parents, and were on the regretful last leg of the visit, with little or no conversation.

Words, Like No Other Words, Ever

In the terminal we found a small table, ordered two coffees, and prepared to have our last closeness for who knew how long. Holding hands across the table, a warm and loving, peaceful conversation ensued. Only 15 minutes before my flight would be called, somehow—from one of us, the subject of marriage came up. Still looking at me with those loving eyes, but reluctantly, she said what I worked out to be: *there is something I must tell you.* What could it be? I at least knew it was going to be something she thought was very important, as she was looking at me with an expression I had not yet observed. I was worried—soon to be justifiably worried. I cannot adequately express my lack of composure after hearing the next words to come out of Mireille's mouth, which ended with *"avec un seul homme."* With my fledgling French, I translated it to be that *she didn't think she could live with just one man!* I could not have been more wounded if I had taken a spear through my heart. In just two seconds my mood plummeted to a sickening deflation, and cruelly, a conclusion that Mireille's unbridled pleasure during sex was not me or us. I had to consider I had stumbled upon the proverbial nymphomaniac. It was a satisfaction she needed, and now—my translation was she was telling me she needed it to be *with varied partners.* She may have been giving me advance notice that for her, it would be an "open" marriage. I had never been this ill.

A Barely Thinking Shadow of a Man

I have no recollection of the remarks that followed; hers or mine. Nor can I remember the boarding call, my path to the gate or passing through the jet way. The first thing I remember is being in the seat, head back, eyes closed, numb to the core—all but dead. Never in my life had I ever been more happy and then, in a matter of seconds—more devastated. I was now saddled with the necessity to discard this wonderful occasion in my life. Force myself to forget! Never ever to reflect again on my greatest pleasure and salvation. I realized I would have to blanch my mind of the many beautiful expectations that had elevated my being for the last two weeks. My memory bank then being erased (assuming that would be possible), I would have to embark on a radically different future path than the one I had been imagining up till an hour ago. This was going to involve a change in attitude and objectives like none other before. I had been living in a beautiful dream dashed to the rocks in a single sentence. My search might well be over. I could not imagine trying again.

Chapter Fifty-One
BACK IN THE STATES AND FACING REALITY

The First Couple Weeks

On the flights back to Florida, no matter how I tried to think of something else—anything else; for ten hours Mireille's last words in the Paris airport haunted me. Even disembarking in Fort Myers, I was still at that table in the Lyon airport. I hailed a cab and was on my way to the safety of my parent's home. My year of aviation jobs having had me out of state or even out of the country half of each month, it made sense (and saved money) not get an apartment; just in between flights, bunk with my folks. My plan was to hide out here in Fort Myers and continue to search for employment, while my heart healed (if that could ever occur). This location enabled me to just drive across the state to visit the kids, which I did the first week—for the whole week (once again staying in a local motel). The times we had together were better than I could have hoped for (as long as I kept my thoughts on this side of the Atlantic). I heard all about their recent activities, new friends and hobbies, and learning to surf, but also another dozen pastimes. And guess what? Sara herself told me that she and the Major had gotten engaged.

There were no cell phones in 1974 and Mireille didn't have my folks' address or phone number, so I didn't have to worry about her contacting me—she couldn't (whether or not she'd even try). And I knew that not wanting to someday be hurt very badly I must persist in believing it could never be; that it would have to remain nothing more than a one-time blessing, and resist any temptation to contact her. (I did have her phone number.) Although I had experienced a first and life-changing experience with her, I was now so wounded, so deflated, I was unsure if I would ever try again, with any woman. So now, to the task at hand: try to forget Mireille and devote all my thoughts and efforts to finding work.

At Last, a Mature and Practical Thought

Finally—instead of just thinking just a month ahead, I at last looked far enough ahead to harshly realize I had no savings, and *no retirement!* My best chance for a retirement income was to add another ten years to my Marine Corps (federal) service; *thus achieving the required twenty years to be eligible for a government retirement.* With only an aviation background one good chance would be with the Federal Aviation Agency. I inquired and received a huge packet of forms to fill out to apply for a pilot's job. I was floored at the number of absurdly detailed forms. Usually when applying for a flying job, they want to know what *types* of airplanes you flew, how many *hours* you have, and what *kind* of flying you had done. However, these forms were ridiculous! I couldn't imagine any applicant—after looking at them, not just throwing them in the trash; deciding no job was worth so much fabrication.

The information they wanted was so nonsensically detailed that it took real innovation to fill it all in. Many of the figures they wanted, *no* pilot would have kept records for! (Meaning for at least a third of the blanks I had to just make an educated guess.) They wanted to know how much flight time you had in single-engine aircraft, how much in two-engine aircraft, how much in multi-engine aircraft, how much in nose-wheel aircraft, how much tailwheel aircraft, and then, and get this: of all those listed hours in each of those type aircraft, how much of it was flown during the day, how much was flown at night, how much was flown in the clouds—for every airplane! It took me a week, but I completed the forms, figuring if I did so I'd probably be one of few to do so—thus increasing my chances to be hired. I put them in the mail, and wait to see if I ever hear from them.

Too-Dangerous Work Again

On my present job search—a break. While in the doldrums of no leads or even ideas, I received a call from Jim Ryan, the one-legged guy that was my boss at Air America in Laos (and who I visited on that trip through Jeddah). No idea how he knew I was staying with my folks. He was offering me a temporary job: remember that single-engine turbo prop aircraft with the 900-round-per-minute Gatling gun mounted in the open side—the Helio Stallion? The one I had flown in Cambodia with LJ Broussard? Well he wanted to know if I would be interested in picking up two of them in Montreal to deliver transatlantic to Angola on the southwest coast of Africa. The agency must have picked me because of my previous experience in this tricky aircraft and my many transatlantic aircraft deliveries. However, just recently—reflecting on the considerable chances of an engine failure, and the sure drowning that would involve, I finally admitted it was almost a death wish to attempt these crossings and I wouldn't do it again. However, these two more trips would net me four months' worth of alimony and child support payments.

Jim gave me a week to come to a decision. When he called—though I'd thought about it day and night, I still had not come to a decision. It was only when he asked the direct question that I said "yes" (though I don't know how or why). The next week, the contract was signed, the advance payment wired, and some important new information received: *Angola was in the throes of a revolution!* Our CIA was training and arming the National Union for the Total Independence of Angola (UNITA), who were waging a live-fire war against the Soviet-supported People's Movement for the Liberation of Angola (MPLA). It was going to be like every other one of these so-called civil wars. There was a regime that we wanted to *"kick out of power"* because it was *not* friendly to our commercial interests; or conversely there was a regime we wanted to *"keep in power"* because it *was* friendly to our commercial interests, but out of favor with its own citizens. Every time, no matter which side we were aiding, the Russians were actively supporting the other side.

These two aircraft would be the start of UNITA's air force. I packed all my maps and survival gear, and after the latest news about the revolution, included my Walther 9mm PPK. (Hard to believe now, but back then you could board an airline with a piece under your shirt.) In Montreal I learned these airplanes were not fitted with auxiliary fuel tanks; no way to deliver them directly to southwest Africa. It was going to be necessary to take my old northern Atlantic route from Newfoundland to Ireland, and then turn south. (I guess that's why they had positioned the planes in Canada.) From Europe it would be south across the Med and then about 3,000 miles through multiple African countries, to Luanda, Angola, where I would deliver the aircraft.

I took off from Gander, Newfoundland at about 4 a.m. An hour later I was being blinded by the rising sun reflecting off the ocean and piercing the arc of my prop. Nine more hours of praying without uncrossing my fingers until I was within engine-out gliding distance of Shannon. Dusk in Ireland. Of course the Gatling gun had been removed and was being flown over on a Miami-based Southern Air C-130 as part of another clandestine cargo trip to Angola. From Shannon it would be six more flights (days) to my destination; first to Nice, France, then markedly substandard airfields in Morocco, Mauritania, The Ivory Coast, Cameroon, and finally Angola.

Each landing and refueling presented its own hardships (similar to when I delivered those W.H.O. planes across the Sahara). Again, I was repeatedly told there was no gas or a special additional payment (and four-hour wait) to get the fuel I needed from some restricted area, and that they couldn't accept my credit card.

Throughout I had my share of obstacles, especially getting through immigration and customs, in fact spent the night in jail in Mauritania. And there were the bribe payments—usually at least two if not three at each stop. At the Cameroon airport waiting for a cab to town, I saw some suspicious-looking characters eyeing me as possible prey, so I walked back in the terminal and chose to sleep in the airplane. A trip the length of the African continent is an ordeal, especially since I had no U.S. government sponsorship. Finally reached Luanda. While the country was at war my arrival went smoothly, minus the fact no one was in the tower, so there was no control of inbound aircraft. I picked the proper runway (into the wind). Just before touching down and looking towards the far end of the runway, *I saw another plane landing straight towards me!* I added power and yanked the nose up, just clearing him and avoiding a fatal head-on collision. I took it around and landed. I found the pilot of the other aircraft on the ramp—a Cuban pilot who apologized to me in his best English. He was delivering a Russian YAK-52 to the "bad guys." (The Russians again.) Instead of my usual routine of faring for myself, here I was met by Agency guys who took me to their compound (where I met a guy I worked with in Laos).

Delivering the second aircraft was just more of the same. First I churned my way nine hours across the deserted Atlantic, then endured the grilling and impositions of transiting five third-world countries, after which I really swore to never do it again. And I found out why they hired me to ferry the planes to Angola. After dropping off the second plane, the CIA station manager made a serious plea for me to stay and train the guerillas who would fly the planes. They had let me ferry the aircraft over to re-familiarize myself with the plane and expose me to the project, in hopes they could talk me into joining it. No deal! Back to my folks' home and a renewed job search.

Oh No!

After six months ago having spent a week filling out that multi-page absurd flying job application for the FAA, I received another packet of forms from them. Updated forms—even worse, being revised with *more* information required. I had to do it all again. Every page. Discouraging as this was I wasn't going to quit now. I spent another three or four days filling out the same seemingly unending list of blanks. And this time it was more difficult because I had to try to remember the numbers I had guessed at on the previous submission. (I suspected not many other applicants would bother with this revision, and my hiring chances should be going up.)

Another Possible Chance For a Retirement

With little confidence in my application for a government (FAA) flying job ever materializing, I realized my only other chance to earn a retirement was to get on as a pilot and get 20 years with an established, large and financially stable corporation such as IBM or Pepsi Cola. But a big problem: They would be operating *jet aircraft,* and I had no civilian jet experience. However I was still qualified for the GI Bill and could use mine to pay for civilian jet training. If so, I'd then be able to add a jet rating to my resume. I checked and discovered the type of jet most in use was the *Learjet.*

Upgrading My Aviation Resumé

I located a Learjet training company in Grand Rapids, Michigan that accepted the GI Bill. The training program consisted of just six, one-and-a-half-hour flights. This was a transonic, complicated, difficult-to-handle jet. I wondered how anyone could merit a rating in it after just nine flight hours? At the end of my first training flight I was real worried about ever mastering the Lear. On takeoff I was going through 2,000 feet before I knew it or had raised the landing gear. One good thing: the Lear they were using was an older model that did not have the updated systems. The instructors told us that if we could handle this old one, we would be able to handle any Lear. A week later, as mystified about it as anyone, I was presented with my Learjet Type Rating (which I personally did not think I came close to deserving).

My First Flight as a Crewmember

One reason I chose the company in Grand Rapids was because they promised that after you got your rating—before you left the area, they would schedule you as *copilot* on an actual charter flight, so you could observe an experienced captain managing a flight. A day after receiving my rating they told me to be on the airport ramp at 6 am, for a 07:00 takeoff— *my first flight as an actual crewmember!* I found the plane, but the captain had not yet arrived. It was still before sunrise, the ramp was dark and abandoned, minus one young kid sitting on a nearby curb. Twenty minutes later—still no captain. While I'm standing by the airplane the kid comes up to me and says, "Excuse me sir, I'm supposed to be the copilot on this flight, are you the captain? *Holy Shit! Me? The captain?* Five minutes later, who arrives but our passenger, Mick Jagger, and I had no choice but to act like I knew what I was doing and take him to Las Vegas.

Now, Trying to Put My New Rating to Use

Once back in Florida, while proud of my new type-rating, it was hard to imagine that a barely qualified neophyte Lear pilot like me could be considered for employment by a respected Fortune 500 company. Still, I sent résumés to about 25 high-profile corporations, and personally visited a dozen corporate flight departments in Florida. After a few weeks of not having received a single affirmative response, I saw an advertisement by a "headhunter." A company hired her because they needed a pilot with three qualifications: (1) A Learjet rating, (2) Both Spanish and French language capability, and (3) Transatlantic experience. *Holy Mackeral! Maybe!* What could I lose? I made a trip to her New Orleans office, produced all my aviation records, sat through an hour interview, expanded on my foreign language and transatlantic experience, and took a weird written test. Wasn't at all sure but hoped it would turn out to be worth it.

Must have been. Two weeks later she contacted me for another interview. I flew to New Orleans again. She wanted to know if I felt comfortable and ready to go in the Lear, and had me repeat what I had told her previously, about my special qualifications. I thought it went well. A week later I got a call from her telling me to call a gentleman named Cliff Ward at a 316 area code. I couldn't pry any details out of her, just that I should make the call. I did and you could have knocked me over with a feather! Cliff was the Chief Pilot for the prestigious Learjet manufacturing company in Wichita, Kansas! They had hired Ms. Harwood. While I had very little of any of those capabilities (especially Lear time), *I was the only guy in the country who had all three!*

I was sent tickets to fly to Wichita for an interview. Cliff told me they were making lots of sales to countries and businesses in South America and Europe, and therefore needed someone with my specific qualifications. Can you believe that? My years of studying Spanish and French before turning out the light, and that crazy time ferrying aircraft from Gander to Shannon, and my decision to get a Learjet rating; all three paid off! *Who'd a thunk it?* Cliff was an okay guy, but not a warm and fuzzy type of guy, so at the end of our time together I wasn't sure how it went. It must've gone well. I was hired, went back to Florida, rented a U-Haul trailer, loaded it, and drove to Wichita. This time actually believing—for the first time in my life, I was going to have a permanent and respectable job as an esteemed "Factory Demonstration Pilot," for the most famous corporate jet manufacturer in the country! (*What would Mireille think now?*)

Chapter Fifty-Two
AT LAST, A RESPECTABLE POSITION WITH A RETIREMENT! (FOR A WHILE)

Welcome to the Midwest

I had seen Wichita two years ago when picking up those aircraft for the Iranian Air Force. But those stays were just one or two-days. Now in 1976 it would be an indefinite domicile, perhaps even my final hometown. Mixed emotions on that one; a job I couldn't turn down, but a thousand miles from the kids. Wichita was ground zero for our country's civilian aviation industry, not only Learjet, but the headquarters and factories for Beechcraft and Cessna as well. I was justifiably excited. At last I would have—not just prestigious employment, but one that would hold a retirement! Coming from Florida with year-round outdoor-activity, most the population was lean and fit. Here in Wichita with much of the year prohibiting outdoor activity, I noticed a large percentage of overweight people, particularly women. (And I never saw so many kids with braces and glasses.) Found and rented one side of a nice duplex.

My Prospective Position

Cliff told me I'd be assigned to the Flight Demonstration Department of which he was the Chief Pilot, supervising about fifteen pilots. All I met were friendly and accepting of me. The mission of the department was demonstrating aircraft to prospective purchasers—usually Fortune500 companies. While I would do some of that, my primary assignment would be demonstrating Learjets to Spanish and French-speaking purchasers from South America, Africa and Europe. And then after they had purchased the plane, they'd send pilots here for me to train (in their language). After they were trained here, I would return with them to their country and fly with them for as long as it took to get them safe in their own theater of operations.

To get me up to speed, I attended a ground school on the model I would be flying most—the new Lear 35. Then I underwent a couple weeks of flight training in it to gain competency and hopefully even an excellence in understanding and flying it. I'm happy to say, both of the above went better than I could have hoped for; especially my final check-ride with Cliff (and two senior department pilots he brought along to observe). I was thrilled when after making my third landing Cliff said—in an almost bored fashion, "Well I've seen enough of this, let's go home." A few days later I heard one of the other pilots say that the guys in Marketing were working on a sale to a company in Lyon, France. You might imagine hearing that caused my heart to skip, remembering my nights with Mireille just 30 miles north of Lyon. Although I thought about her often, my overriding fear remained, that her expressed need for more than one man would have surely broken my heart.

Awaiting foreign pilots, I demonstrated aircraft to stateside purchasers. One company needed to operate out of short runways and arriving at Tucson, asked me if I could demonstrate a "short-field landing." The Tucson weather was *not* conducive to attempting a short-field landing. There was a 20-knot tailwind which would markedly increase the landing distance. And it was over 100 degrees, causing strong updrafts which would loft me higher, make my touchdown late, resulting in a longer landing. I tried my best, battling the elements. To get her down I had to chop the power, but just as I did the updraft quit and "the bottom dropped out." We hit with a resounding smack! Bounced and hit again. It was more than just a little embarrassing.

As I was humbly walking to the terminal the head passenger asked me, *after they'd bought the aircraft, how would his pilots get trained?* I responded that all new buyers got a free week of training for their pilots. He then asked, "Well who's going to train them?"

I said, "I will."

He stopped in his tracks turned to face me and said in wonderment: "*You* will?!"

Doing What I Was Hired For

The first group of foreign pilots were from a Chilean Air Force squadron that had bought a camera-equipped Lear to map their country. The cadre of pilots included an older gentleman—a colonel who was the squadron commander, one major—the executive officer of the squadron, two captains and two lieutenants. Only two of the older officers—the colonel and the major spoke passable English. The younger pilots spoke no English (but were much better pilots).

I started a three-week training syllabus that went as well as I could expect, minus the absence of progress I was making with the colonel. As the squadron commander I knew it was imperative that he do well enough to graduate from the syllabus. His *not* making it would be an unbearable "loss of face" for him and upset the morale of the whole squadron. I shared my concern with the major—Carlos (a fine man and a real gentleman). I learned from him that the colonel had never flown a jet before, *any jet*. For the last five years he had only flown slow, propeller-driven aircraft, and then only rarely.

Just walking to the aircraft the colonel's nervousness was readily apparent. My heart went out to him. He fully recognized his lack of ability and the potential consequences. In the cockpit doing the checklists, I could see his torso shivering and his legs shaking. With the other pilots I taught a wide variety of maneuvers (often with one or more aircraft systems purposely failed). However, with the colonel—ten days into the syllabus I was still working on the most basic profile; the five minimum maneuvers required on every flight: takeoff, climb, level-off, descent, and landing. We did this same profile—nothing more, two or three times on every training flight. I was much relieved when halfway through the second week, he was able to accomplish these five phases of flight, if not smoothly (or with any confidence)—at least hopefully safely. I was able to graduate him, and in so doing, I'm sure earned his eternal gratefulness. (I did make the major promise me that he would never schedule the colonel for a flight without one of the hot-shot lieutenants in the copilot seat.)

Oh No, Not the FAA Again

You're not going to believe this: while there in Wichita I received a *third* pack of new forms from the FAA; another revised multi-page questionnaire to fill out if I wanted to keep my job application current. Geez, can't they just use these updated forms for new applicants? I spent another week devoted to the task. After what I'd already done I wasn't going to give up now. I felt that most guys, if they hadn't already given up—receiving this last pack of forms they would surely give up, and that would increase my chances to get the job (and in just ten years earn a *government* retirement)! Finished, I put this third set of ridiculous forms in the mail.

A Humorous Incident Worth Recounting

When the program with the Chilean pilots was all but over, I hosted a party for them. During the evening Carlos confronted me with a mystery they had not been able to solve—even after many referrals to their English dictionary and calls back to their friends in Santiago. They begged me to explain what one word meant. I said sure, just tell me the word. Each of them took a try at it. It sounded like "*Toobouie.*" I told them I had never said that word and in fact had never even heard it. They exchanged skeptical expressions, indicating they continued to believe I had said it. But being gentlemen, in spite of my incredulous answer they were willing to let it go. The following day we had our last flight, during which the mystery was solved. The training pilot did an excellent job on a simulated loss of engine landing, and when he had rolled out, I slapped him on the back and said "Attaboy!" He and the two pilots observing were all but in my lap shouting and shaking their finger at me. That was the "*toobouie*" they had heard. "Attaboy" was an expression I evidently used frequently without being aware of it.

The Last Project and Goodbye
The training finished, we left on the flight back to their base in Santiago. To give them confidence and get a better evaluation of them, I risked it: I rode in the right seat just performing the copilot duties, assigning alternate Chilean pilots to fly the left seat and act as captain on each of the five legs. They sincerely appreciated this. I stayed in Chile—flying with them daily for about ten days. When it came time to leave it wasn't without some sadness. I had grown attached to these pilots—who to-the-man were the most polite and respectful individuals I think I ever met. I will always think highly of Chile because of them.

A Differing Foreign Training Experience
Unlike the smooth-running Chilean program, I had a tough one with the pilots from Bolivia. Their Air Force purchased a Lear so they sent three pilots to Wichita for me to train. They all must have seen a "*Top Gun*" type movie. Each one showed up with their flight suit front zipper open down to their navel. No tee shirt, nothing but bare skin showing. Not only that, (the sign of a really "hot pilot") they even went to meals wearing their yellow leather US flying gloves. And they had learned the mark of a "super-hot" pilot: peel the gloves off forwards, until the wrist opening is stretched tight across the knuckles, leaving half the hand ungloved!

The Wichita training syllabus completed, I flew back to Bolivia with them. During this flight I purposely offered little help, letting them make the decisions regarding altitude, power settings, and fuel usage; hoping they would make the right choices. The flight went apparently okay until about 800 miles north of our destination—La Paz. According to my calculations *we were not going to have enough fuel to make it.*

I bounced a few cutely designed questions off them, until their own answers caused them to recognize they were going to run out of fuel before reaching their destination. They agreed, we were going to have to land and refuel as soon as possible. But we were overhead Peru which had broken off diplomatic relations with Bolivia. However we had no alternative but to land, and did so in Lima—unannounced! Rolling out on landing, military vehicles sped down the runway alongside us. As soon as we came to a stop we were surrounded by jeeps with hood-mounted machine guns! Miracle of miracles: Six months earlier the Peruvian Air Force had purchased a Learjet, *and the colonel now approaching the aircraft was who I had trained to fly it.* It was only our prior amicable association that allowed us to be refueled and take back off.

After finishing their training in Bolivia I did not sleep well for months. Every aircraft has a "Performance Manual" with charts showing the aircraft's maximum allowable weight for takeoff at every elevation and temperature. (If the elevation and the temperature are too high, even an *empty* aircraft may not get airborne with the available runway!) The Lear 35 manual only has charts for airfields up to 10,000 feet of elevation, and the airport at La Paz is 13,200 feet above sea level. I modified all the charts (fingers crossed) drawing upward sloping lines, indicating the limitations I personally calculated these pilots would have to adhere to when operating out of their airport. There was no way I could know if my projections were accurate or would prove fatal.

Thankful For My Career at Learjet

Two years at Learjet. Everything was going smoothly—more smoothly and satisfying than ever before. I had rewarding experiences with crews from all over the world. Cliff retired and I was promoted to his position. I was now the well-paid Chief Pilot of the Learjet Demonstration Department. I was content and well-respected by management and my pilots. A type of prideful, professional feeling I had not yet ever had. After many years, I now had it with Learjet. And if Learjet sees no reason to tire of my services for another eighteen years, I'll at last have earned a retirement!

And Then!

Eight p.m., April 1978, relaxing at home. But not for long. The phone rings and it's my son Mark calling from Florida.

"Dad, dad. We have a huge problem!

"What kind of problem? What do you mean?"

"Mom and that Air Force major are getting married."

"So, that's probably good."

"He's being transferred to Okinawa and Mom's going with him, and she says we're going to have to go with them!"

"Yes..."

"We don't *want* to go! We *have* to stay here. We started high school here in Hobe Sound, and we want to graduate from high school here. We know everybody. Everybody knows us. Each of us are on the honor roll and I'm on the football team and Samantha is captain of the cheerleaders. Dad, we just have to stay. We need you to get a job here in Hobe Sound, so we can live with you and stay here and graduate from St. Michaels!"

Holy Christ. What am I going to do? Hobe Sound doesn't even have an airport, and I'm not qualified for any other line of work. And at last I'm finally settled in my life; secure and happy, and qualifying for a retirement.

"Dad, dad are you there? Did you hear me? What are you going to do?"

"I'll call you back in a couple days Mark. Let me think."

Maybe There Is a God

When I hit the rack that night and the following night, I still didn't have a glimmer of an idea. I'd spent every waking hour weighing every possibility, dreading the thought of giving this up and trying to start all over again (for about the fifth time) and having to do it in a small beachside town, all so my kids could continue the life (that I in truth had thrust them into). I understood this was critically important to them, since the alternative was to move to a small island in the South Pacific.

About 10 the next morning the phone rang—striking terror in my heart; expecting it would be Mark. Reluctantly I answered and breathed a sigh of relief when it wasn't Mark.

"Rog, Stu Carlton here. How you doing?" It was that old friend from Banner Flight in upstate New York. Remember? That short employment disaster in the end of 74, where Earl Richman's company went bankrupt. I hadn't spoken to Stu in at least a year.

I answered him "I'm doing just great!" (At the moment, a major untruth.)

But what I was about to hear was a possible solution to my dilemma. "Rog, I know you got your family here in the Palm Beach area. Well as you might have heard, I fly for a big high tech company—SSL Systems, and we keep our planes at the West Palm Beach airport."

"And you're calling because..."

"We've requested a Lear 35 demonstration flight! I think for next Wednesday. You may want to schedule yourself for the flight, because I know we're looking to add another pilot, and you could be the one!"

Holy Shit! A long shot, but it could be the solution to a huge problem. I checked the pending demonstrations and there it was: "*SSL Systems in West Palm Beach.*" I wasted no time in putting myself on the flight, on the chance I could be the pilot they were looking for. (Being able to hire a *factory* pilot is always a priority to new purchasers; the best way to learn the ins and outs of operating the new aircraft.) The next day—as preoccupied as I was, it was hard to even function. I felt guilty while in the comfort and security of walking around the now-familiar Learjet property, visiting the flight offices, the factory floor, the hangars and the ramps. This was my home now. I tried the best I could to get out a cheerful "Hi" when one of my pilots passed, while contemplating a possible end to it all.

The Demonstration Flight

It called for two days of flying. I told my copilot to go sit in the back and had the SSL Chief Pilot (Perry Dawson) ride in the right seat. He was a polite, tall and impressive-looking guy, but with a not-forthcoming personality. It was not easy to feel as if you were on the same frequency as him. Just a shade unnatural. Still, him sitting next to me gave me the chance to try to (tactfully) impress him with my proficiency, and display a friendly, outgoing personality. The first day was from WPB to O'Hare airport in Chicago; a few hours there and then a long leg to Los Angeles. We overnighted in LA and ate dinner together. I used the occasion to make comments that would strike Perry as me being a team-player, not infused with self-importance, and be glad to carry out any instructions he issued. My efforts must have been successful. The next day, just before the flight back to Wichita, *he asked me if I would consider resigning at Learjet and hiring on with SSL.* I told him I'd be honored to be a member of his flight department. I was hired. *A miracle!* (Thanks to Stu, an unthinkable dilemma had been avoided.)

Departing Wichita, and This You're Not Going to Believe

I was standing in the street alongside my fully packed car, ready to start the journey to Florida and my new job. The movers had made their final trip out of the house and were closing up the truck when the mailman came—putting his last handful into the box. I took it out and perused the envelopes. One was from the FAA. Oh no, not *another* set of forms. You could have knocked me over with a feather. My repeated submissions had worked! The FAA was offering me the position of Chief Pilot for the US government National Park Service, to be stationed in Lake Mead, Nevada! *Holy shit!* All my work had paid off! A way to qualify for a government retirement with just ten more years of work. But tragically—too late now, I'd already signed on with SSL.

Arriving Florida

I arrived at my destination on the east coast of Florida in three days. And I was *really* lucky; purely gratified. Things went like clockwork. I only had to stay in a motel a week, before Sara and the major moved out of the house and caught a military flight to Okinawa. It had come to pass: Mark and Samantha's father had indeed come to Hobe Sound, and they were able to stay in St. Michaels with all their friends, and in the same house!

Chapter Fifty-Three
THE SSL FLIGHT DEPARTMENT AND A HAPPENING

With My Kids Again

I had to admit, that minus leaving my prestigious job with Learjet and two years earned towards a retirement, the move here had been a blessing. Things had gone just fine—in fact, better than I deserved. It was a refreshingly wholesome time learning to be a "head of household," even doing all the grocery shopping! I was able to spend almost every evening and the weekends with the kids. They were having a great time at St. Michael's and still getting good grades, which may not have been an accident. Soon after we were all in one household I realized space-wise there was no place for the kids to do their studying. To correct this I knocked out a back wall and added another room. Along one wall I built a long counter with a divider positioned so two kids could study without distracting each other (even seeing each other). The room had no TV or radio, and each of them knew upon arriving home from school, he or she had to spend one solid hour at the counter. If they said they already did their homework in study hall. I responded, "Then go in there and read over what you're going to cover next week." Every week I attended at least one school function, a sporting event, an academic competition, or school play.

Flight Duties at SSL

The SSL flight schedule was easy. The same month after month. I normally flew two or three days each week, occasionally having to overnight in another city, and flying only one weekend a month at he most. Couldn't complain. It soon became "old hat" although occasionally we had different—even emergency, flights. One night I had to rush a newly born "blue baby" (suffering from oxygen loss) to a hospital in Atlanta. I knew how long the flight would take and how much oxygen would be needed for it. Before taxiing out I asked my copilot to check that the oxygen bottle was full. He checked and the nurse assured him it was almost full—1,800 psi. Twenty minutes into the flight I told him to go back and check and see how much the baby had used so far. He comes crashing back into the cockpit shouting that it's already half gone—down to only 900 pounds! While the nurse was right; the bottle had enough pressure, *it was the wrong sized bottle; too small.* We weren't going to make it to Atlanta. We'd be out of oxygen in another fifteen minutes! Okay I can't make it to Atlanta. What can I do? Jacksonville was about 40 miles in front of us; the crash crew there should have oxygen. But if I landed and something went wrong and the baby died, how culpable would I or SSL be? I contacted the JAX tower and had them connect me directly to the crash crew chief. *Great.* He said they *did* have portable oxygen! He told me to check the fitting on the oxygen bottle. We checked and told him. He said he knew that one and had the mate. Rolling down the runway the crash crew vehicle was right alongside us. The copilot opened the cabin door before we had come to a stop and the crash crew guys came thudding inside and in thirty seconds had the new oxygen bottle hooked up. The baby appeared no worse for the wear and we were able to takeoff for Atlanta with sufficient oxygen. The copilot and I got an award from the local hospital, and a letter of commendation from the company.

Unfortunately, Some Non-Standard Pilot Duties

During the second year, Dave—the Assistant Chief Pilot (the guy who had checked me out while surprisingly bad-mouthing Perry the whole time) quit. I was appointed to replace him, and it wasn't long before I began to share his evaluation of Perry. For instance, on our non-flying days, Perry insisted we all come in for an hour or two, just to see what was going on (which the pilots hated and referred to as "logging face-time"). To add insult to injury, there was a patch of grass on each side of the hangar, and Perry would assign one pilot a week to mow them. Last Christmas he called us in to make an announcement about the grass-cutting, that he assured us we would all appreciate. We suspected it would be the end of that job, so showed up in gleeful anticipation. Guess what the good deal was: the company was buying us a *riding* mower! Things like this were not good for morale and resulted in a resentment of Perry. (This grass-cutting duty had caused my good friend Stu to quit.)

The previous two activities were bad for morale, but at least they didn't impact flight safety. The worst of Perry's shortcomings related to the duty hours he assigned our 5-man aircraft maintenance staff. According to FAA regulations, before a pilot can depart in an airplane, it must be released by a certified mechanic, and when it returns at the end of the day a certified mechanic must meet it and inspect it for any discrepancies that had occurred on that day's flight. To accomplish this, since we usually departed at 6:30 a.m. and returned about 8 p.m., it would have been necessary to do like most other corporate flight department: split the maintenance shift. Have some come in at 5 am and go home at 1 p.m., and others come in at 1 pm and go home at 9 p.m. Instead of this, Perry (intimidated by the raw-boned Chief of Maintenance) allowed the whole maintenance department to stick with normal 8 to 5 office hours. This meant, based on our early takeoffs and late returns, sometimes for four or five days straight *no certified mechanic checked the airplane either before a flight or after a flight.* This was a serious "Safety of Flight" omission and I continually urged Perry to alter the maintenance department workhours. I never succeeded.

Scoring Points With the Company

When I was with Air America in Saigon there was a tech rep who I forever credit with most of what I know about jet engines. He explained to me an ingenious way that a pilot could—just by comparing the readings of three engine instruments, recognize an engine that may be going to fail in the next few weeks. I implemented this system here with SSL. On every flight we took along log sheets to record the details of that day's flights. I reprinted these forms to add specific blanks for these three readings. At least once every flight, at a precise altitude and after setting a precise fuel-flow (both critical parts of the equation), the pilot would record the readings of those three engine instruments. If a pilot noticed a comparative deviation, he could flip back through the carbons of the previous days' log sheets to see if there was a trend; an indication of the engine slowly becoming less efficient (in the process of failing). We began using this procedure. It was well received by the pilots and once understood by upper management, them as well. When word of it got to The National Business Aircraft Association, they published an article about the SSL flight department and their new procedure; one that included a photo of me holding the new form. *(Thanks Alex.)*

If the Maintenance Chief Said It, It Must Be True

I mentioned that none of the maintenance staff were staying late enough to meet us when we came in after five. One time taxiing onto our ramp at 4:50, I saw the last maintenance guy arm the alarm system and start running towards his car. Perry's deference to whatever the Maintenance Chief said got worse. For instance, he told Perry that refueling a Lear and letting it sit all night with full wing tanks, would cause the wings to spring leaks. Terry believed him and relieved maintenance of fueling the planes after they had returned. Guess what this meant: when we pilots came in for our 6:30 morning takeoff (with no maintenance staff at work yet) we had to hook up a tug and pull the aircraft out of the hangar and to the gas pumps. It's not easy to tow an aircraft, and throughout the industry pilots are not trusted to do so. And when we got it to the "Fuel Farm," wrestling with those thick black rubber hoses was a dirty job. Knowing this Perry provided us with bibbed overalls and rubber gloves to don before commencing the refueling. This kept your white shirt clean, but also resulted in it being soaked with sweat by the time you were done. Assigned this pre-launch manual labor, two pilots threatened to quit, and one did (joining Stu, who was now flying for a BB&T Banks in Charlotte).

An Operational Audit

All corporate flight departments are subject to operational audits. Top management wants an outside opinion as to how well-managed, professional, and safe their flight department is. SSL contracted with one of the better organizations to conduct this audit. When the word came down that we were in line for this, I was worried and warned Perry about several of our defaults (such as the ones mentioned). We still had six weeks—enough time to implement the procedures we *should* be doing and eliminate the procedures we *shouldn't* be doing. One I didn't mention was the excess duty times Perry had us flying. The FAA stipulates how many duty hours a pilot can have in any 24-hour period. Against my repeated protests, Perry continued to schedule pilots in excess of this maximum. I finally presented him with a list of eight procedural items that I deemed would have to be corrected before the audit, or we would fail. He said my list was just minor things that many flight departments were doing and weren't that important.

We had the audit and failed—miserably. Perry called me in and accused me of having given the examiners the list I had given him—since six of my items were on the list of violations. Of course I told him I had not mentioned the list, and in fact was hoping like hell that they would miss at least some of them. About ten days later the VP of transportation had the audacity to call a meeting of all the pilots and announce that Perry had personally decided he no longer wanted to be in management and was going to seek a line-flying job elsewhere. *Can you believe the company offered this explanation with a straight face?* All the pilots assumed I would be promoted from Assistant Chief Pilot to Chief Pilot, but it was not to be. On the sly the company had already hired Perry's replacement; a guy from Wisconsin named Jonathan Jeffrey Symington III, and that name should tell you something. (Also maybe a factor—his father was on the Board of Directors of Procter and Gamble.) And Perry didn't go quietly. He informed every vice president who would listen, that we had failed the audit because I had given the examiners my list.

The New Boss

Ten minutes after meeting the new chief pilot, I knew I was in big trouble. I could sense he was worried about my Learjet experience and relationship with the pilots. The first six weeks he was only in West Palm Beach a couple days a week; the company had to give him time off to travel back and forth to Houston and Las Vegas to address family problems. His son had joined a rock band and was now in some kind of trouble, and there was an even more unsettling problem with his daughter. I drew some consolation comparing his parenting with how *my* kids were faring. Samantha was on a generous Marine Biology scholarship at the University of Miami and involved in several south Florida environmental groups, and Mark was a sophomore at the University of Florida; a Dean's List student and a 162-pound wide receiver for the "Gators." With Jonathan's lack of regard for me, this offspring comparison lent some assurance of my worth. When Jonathan *was* there, he never took me in his confidence, never asked any questions about existing flight department operating procedures (or if I had any suggestions). He *did* call long-lasting, entirely non-productive meetings, with frequent coffee breaks and smoking breaks, and discussions about current movies and popular sports teams.

Seven Years and Nine Months

I was worried and I well should have been. He'd only been our chief pilot for two months when he called me into his office and spoke: *"Roger, I just can't manage effectively with you staying on board, so I'm terminating you. You'll have to turn in your keys."* To say I was stunned—speechless and barely on my feet, would be an understatement. I knew we'd never be confidants, but this was something I hadn't envisioned. *Turn in my keys?* Did he think I was going to come back at night and steal something? I was numb and had not yet responded when he continued, *"And it's of right now. You can empty your desk and leave."* I managed to ask why. What happened? What the heck have I done? He responded, *"I was hired 'carte blanche' with the approval to do whatever I want personnel-wise, and I just won't be able to manage effectively with you still here."* No reason.

A done deal. Shakily I gave him my keys. He added that I was to report to Bill Goodwin in Human Resources right away. I made my way to my office, filled up a cardboard box with items from my desk and the plaques and certificates that had adorned the walls. Leaving, I passed a couple of pilots in the hall, but they were a blur going by; couldn't even voice a *Hi*. Think I made a waving motion.

A Human Resources Wimp!

I went directly to the HR office, hoping I might be able to make some progress there; maybe even get this thing turned around. One thing that didn't help: Bill had only been with the company for a few weeks. When he arrived Jonathan was already here, and as far as Bill knew—Jonathan was the established and respected chief pilot. And Bill knew nothing of my reputation and years of exemplary performance. Of course I told him I had no idea what I had done that could have prompted Jonathan to come to this decision. After saying that Bill looked up at me with a sarcastic expression on his face and spread two pink sheets across his desk. I looked at them unknowingly, not understanding what they were. "Well Roger, I don't understand where the mystery is. Here are the two reprimands Jonathan gave you last month." *Two reprimands? In a month?* There *were* no reprimands! No meetings. Not even any conversations that could have been interpreted to have been disciplinary in nature. Bill went on: "And look, right here on this second one, it says one more occurrence would be grounds for termination." I was at a loss to speak and almost unable to remain standing. It wasn't that Jonathan had exaggerated meetings we had. We didn't *have* any meetings. None! *He had completely forged the reprimands.* There never was a single one. Not one meeting occurred!

Knowing Bill had been a personnel officer for his 20 years in the army (and got out as a Major, a rank usually achieved in nine years) I pointed out one undeniable item: "Bill, with all your experience, have you ever seen an employee receive a last—final warning before being fired, without signing the document or having a witness present? "Look! There's no witness, and you don't see my signature there— right there in the block specifically designed for it." This *did* cause him to pause—a fleeting realization he could not disguise. But evidently he understood it had to be a done deal and was able to somehow discount it. After a slight pause he mumbled his way to finally informing me that I was being *"Outplaced for Management Convenience."* When a pilot is let go for this stated reason, it is usually because the real reason is too dastardly to mention, thus identifying the outplaced employee as one to be avoided. Being terminated in this fashion I was in big trouble, unable to even begin considering a "what next." Drove home, only a shadow of the man I was when I woke up.

What Can I Do, and What Will This Mean

The following day I asked each of the pilots if they would write a testimonial letter as to my flying skills, management techniques, and ability to carry on an amiable relationship with just about anyone. I was humbled by the sincere and convincing letters I received from each of them. Along with these letters I made up a chronology of my history with SSL, pointing out innumerable pluses, and delivered the packet to three vice presidents I knew. (Unfortunately, two other VP's I knew really well and who had high opinions of me had just recently left the company.) The ones I did give it to, read the materials and confided in me that it sure looked like I was victim of one person's personal motives, but in view of the new chief pilot's "carte blanche" I was screwed. One VP said, "Don't worry this happens to senior managers all the time."

I was able to get a meeting with the president of the company, who was sincerely sympathetic and said the company would offer me a settlement. But in spite of the pilots' letters and my past service, he could not overturn Johnathon's decree. *Seven years shot and now I don't have enough employable time left to acquire a retirement!* As I said earlier, the wording of my termination is usually to disguise some other shameful act best not to mention. Terminated for this reason it was doubtful I'd ever secure another position with a respected corporate flight department. Now once again, in 1984—even later in my life, with less time remaining to recover, I was indeed at a loss, with no plan and little optimism or energy.

With the kids now calling my home theirs, and my wife now being married, I was no longer paying child support or alimony, but with the unanticipated college expenses and a couple other surprises, money was still an issue. I began sending out résumés, but even though the "positions held" looked pretty good (Factory Test Pilot and Assistant Chief Pilot for a Fortune 500 company), that *"Outplaced for Management Convenience"* was more than any prospective employer was going to risk.

Unemployed, and a Chance for Some Temporary Income

A month after my termination, and shortly after the notorious Mariel boatlift scandal—where thousands of Cubans—poor, ill, illiterate, and often felons crammed themselves into barely sea-worthy boats to escape to Miami, I got a call from a CIA case-officer I'd known in Laos. In Cuba there still were well-to-do informants working for the Agency, who also wanted to get to the states, but not in one of those often-capsizing boats. Steve informed me of a plan he had for me, and that I'd find a single-engine Cherokee Six plane parked in front of Atlantic Aviation at the West Palm Beach airport.

The project lasted several months, while I continued to send out résumés and make calls. A couple times a week I made clandestine late-night roundtrips to Cuba and back. I'd takeoff about midnight and wrap up about dawn. I'm sure the guys working in Cuban Air Traffic control were in on the thing, because for sure they were tracking me, but without any objections. Arriving in Cuba I'd land on a homemade strip in the middle of a sugar cane field in Cienfuegos, on the south side of the island (where the CIA made their invasion of Cuba in April of 1961). The hardest part was the return flight. Obviously, even at 3a.m. I couldn't land at an airport with Customs or Immigration, or any local authority, *so I landed in the middle of the Everglades!* Before I started Steve had taken me into the glades, where he showed me a short, bumpy raised dirt dike (with a canal on each side) that was to be my return "airport." These landings turned out to be heart-in-the-throat white knucklers (maybe even worse than Laos), but not only did Steve pay me a thousand dollars a trip, almost every trip the passengers tipped me handsomely.

A Search on Hold

During my seven years in Hobe Sound I was still painfully aware of my shaming male deficiency, but as a new head of household and all the kids' school activities, with some effort I was able to diminish its disabling effect on me; faring better than when it first got hold of me. I just kept it my own secret. Since arriving in Florida, only a couple of times did I end up in a woman's bed, and I'm sure they would testify to a non-memorable event (at least to them; still memorably humbling to me). Reflecting on my miraculous success with Mireille, I had to accept it as a one-time fluke, with *her only*. She may have been the only woman living who had the chemistry I needed.

A Long Overdue Conclusion

After my unceasing subsequent failures, at long last, I was finally ready to accept it: *it may not be a "chemistry" thing. It's me!* It was time to admit that my problem was mine alone, that there *wasn't* that one woman still out there. I would have to rescue myself from years of despair, *not* by succeeding, but by resigning myself to the fact I would *not* succeed—ever. I would just live bearing the weight of that awareness; knowing the vitally critical role it plays, and that I would have no part in it. Just forget the "what would have beens," the fulfillment, pride and power Mireille had gifted me with for a few days in Dakar and that week in France.

Chapter Fifty-Four
AN INCREDIBLE PAIRING! A MIRACLE!

Something New and Wonderful

Some months ago I had decided that I might want to buy a piece of property that would appreciate, and that I would be able to sell fifteen years from now to help fund my old age. To help me find such a piece of property I had used a real estate agent named Kathy; a cheerful, always smiling woman, just a few years younger than me. Although no purchase ever came about, there was a big plus to the effort: I found—perhaps for the first time since June, and who knows why—a totally non-stressful, complementing person. A person in whose company I was always at ease. We started dating. I guess you could say we quickly became a couple, often seen hand in hand, both perfectly content doing normal even mundane everyday things together. (And gratefully, without her giving any indication of being desirous of that—for me, always worrisome, humiliating and never successful intimate act.)

I Could Hardly Believe My Ears

After several weeks together, Kathy evidently felt comfortable enough with me to say she had a confession to make; one that she said would certainly disappoint me and likely end our relationship, but she had to tell me. Hesitantly she began: "Roger, there's something I dread bringing up, but have to. Many years ago I had uterine prolapse surgery, requiring a mesh implant. It slipped, penetrating the wall of my vagina. After two surgeries the doctors concluded the protrusion was irreparable, and more corrective attempts were not recommended. But forever more, intercourse —if even possible, would be painful to me, not to mention my male partner. I was part of a class-action suit and did receive a sizeable settlement; not that that would ever make up for my deficiency. So now you know. That's what a guy would get with me. It's why I will never marry."

I was stunned. Incredulous. An answer to the unanswerable. A miracle! I had met a woman who also "couldn't do it." A woman whose pleasures were such that I could provide them. One who didn't need that *other* satisfaction that I was unable to provide. *No more prayers to the gods of lovemaking!* All this being true, it was not a long courtship. Three months later I bought a ring and proposed.

Kathy's situation, although unknown as such by her, if not saving my life, was going to allow me to live it out free from recrimination and shame. Although I must admit, like the reason for my first marriage, there was a bit of the same motivation: rescue a woman; *bring something into Kathy's life she never expected.* In my first marriage I failed to realize the gratification of "saving someone" is only short-lived, and certainly nothing to make a marriage decision on. But here, this was *way* different! Now with Kathy, in spite of years of disgrace, I was experiencing happiness and fulfillment. Things went great, from morning to night, at home or out, every day and night. (While I could never forget her, I was able to reflect less often on my performance and the euphoria I had experienced with Mireille.)

Chapter Fifty-Five
RICH AND THE DEA

One of Those Kinds of Flying Jobs Again

My next revenue-producing activity displays as well as anything my inability to consider possible consequences (or even *likely* consequences)! One of my Laotian Air America pilots—Colt Chance, phoned me from Georgia, and said he was going to be passing through West Palm the end of the week and suggested we have a beer together. Great, some reminiscing sounded good, especially now (me spending most my time sending out resumes and making phone calls). We met at a local hangout—"T J Gators," and after some fish and chips and a couple cold beers, he shared something with me; something a little scary.

"Rog, I know you're out of work so you may be interested. A friend of mine is a professor at Valdosta State College. He has a brother in the Keys who owns a small trailer park in Marathon and works for the DEA. The professor put me in touch with him and you should see what he's got me doing." I knew Colt was ambitious and not averse to taking risks, so not sure I wanted to hear about it, but told him I was listening. Colt said after a couple meetings, the brother—Rich, flew Colt back up to Valdosta Regional Airport. There, parked on the ramp was a single-engine Cherokee Six, *for Colt's personal use!* Although part of this use would be making frequent trips to the Homestead airport just south of Miami.

"I was told that after landing at Homestead I was to taxi to Stewart Aviation and find two guys. Rich gave me their names and photos. I was to strike up a conversation with them and work at becoming friends. I of course asked him why. He just waved a hand and said they were a couple pilots who flew their own planes back and forth to the Bahamas, and the DEA needed more information about them. Rich said they would be easy to find, because almost every day they'd be at Stewart; on the ramp, in the hangar, or having a coffee inside in the luncheonette."

Colt said he was not only able to find them, but being a renowned aviation storyteller (and knowing more risqué jokes than any standup comic) he was able to develop the relationship Rich had wanted (though still not knowing why). "After a couple weeks I had their confidence and they were less guarded in their comments, and I might have found out why they didn't appear to have a job. Some of their remarks indicated that their source of income could be *smuggling.* That night I phoned Rich and told him while the guys never outright admitted to it, they hinted about smuggling. Rich laughed and said being with the Drug Enforcement Agency he already knew that and needed an outsider to infiltrate their operation. He said he could not have shared that with me at first, because if he did those guys would have smelled it on me."

"What else did he tell you? What was the plan?"

Colt finally got to the heart of it, saying "My job was to keep the friendship going until I'd gained their complete confidence, and they asked me and my Cherokee to join them on one of their runs to Colombia and back."

"Holy Shit Colt, was he asking you to actually take part in a smuggling mission?"

"Sure sounded like it. Of course I questioned that, which Rich was expecting. He said he understood I had a couple worries: first, they'd be caught—me among them, and I'd be thrown in jail while babbling about actually working for the DEA and waving the one blank card I had with a phone number on it. Or worse, the two guys might find out I was a "plant." And if so, I'd leave on a trip and never come back. Rich said he was in a position to take care of at least the first concern. He also said that while he didn't know how much, I'd be well paid for any trip I made, and that the money did not have to be accounted for! I must've been doing okay feeding the trip info to Rich, because one day he asked me if I knew anyone who might be interested in working with me to break up this ring, and I thought of you."

Can't Believe I Did It

Maybe because of no job, no income, and still no retirement, I agreed to at least meet Rich. Colt set up a meeting in a high-rise in Fort Lauderdale. After listening to Rich I heard the words—not believing I had signaled my vocal cords to produce them, that *I'd be willing to give it a try.* Perhaps it was foolish, maybe because I didn't want to let Colt down, or appear like a wimp to Rich. And not only did I have serious reservations about this forthcoming escapade, you can guess my dear Kathy—even knowing my concern, in fact fear—for our future financial security, was not at all convinced I should get involved. She never argued (perhaps like Sara, thinking I knew best—which of course by now even you know I rarely if ever had)!

My commitment to come onboard resulted in Rich positioning a Cherokee Six on the ramp at West Palm Beach—for my use. Colt said the Cherokee Six was the "plane-of-choice" because it had a 300-horsepower engine that would be necessary when taking off and trying to climb while in an over-loaded condition. Colt asked the two guys if they'd ever thought about one more plane: more pot, more revenue! When they agreed, he told Carl and Daryl that he knew a guy (me) with his own Cherokee Six. And that he had known me for years, that I could be trusted with anything, was a great bush pilot and had done things like this before. After two months, many flights to Homestead, many meetings at Stewart Aviation as well as having my share of beers with them at the nearby Blue Boar Tavern. I was part of the team.

Fearful as I was, the Day Arrived

Finally Carl said it was time for our first trip—to Colombia and back. We would leave from the Lauderdale Executive airport at eight in the morning—for a couple reasons: there were a lot of departing aircraft at that time and it was shift-change in the tower. But Carl also warned us, if a guy in the tower spied a plane taxiing out with no seats, they would suspect that was because they may need the empty cabin for bales of pot. So before positioning the plane to Fort Lauderdale they were installing throwaway Volkswagen seats that he said fit perfectly on the Cherokee seat tracks. What we couldn't hide when taxiing out was a half bladder of fuel stuffed in the row between the seats.

Where Would We Land on Our Return?

In a huge F550 truck (completely painted camouflage) Carl took us into the Everglades (not far from where Steve had taken me). A half mile inside we came to a locked metal gate, with a sign on it that read *"No Trespassing by order of US Bureau of Land Reclamation."* Carl had Daryl jump out and unlock it. No idea how Daryl got the key. (I later learned these guys had high school friends working for just about every county commission). We went through, driving atop narrow raised dikes, until coming to one that was straight, hard-packed and about five hundred feet long *that was going to serve as our 4 a.m. return runway.* I could see why they wanted a bush pilot. It would be pitch black and Carl said we could not turn on our landing lights until we were only 50 feet above the ground! If you went off the end or over the side, the airplane was wrecked and you were marooned! Just before touchdown we would have to clear a 25-foot high tree line, drop down quickly, and hit close enough to this end of the dike to leave enough distance ahead to get it stopped. To the left of the far end was a fifty-foot-wide flat area where we could park and unload. As I viewed this dangerous landing site I began feeling less confident; that I was about to do something really foolish (and dangerous).

Learning More About Carl

Before dropping us at the motel Carl bought us a beer at a local dive (that besides selling beer mostly sold smelly bait). Colt asked Carl how he got into smuggling. He answered that it wasn't too long ago. "My wife Shirley made me promise it would only be temporary. Our son was born with about the worst Talipes condition the doctors ever saw; not just a regular club foot, you know—turned down and inwards, but Skip's was rotated a full 90 degrees inward. To correct this requires at least two if not three surgeries—about six months apart. The best surgeon for this procedure is in Germany, and it costs $175,000. The day I have enough money for it, I'm through with this shit!" *Boy, what you don't know about people till you ask.* Colt then asked Carl why he didn't bring in cocaine, which in one trip would bring in enough money for his son's surgery. Carl took on a look of indignation as if he'd been offended. He pulled his head back and said "That shit's ruining the country. It's bad stuff! I promised myself I wouldn't touch it and I won't!" I was surprised to hear this. We like to say "there's no honor among thieves," but *this* guy had staked out a position and was sticking with it.

While walking to the truck, thinking about Carl's need for money, Colt asked him when he had saved almost enough, why couldn't he just sell his airplane for the rest. "Shit Colt, the plane's not mine. The main guy—Sinclair, provided it for me. And Daryl's too. (Daryl was Shirley's brother. It was a family project.) On the ride back to the motel Carl told us to buy gloves. Back at the motel, after a quick trip to an ACE Hardware to pick up gloves, Colt phoned Rich. He told him that neither of us understood the real endgame here. Rich answered that he couldn't tell him everything yet, except, while they knew who *these* two guys were, they didn't know who was getting the stuff—what organization they were working for. And that was what they needed to know. Colt then remembered Carl having referred to the "main guy," Sinclair, and relayed this to Rich, which *did* get his attention.

Rich asked, "Is Sinclair his first name or his last?" Colt said he didn't know. Rich told him that was his next project: find out as soon as he could and let him know.

Final Preparations

The day before "D-day" Carl had us fly to a rural area west of Kendall Lakes, on the east edge of the glades. No residential developments nearby—just miles of cultivated fields with a barn or warehouse every so often. Our landing area was a pasture next to one of those barns. After plowing through the high grass to a stop, we were met by a guy we'd never seen before. He had us hurriedly taxi *inside* the barn, which was more like a hangar—with a concrete floor. It was completely empty minus a machine shop on one side. We just wasted time while the unknown guy installed the big rubber bladder that would be our extra fuel tank. It was not an easy modification, involving cutting metal, installing valves and connectors, and then hooking up hoses from the bladder to the engine fuel line. The only control for the pilot was a large "T" handle that when turned would *close* the valve in the *normal* fuel line from the wing tanks, and at the same time *open* the valve in the line from the *bladder tank* to the engine. When he was finished we installed the Volkswagen seats on the tracks on each side of the folded bladder. The guy who had led us in gave us some alcohol rags, told us to put on our gloves and wipe down the whole airplane, inside and out; anywhere and everywhere he or we might have touched.

The Trip Down

At 7 a.m. the next morning I was parked on the ramp at Fort Lauderdale Executive, not far from Carl and Colt in their planes (no Daryl—just a three-plane flight). At 8 am sharp we called for taxi clearance and started out to the runway. I was nervous as hell and wishing I'd never gotten myself into this. I was just praying there was nobody in the tower with binoculars; afraid to even turn my head in that direction. One by one we were cleared for takeoff. As my wheels came up I thought: well *one* thing under our belts: we're airborne. As a pilot, once you break ground there's a feeling of satisfaction and well-being, but not this time. We headed southeast over Biscayne Bay, on our initial heading towards Haiti; 700 miles—about five hours. Rich said that if the DEA caught Carl and Daryl before his sting was completed, they'd never find out the scope of the ring; the upward flow of the pot. I spent the first thirty minutes scanning the sky for a King Air or

Cessna Citation that Rich told us his DEA buddies were flying.

Though I couldn't relish it today, the turquoise and emerald-green water surrounding the Caribbean islands was mesmerizing. About 1:30 we approached the gap between the east end of Cuba and the west end of Haiti. There we made our turn due south toward Colombia: 540 miles and another four hours. Not another plane. Not a sound on the radio. Four hours and twenty minutes later Carl made a slight heading adjustment. Ten minutes later I had Barranquilla in sight. Shortly thereafter, even in the now limited daylight I had our destination in sight: a dirt strip carved out of the jungle; not a wide or long strip, but no worse than the ones I landed at in Laos. Carl made a transmission: "Get in a thirty second trail and follow me in. Don't circle overhead, just land straight in." Colt adjusted his position and I reduced power to slow down and get spacing behind him. We all three landed no sweat (except for teeth jarring bumps) and taxied back to what would be the loading area.

Somewhere About 25 Miles Outside Barranquilla

On the ground I was ready for chaos, but it was pretty well organized, though not a single guy cracked a smile. Some were in a military uniform. First all the seats came flying out and then the bladder was unfolded flat on the cabin floor. The 55-gallon drums of fuel had already been dollied over. A hand pump was mounted on the drum and a long hose was being connected from it to the rubber bladder. Filling the bladder took longer than I expected. I watched mine expand and finally be declared full. Soon as it was, the marijuana bundles, heavy 2-foot square compressed cubes wrapped in black plastic, were being stacked in on top of the fuel bladder. When fully loaded there were four rows of pot—two across and two high from the back wall to right up against the pilot's seat; 16 bales in the cabin plus 2 in the copilot's seat made 18 bales total (and way more weight than the aircraft was approved for)!

The Trip Back

It was twilight when we positioned for takeoff. I was third. The acceleration on takeoff roll was frightfully (alarmingly) slow—as if I was towing a trailer with flat tires. Halfway down the dirt strip I considered aborting the takeoff; fearing I was so heavy I might just plow into the trees at the far end! I kept going (and praying). When I had enough speed I eased the yoke back. The nose wheel *did* come up, but the main gear—supporting most the weight, were still heavy on the ground. The tree line was rushing up. Waited as long as I could and when I'd gotten as close to it as I dared, I yanked the nose up, and *thank God* I broke ground. *I was airborne!* But none too soon. Before I got the wheels up I heard them snapping limbs in the tree tops. Incidentally, so many guys did crash on these overloaded takeoffs that even tonight, parked alongside the strip was a bulldozer *to dig a hole and bury the remains of a crashed plane.* (If the pilot lived and was lucky, he might be able to talk one of the other pilots into not taking the two bales in the copilot's seat, and let him ride back in the vacated space.)

Performance of an Over-grossed Aircraft
I was at full power. The engine was screaming for me to give it a break. I was climbing, barely! Maybe 50 feet per minute, as compared to the normal 1,500 feet per minute. If I would have acquiesced to the engine's plea, pulling off even the slightest bit of power, I would have stopped climbing and started descending. Rolled into a normal 30-degree bank to make my right turn to the north. My rate of climb went to a *negative* 100 feet per minute—down! In a bank the vertical component of lift is reduced. So quick—lessen the angle of bank! Usually, to get to ten thousand feet would take six to eight minutes. It took me fifty minutes—almost an hour (and I was never sure the airplane was going to make it). Soon it was pitch black; blacker than you would be familiar with. On land—always near a town or city, there is a lot of light trapped in the lower atmosphere. Out here in the middle of the ocean, you have none of that. (As I said earlier, "like being inside an ink bottle in a coat pocket, hanging in a closet.")

Having Enough Fuel to Make It Back
Once stabilized at altitude the most worrisome time is when you to must switch the engine to the bladder fuel (all of which is needed to make it back). This is done by rotating that recently installed "T" handle, which opens the valve to the bladder, *but at the same time cuts off the normal fuel flow from the wing tanks.* There are several things that can go wrong when attempting this: all resulting in the engine quitting! Starting the process you first advance the mixture control to "Full Rich," then activate the auxiliary fuel pump, then and only then do you muster the nerve to rotate the "T" handle. Even when it works perfectly, air trapped in the bladder line will cause the engine to cough and sputter for fifteen seconds. A big breath and I did it. Several slight coughs and the engine began running smoothly. *Thank you God.*

And, if *beginning* to use the bladder fuel isn't enough of a challenge; since we have no fuel gauge for the bladder we don't know when it's going to run dry. The best you can do is divide the gallons in the tank by the gallons per hour you're using and come up with a rough estimate of the time when you *expect* it to run dry. But the way you know exactly when it's running dry is *you hear the engine quitting!* (And unfortunately, you *do* have to let it run dry.) A half hour before the time you estimated it would run dry, you reach down and position your hand on the "T" handle, so it will be there when the engine starts to quit and you can immediately rotate it back to the normal fuel flow from the wing tanks.

Arriving Back to Florida and Getting Past the Radar

Our takeoff time from Colombia was calculated to have us crossing over Biscayne Bay within a 20-minute window. Remember? One of Daryl's high school buddies worked for the Water Reclamation Bureau and had given him the key to that gate in the Everglades. Well Carl's cousin was the senior radar operator at the Air Traffic Control Center in Richmond (just southwest of Miami). Once we were within fifty miles of the coast, even though our small planes only made a tiny blip on a radar scope, there was a chance we could be spotted. Carl's cousin—soon as he could make us out on the scope, would give his guys a break or send them on a pizza run, and watch the scope himself. For us, monitoring the Miami tower frequency we were able to hear the current barometric pressure and set our altimeters. We'd need it exactly right to make an acceptable touchdown on the dike.

Finding the Dike, Landing, and Unloading

On the trip back none of us had our wingtip or tail lights on. I therefore had no way to see Carl or Colt's airplanes, and of course our landing area was in no way illuminated, so it was just part of the black expanse. Finding it was *not* easy. We were looking for tiny white specks that would be flashlights. On the far end of the dike was a guy shining his towards the landing end, and on the landing end—another guy was standing, shining his flashlight towards where he heard us. After a good ten minutes of searching, twisting and turning at around five hundred feet, without being able to make out a single feature on the ground, I heard a long series of clicks. This would be Carl signaling he had spotted the flashlights and found our dike. Passing east of the strip, and looking back in its direction, I was lucky enough to see a set of landing lights go on, meaning Carl was about to touch down. A moment or two later, though now west of the dike, I wasn't able to see Colt's landing lights, but I did see the dike surface brighten up. He'd touched down and was rolling out. *My turn.* I maneuvered the aircraft so as to line up both lights, putting me on a final approach course. Keeping both lights aligned, I put the gear and flaps down and continued my descent. Going through 50 feet I flipped on the landing lights, crossed right over the first guy with the light, chopped the power, and thudded down like a ton of bricks, jamming the rudders and stomping the brakes to stay centered on the narrow dike. At the end, just to the left, the other two planes were parked, engines off, doors open.

Off-Loading and Escaping

As best I could see in the dark, there were about five guys, shouting at each other and working at a frenzied pace. It didn't look organized but at the rate things were happening, it must have been. After getting bumped into and almost knocked off my feet twice, I backed up to the edge of the activity. Besides Carl's big 550 there was another huge four-wheel-drive vehicle. Bales were going into the trucks right and left, sailing through the air and thudding into the beds. As soon as the planes were emptied of their cargo, the bladders were coming out. Soon as they were out, from somewhere the original seats were being thrown into the planes. I'll bet we weren't on the ground ten minutes when the job was done. Someone thrust a Dustbuster into my hands, shoved me back into my plane, and told me to get the hell back in the air. Being the last into the widened area I was first off; taking back off the opposite way we had landed.

Airborne—still with no exterior lights on, I climbed to about a thousand feet, and flew west till I was over the darkest, most uninhabited area I could locate. There, I set a certain engine power, trimmed the airplane up best I could to "fly itself," *got out of the pilot's seat and went back into the cabin!* (No one is flying the airplane now.) On my hands and knees in the cabin I began using the Dustbuster to vacuum the airplane; suck up every seed, every twig, every piece of a leaf. This took me about fifteen minutes—during which time I had to rush back to the cockpit twice to right the airplane. When finally the job was done I threw the Dustbuster out the window. (I could imagine reading in the Miami Herald, *"Camper in the Glades killed by falling Dustbuster."*) But that wasn't my only job. Now, while the airplane was still doing mostly okay flying itself, I had to install the six seats. I can tell you, by the time I was done with this I was exhausted and drenched with sweat.

The plan was for each of us to go to a separate airport; for me it was the same airport I'd taken off from in the morning: the small Fort Lauderdale Executive airport. No airlines flew into this airport, just small private planes, and there should be zero activity at this ungodly hour. Still, you can imagine, after landing and taxiing to a parking area I was shaking with fearful scenarios that could occur; the police or some DEA agent—not aware of Rich's assignment for us, just being there, or bored personnel from the facility delaying me in a long conversation. I had to sign in and order fuel; didn't use my real name of course. We always bought fuel with cash—though I would not stay and pay now. I'd do it when I returned tomorrow afternoon. Right now I just wanted to get miles between me and the airplane. Didn't hail a cab; walked a mile to a mom and pop motel, checked in and tumbled into the hard single bed.

Payday and More

I slept past checkout time, walked to the airport and thank God was able to pay for the fuel and leave without any conversations that could make me memorable. I was due to meet Colt at the Homestead airport at five. He was in the luncheonette. He had met with Carl, who had already met with his "main guy"—that *Sinclair* fellow, about whom (remembering Rich's request) Colt asked a couple probing questions. Carl wasn't answering, but he was in a good mood. His son Skip—the one with the acute Talipse of the right ankle, in spite of his significant handicap, had just won a jet-ski tournament in Miami. And some good news for us: Carl had given Colt our compensation for the trip. With a grin Colt handed me a paper bag. I went straight to a Men's room stall, opened it and pulled out $18,000—*for one night's work!* I was shocked, excited and worried; not at all sure about anything. When I described the details of this first trip to Kathy, it did nothing to enshrine the project with her! In spite of the financial reward (or because of it) she still held serious reservation.

Colt said that he'd been called by Rich and had to meet him this evening. I gave Colt a couple questions to ask Rich, and Colt said he damn well had a couple of his own. About ten Colt returned, with only a few sensible answers. Even though Colt had no more info for Rich, about this guy called Sinclair, Rich wasn't upset. He asked Colt exactly how many bales we brought back. Colt told him, that he thought we each had 18 bales, so with three aircraft, the total would have been 54. Colt said that for some reason Rich looked askance at the number quoted, jotted it down and told him that on the next trip be sure to get the exact number.

Sooner or Later Things Weren't Going to Go Smooth

It was another week before we attempted it again, another three plane flight; me, Colt, and Carl's brother-in-law—Daryl. Everything went exactly like the first trip: our departure, our flight down, the hectic loading, the white-knuckle takeoff, the laborious climb to altitude, the flight back, *switching tanks*, and even the landing on the dike. Just as we were finishing the unloading; in the midst of bales sailing through the air, lurching black figures and bobbing flashlights, the air was pierced by a shout of alarm, "*Look over there! Look over there! Jesus Christ!*" I saw where the guy was pointing and whipped around to that direction. He was pointing out to SW 217th, where speeding northward on it, soon to be at the dirt turnoff leading to us, were at least *three police cars with flashing red and blue lights.* Uh Oh! The cars turned in on the dirt road and were roaring towards us, sirens wailing! In the next ten seconds, without having time to throw the seats in, Daryl, Colt and I were in our cockpits and cranking the engines. My heart was in my throat watching the cars' headlights getting brighter. We hurried onto the dike and simultaneously poured the coal to it, thumping down the dike—only a few yards behind each other (something that's never done). Once airborne I rolled into a steep bank and looked down at the headlights and flashing lights. In the few seconds I had to scan the area, it appeared that the cop cars were speeding westward on the dirt road, at the same time our two trucks were speeding easterly *on the same road!* Had to roll back and couldn't see what was going to happen.

I didn't think I should return to my designated recovery airport—Fort Lauderdale Executive, or any other airport here on the east coast. Checked my fuel gauge and had enough to make it over to Naples Municipal Airport on the west coast. On the way, I did the same drill with the Dustbuster, but didn't have the original seats to install. Luck was with me—the airport was deserted, and one half-asleep lineman parked me. I signed in (once again with a made-up name and address), left a fuel order and walked out without seeing a single official. *Thank the Lord for small favors.* Checked into the first motel I came to and tumbled into the rack.

In a few days I found out what happened at the Everglades unloading. The drivers of both trucks (Carl being the driver of the first truck), played a game of "chicken," acting as if they were going to ram the incoming cop cars—head on! Their bluff worked and the drivers of the cop cars chose to yank the wheel and go over the side of the road (down into the canal), rather than risk a "head-on." The trucks roared by, turning right and sped south. They escaped with the load without being caught! In spite of this huge scare, Colt and I stayed as Rich's plants, supplying him with names, dates, and particularly, the number of bales we brought in, and what little we could find out about this guy named Sinclair. We both were waiting for Rich to tell us *"Next trip we're going to bring em down!"* The delay continued, either because of the DEA's ultimate objective, that we weren't privy to, or because the DEA is just another example of federal bureaucracy. In any case we just hung in there (accepting the paydays). You can imagine I chose not to share the details of this trip with Kathy.

A Month Later and a Different Kind of Flight

On a trip I wasn't on, *Colt had gotten captured in South America!* Carl's connections in Barranquilla must have missed a payment to the local police, because they arrived before Colt could take off, blocked the runway and grabbed him. It took two weeks to find out where he was being held, and then a couple more to get the payments made to get him freed. (Oh, turns out Colt wasn't completely retired. According to his wife he was working at home as a manager of some pension plan for the state of Illinois, and a week after no one could contact him, the SEC shut down all trading of the parent fund.)

The right people were paid and the day to spring him was set. Since Colt was my friend Carl assigned me as the pilot to fly down there to bring him back. He ushered two rough-looking Cuban guys into my plane—each carrying Uzi's (600 round-per-minute submachine guns). This made me think Carl wasn't sure things were properly laid on. I landed at a jungle strip just outside Barranquilla (not the one we used on our previous trips). We were met by a military guy driving a jeep. My two Cuban guys got in *and waved for me to join them!* In the jeep I saw them pass an approving look when they saw the 9mm in my waistband. I was wondering what my exact role was going to be.

It was a ten-minute drive to a small village. Only a few shutdown businesses and a building with barred windows that I took to be the jail. The two Cubans leaped out of the jeep and ran full speed into the building. I heard three or four shots, and a minute later they came out with an old skinny guy with a white beard, wearing a straw hat. They threw him into the jeep on top of me. *Shit!* I hollered to them that it wasn't Colt! *They had the wrong guy!* In fact I was trying to push the old guy out of the jeep myself when he shouts at me, "Rog! What in the hell's wrong with you"!? Holy Shit, it *was* Colt! He must've lost twenty pounds. And with the beard and the hat he didn't look at all like the Colt I had last seen! It was a high speed, careening trip back to the strip; a quick embarking, engine-start, and takeoff. Safely at altitude Colt began telling his story, and that he only had one friend in jail, a guy named "Mata" who no one else would associate with. I told him that "mata" was short for "matador" which is the Spanish word for "killer." The flight back and landing was uneventful (and it was a comforting feeling knowing for once the cabin contained no contraband).

The Most Terrifying Flying Story I Ever Heard, and It Happened to Me
On the way back from my fourth trip, having just reached altitude, I think about 2 a.m., it was that harrowing time to use the "T" handle to start using the bladder fuel. You can't make it back without using all the fuel in the bladder. If for some reason it wouldn't transfer, you'd exhaust the fuel in the wing tanks, the engine would quit, and you'd glide down through the blackness, into a crushing wall of wet blackness, *and a life of blackness.*

I did the "T" handle rotation, the engine sputtered (which I was expecting) and then *quit completely,* which I wasn't expecting! I immediately turned the "T" handle back to the "wing fuel" position, and after a couple coughs the engine began running. I selected bladder fuel again—twice! Each time, two seconds after rotating the "T" handle to "bladder fuel" a cough, a sputter, and the engine quit completely! Rotating the "T" handle back to the wing fuel position caused the engine to start again. *Great, but I had to get that fuel from the bladder!*

A night ditching at sea had not yet been lived through—ever, and even if I survived the crash, I'd have drowned by daylight. I have to come up with a fix. Maybe one of the bales in the far rear of the cabin (where the rubber hose came out of the bladder) was *pinching the hose closed.* But how could I ever get to the back of the cabin to fix it? I was pinned in the cockpit; my right shoulder was against the two bales in the copilot's seat, and the back of my head was hitting the top bale stacked behind me. Behind it were another three rows of side-by-side stacked bales. This could be the end of my life. It would be almost impossible to make a tunnel back through the bales and get to the pinched hose. I couldn't even start by pulling one bale forward, because there was nowhere to put it. Lemmee think: If I moved the top bale off the copilot's seat—put it somewhere, I could use the vacated space for the first bale I would drag forward. I sliced that top bale into two pieces and was able to jam each half on top of one side of the instrument panel. After doing so I wouldn't be able to see out, but that wouldn't matter because I was flying on instruments anyway. I radioed Colt with my problem, told him my tunneling plan—that I would be out of the cockpit and unable to communicate with him (or control the plane).

After accomplishing the above—with the top bale out of the copilot's seat, I gained one vacant cube of space. I unstrapped, half stood up, grabbed hold of the top bale behind the copilot's seat and drug it over the seat, plopping it down where the other bale had been. *Whew*, one hole! Standing (bent over) and facing rearward I was able to grab the bottom bundle behind the copilot's seat, lift it, turn, and plop it down into my now-empty pilot's seat. This gave me a chance to scan the flight instruments, and noticed I was in a slow left turn off course. I returned the plane to on course and rolled in an eighth of a turn of right wing down trim. I was out of breath but *now had a place to begin my rearward burrowing.* I dropped to my knees, rolled onto my back, and using my heels pushed my way rearward until the top of my head hit the next stack of bales. I first pulled the top one, then the bottom one, out of the stack, dragged them over my head (face) and chest, and pushed them towards the cockpit.

I was now flat on my back in the cabin, in the dark, with two bales of marijuana on my chest. *Uh Oh!* The sound of the airflow passing the airplane was getting louder. I was gaining airspeed. This meant the nose must have dropped and the plane was in a dive! *Quick—up!* Wrestled my way past the two bales, into the cockpit, grabbed the yoke and pulled the nose back up, arresting the descent. Added a bit of power and a hair of nose up trim, and back to work. Still lying on my back, squirming my way rearward, I was removing and replacing one bale and then another. Finally, *there it was!* With my fingers shoved under the last bale, I felt the kinked rubber hose. *What I was praying had been the problem.* I straightened and rerouted it, and then spent at least five minutes working my way back to the cockpit, restacking the bales behind me as I went. After removing the bale from my pilot's seat I plopped down into it, drenched and exhausted. Now, pull the half bales off the top of the instrument panel and put them back on top of the bale in the copilot's seat. I had solved the problem! Ready to resume the flight I noted I was looking at blurred engine instruments, and realized somewhere in the back of the cabin, *I had lost my glasses.* After my calves stopped shaking and my heart rate was down to normal, I rotated the "T" handle to access the bladder fuel; a cough, a sputter, and the engine began running! Crossed Biscayne Bay at 3:20.

Plan B, Landing at Key Largo

My pulse almost back to normal and about fifteen minutes from landing, I heard Daryl's voice: "Goatfuck, goatfuck, goatfuck!' This was a briefed call meaning *Don't land, divert to another location.* Even though we had switched to a new landing site, I guessed it meant something went wrong. I didn't know what to do, but right there and then I swore to myself that this was my last trip! I was done! *Here I am sitting in an airplane loaded with marijuana, with no place to land!* It had to be a decent runway, but also had to be a small airport that would not have any personnel on it or even near it. I had flown into the Key Largo airport last week and knew it closed at sunset, and not only that, it was a good half mile in from the Overseas Highway. Only thing was—the runway stuck out in the water, and even in the daytime it was a tricky landing because there were always a couple dozen sailboats moored right off the end of the runway. To land you had to weave your way between the masts. With no other ideas I was on my way there.

Overhead the airport. Great—as best I could see, it was deserted. No activity, not a single solitary glimmer of light. I didn't want to stay airborne any longer than necessary, where I could be seen or heard by anyone on the ground. I positioned myself on about a mile final, three-hundred feet above the water, descending and heading for the end of the strip. In the blackness under and in front of me I could make out grayish blobs that I knew were the hulls of the sailboats, but could not see the masts. Waited till as low as I could before switching on my landing lights, and good thing I didn't wait a second longer. I narrowly avoided hitting a mast! Was too high and landed long, but got it stopped at the far north end, spun it around and taxied at max speed back to the south end parking area. Pulled into the first empty space.

I leaped out of the aircraft and started running towards the dirt road that would take me out to the Overseas Highway. *Uh, Oh! Big trouble.* Just as I turned onto the dirt road I heard sirens and could see the flashing red and blue hue in the sky. Someone had seen me landing. In a second they'd be turning in on the same road I was running out on! *They did.* With their headlights looming brighter, I made a sharp right turn into dense underbrush, which suddenly became a swamp—now finding myself up to my crotch in slime.

I was only a hundred feet off the road when the cop cars went streaking by. In about ten minutes, based on the shouts and increased commotion, they must have found the airplane. All kinds of activity followed. It was a good two hours before they had all cleared out (minus I think—one cop left to guard the airplane and its cargo). Soon as I could I left my hiding place and started sloshing—still in dense wet undergrowth, towards the main highway. I stopped about fifty feet from it, staying hidden in the scrub brush. I laid there until dawn, exhausted, and out of ideas. I then (staying sufficiently off the highway) walked a few miles north to John Pennekamp Park. There were lots of people there visiting the Welcome Center and using the restrooms and phones. I had no idea where Colt or Daryl were. I called a South Florida friend (telling him a halfway plausible story) to drive an hour south and pick me up at Pennekamp Park.

Everything Must Come to an End

Carl contacted Colt and asked us to meet him at the Stewart Aviation luncheonette. We did, and noticed he was a different person; calm and satisfied. He spoke first: "Guys, it's over, you can retire. I've got the $175,000 and we're already scheduling our trip to Berlin for Skip's first surgery. I promised Shirley and I'm doing it. I'm counting my blessings, knowing full well I could be in prison or dead. I'm quitting this whole ugly thing, for good!"

We didn't know how to react. For one, I breathed a huge sigh of relief; never did feel right while involved. *Finished was surely for the better.* My screwed-up life had left me with one interesting observance: sometimes when you can't make a decision; it gets made for you. We didn't argue with Carl, in fact I think we were genuinely pleased that he had achieved his personal goal—he had what he needed and was going to get Skip's ankle fixed (and we may have felt relieved that we were not going to be responsible for him going to prison).

Don't know about Colt, but during the past few months I had been having a more and more skeptical opinion of Rich, and if what I was doing might be exactly what it looked like I was doing. *Not* what he had said! Of course the big deal now would be: what happens when we tell Rich it's over? As much of a surprise the end of the operation was, we got a bigger one when we met with Rich. It was true he *was* with the DEA, and thus knowing the ins and outs of the South Florida smuggling operations, he had decided to try his hand at it! Carl and Daryl were *his* guys! *And Rich was Sinclair!* Rich had gotten us involved to add to his take; two more planes, twice as much pot, twice the profit! Then he got worried when Colt told him that Carl had mentioned a guy named Sinclair (*who was him—Rich*)! That's why he kept asking Colt what if anything Carl had told him about the guy named Sinclair. Later, Rich suspected that Carl was skimming off some of the incoming stuff, and that was why he wanted Colt to keep track of the exact number of bales. Rich thanked us (like we had just babysat his kids for the afternoon), told us we could each fly our planes back to our airports; just leave the keys in them. He'd have one of his guys pick them up. *I would sleep much better in the nights to come than I had for the past months.*

Reflecting on a Flawed Life

Way too late in my life, but finally, I could not avoid reflecting on the inconsiderate, inexcusably selfish life I had led. Irrespective of what I say drove it, the pattern of my behavior would be viewed by any third party as unpardonable: with my parents—the infrequency of my adult visits; with my children—my prolonged absences; and most especially with my wife—my infidelity. To another man (if it ever occurred to one) my total impotence may not have been the all-controlling factor I profess it to be, though with the shame and humiliation it brought, I truly believe it was. You have seen how I sought a cure with a variety of women who were perhaps little more than unfortunate candidates in my search for the ultimate intimacy. We know of course how my activity impacted Sara, and though I failed to consider it, I suspect on June as well. Perhaps I could, in a small measure, salvage myself as a man and worthy person by being a truly devoted partner with Kathy.

Chapter Fifty-Six
A STAGGERING REVELATION

You Won't Believe What Happened Next

It was a couple weeks before I wound down from my work with Colt and Carl. (Thankful and grateful weeks, that I emerged from it unscathed; I fear undeservedly unscathed.) It was at the end of the second week that I got a call from that For Lauderdale charter company I had flown for before. They knew of my transatlantic experience and that I spoke French (or some people thought I did) and they wanted me to fly some scientists to a small airport not too far from Lyon, France. *Near Lyon?!* Of course hearing that my heart skipped a beat. It was almost as if it was ordained. The last time I was in Lyon was with Mireille—sixteen years ago. Was it wise for me to even allow myself to get that close to her again; to relive that pain? In spite of that danger, and my debating of it, I accepted the trip. It was going to be a different Atlantic crossing this time because they had an older Lear, and I would not have enough fuel to do it like I used to—from Gander, Newfoundland to Shannon. I would have to leave from Goose Bay, Labrador to Reykjavik, Iceland, refuel there, and then down to the shorter runway, Lyon-Saint Exupèry airport.

The Big Debate

After spending 18-plus hours in accomplishing everything involved in the crossing, including a bunch of paperwork at the airport, I got a room for the night in a small but charming mom and pop hotel there in Saint Exupèry. But instead of turning out the light like I should have, I sat on the edge of the bed, head in hands, arguing with myself. I was only thirty miles south of St-Martin-du-Lac, Mireille's town. I could not overcome the lure of at least trying to give her a call.

*Why Hadn't It Been the Beginning of a Beautiful New Life
With Mireille?*

Sixteen years ago, my dreams of an incredible sexually and blissfully fulfilled life with her were dashed when just before I boarded my flight back to the States, in her native language she made that shocking confession to me—that as best I could translate meant *she did not think she could live with just one man!* When I had digested these words and was able to regain my sensibilities, I had to numbly conclude her pleasure was not because of me. It was the pleasure of having a man inside her, perhaps *any* man. I knew then, if I married her there would come a day when she would surely break my heart. But now, should I try to contact her, after all these years and irrespective of her shocking admission to me? And now with me being married, I probably shouldn't even be considering it. But if we only touch base, say "Hi" and reminisce for a few hours tomorrow, that could be okay. *I decided to do it!* (And maybe any thoughts of not doing so, had received only token consideration.)

Making Contact

I had long since lost her phone number. The French telephone information service gave me the phone number of a person with Mireille's last name, living in her area. Perhaps, just perhaps. I called it. An elderly woman answered. I was about to hang up when she told me that while she wasn't Mireille, she had received calls for her before, and had her number! *She was giving Mireille's number to a complete stranger!* I called the number and good news—a woman answered and I asked if I had reached Mireille Piccio. Before responding that I had, she blurted out "Roger c'est vous? C'est vous Roger?" *She recognized my voice in just a dozen words, and after sixteen years!* Through a stumbling conversation, all in French, I believe I was more thrilled than I should have been to hear her say, "Oui, oui." She was fine with me stopping by tomorrow. She said that she was still in the same stone cottage atop the high meadow.

Arriving at Her Home

The drive north was sometimes familiar; especially when I went through the center of that one small village on that barely two-car-wide road. When I arrived at the outskirts of St-Martin-du-lac, I barely recognized it. The years had made a big difference. Many new structures and a confusing change of appearance in the roadside foliage. I was hoping that even with the changes I would be able to spot the partially hidden, right-side turnoff to the private drive; the one that led up the long hill to her house. I came upon what had to be it, even though it now only bore a slight resemblance.

After turning into it and venturing uphill through a wooded area, I wasn't so sure. Then the grassy meadow appeared on the left. Another hundred yards and I saw the two stone pillars with the wrought iron gate.

I'd made it. Within a minute of turning off the engine I spied Mireille, out of the cottage and walking towards the gate. As she got closer I was taken aback by her stern expression; no smile or indication that she was glad to see me. And then I thought back, about me leaving and never contacting her again; why *would* she be glad to see me? We had what would be called a civil greeting, with no embrace. The first surprise was, there was no husband. She had not remarried; was still single (*making my visit as a married man even less appropriate*).

The Stinging, Numbing, Mind-Bending Truth

During the next couple hours Mireille slowly warmed to my presence, and every once in a while I may have seen the hint of a smile. We sat in two chairs facing each other, speaking mostly French (although her English had improved). It was not long before Mireille brought up the subject of my unexplained, sudden and permanent disappearance. Her question was in earnest and with gestures and expressions of dismay and concern. *"Pour quoi, pour quelle raison?"* Why, for what reason, she asked. Certainly I knew the reason; that damned thing about *not being able to live with just one man!* But how was I going to accuse her of being a woman whose sexual appetite required more than one man. I had no choice but to do so. It took a couple minutes to get it out, but I refreshed her memory of the statement she had made. As I was finishing, she appeared stunned—bodily wounded, raised both hands to her face and stood up abruptly, not speaking, just twisting and turning, in fact—moaning aloud! When she calmed herself, she dropped to her knees on the floor in front of me, put her palms on my knees and looking into my eyes, exclaimed that *"living with just one man"* in French, is an idiom meaning *"being married*!" And the reason she said she didn't think she could re-marry, was *because she still loved her first husband so much!*

Oh my God! Here was a woman who was the opposite of what I had thought she was! Rather than being promiscuous she was the epitome of loyalty and devotion. Because of my lack of familiarity with the French language *I thought she meant to admit something entirely contrary!* My erroneous translation had caused me to throw away my dreams, leave and never contact her again; mistakenly resign myself to a life without ever knowing again what I had known with her.

That Night

Shortly after I arrived I had told Mireille I was married, and happily married; something she may well have guessed after all these years.

I suspected at this late date, neither she nor I harbored any thoughts of attempting to recreate a life together and discover the bliss we had known so many years ago. Upon arrival she asked me if I would spend the night. I agreed to but threw my overnight bag on the bed in the guest room and hung my jacket over a chair at the foot of that bed; making it apparent I was not planning on us sleeping together. She prepared a delicious meal for us (with my favorite Bordeaux). While the meal was great, it was quiet; both of us preoccupied with "what-ifs."

When it was time to retire, I gave her a polite kiss on each cheek and walked straight to the guest room. On a later trip to the bathroom, through her partially open door I could see the flickering light of a candle. I returned straight to the guest room and was proud of myself for ignoring the wonderment that was in my mind. As you might imagine I did not soon fall asleep. As I was slipping away *I felt Mireille's body next to me*. In spite of everything—especially my thoughts of Kathy, I immediately felt the same strong and capable arousal I had felt with her each time before, but with no woman since. I resisted, attempting to be caring without taking any action that would encourage her. But it was no use. She began kissing me and soon was positioning herself over me. It was happening! In spite of me being wracked with guilt I let her slide down on me. And it was just like Dakar.

After lying there the time I knew I must, as soon as I could I left the bed and went to the bathroom. There, alone with my culpability I took a shower, almost scrubbing the skin off my bones; racked with guilt—severe and deserved guilt! I could not believe I let it occur, with a loving wife back in Florida, likely incapable of imagining this behavior on the part of her husband. I was sick—physically sick. The next morning I left early, but not before Mireille said in French *that she had lost me once and didn't want to lose me again*. The drive back to the hotel and the small airport was mournful—me only a shadow of the man who had left the states just two days ago. Throughout the multi leg flight back to Lauderdale I was haunted by my transgression, which I didn't even need to vow would never happen again. I made a personal pledge to spend every day the rest of my life making Kathy happy and proud. Though I knew, nothing now or ever could erase my wrongdoing.

Back in Hobe Sound

Five minutes from the house, no matter how hard I tried I could not erase the image of Mireille's face, or cease hearing her saying *I lost you once and I don't want to lose you again.* Even if *she* didn't, I knew it was over—never to be. Upon meeting Kathy, if you suspected my guilt and deserved discomfort would be difficult to hide, you would be right. I couldn't believe the regret and sadness I felt wasn't apparent on my expressionless face. I don't know if Kathy's joy at seeing me made things better or worse. And as you might imagine, that first day back I dreaded when the hour would come that we would retreat to the bedroom; just hoping this would be one of the usual "holding hands" nights. It wasn't. As much trouble as I had on the rare occasions that Kathy felt up to it, tonight, I was mercifully up to it. Undeserved as I was. The next day came and went, then a week, and more. Wounded though I was, I was going to be able to make it, and was gratefully able to make myself bit by bit think less about Mireille.

Chapter Fifty-Seven
NICARAGUA

Taking the Only Work I Could Get

In view of that *"Outplaced for Management Convenience"* thing, my resumés only netted responses from bare bones Charter companies (such as that one in Ft Lauderdale) that weren't carrying executives on boondoggles. They were carrying passengers who had paid good money to get someplace regardless of the weather. So these companies didn't care why I left my last job, they just wanted to be sure I didn't mind flying in sleet and blowing snow, making zero-visibility, zero-ceiling approaches, and landing on a frozen runway at 2 in the morning. I hired on temporarily with several of these "shoestring" operations, most being in declining cities, operating old aircraft weren't new or well maintained, and the pay was nothing to brag about. Those checks plus the proceeds from Colt's DEA project were getting us through. But it wasn't going to last forever and I was still hoping for a miracle hiring.

A Voice From the Past and a Job

In the spring of '86 an old friend from Air America, still with CIA connections, found out I was available. He called me while on a break from his assignment *in Nicaragua!* At this time Nicaragua was in the midst of a civil war. In a not very well disguised fashion (which resulted in the Oliver North *"Iran-Contra Scandal"*) the US was arming the Nicaraguan "Contras" (the guerillas) who were attempting to defeat the "Sandinistas" (the government militia) and overthrow Daniel Ortega, the Communist leader of Nicaragua. My friend asked me if I would like to do some flying not unlike what I had done in Southeast Asia. And he said the job would pay really good. Knowing little else I accepted and was told I'd soon receive an airline ticket from Miami to Comalapa airport in El Salvador. Once again (similar to my midnight to dawn back-and-forths to Cuba) this venture was not popular with Kathy. The risk involved was not clear, and I'd be away—in fact out of the country, for an indefinite time. I assured her I knew these guys from Air America, and while they were adventure-prone, they were longtime friends, smart and cautious.

Arriving in El Salvador

The airport was reasonably modern and I felt mostly safe. John met me and started the drive to San Salvador. There wasn't a building of any sort on either side of the road (or even in sight)! Just rolling bluffs of bright green foliage and taller palms. He noticed my concern and told me the airport was 30 klicks (kilometers) out of the city. As we approached our "Safe House" in an almost middle-class neighborhood, John advised me that I shouldn't wander more than a hundred yards from the house. Kidnapping Americans for ransom was an ongoing activity here. John told me that our airplanes were based at a small military airport—Ilopango, located just a few miles outside city. That's where we would launch from.

Some Old Friends

Entering the safe house I was pleased to see two other Air America pilots (Bill Copper and Buzz Sanders) and two "kickers" I knew from Laos. A series of hugs and back-slapping ensued. So far I had no reason to suspect the danger in what I would soon be doing. Although they weren't with us in the safe house now, two notorious Cubans (who worked for the CIA since the failed "Bay of Pigs" invasion in 1961) were supervising this operation. They were the intermediaries between the Agency and our manager (Bill), telling him where and when we would go, and what we would carry.

How the Operation Was Being Funded (This will be Important Later)

The financial support for the operation came from two USA-based fund-raising groups, *each supporting a different set of guerillas.*

Funding group "A" delivered the supplies for their contras to the airport here in San Salvador, and provided an old propeller-driven cargo plane—the C-123 "Provider" to air drop the guns and ammo to their contras in Nicaragua.

Funding group "B" delivered the supplies for their contras to a small airport (Aguacate) in Honduras, and provided a Vietnam-era, US Army propeller-driven cargo plane—the DHC-4 "Caribou" to first fly to Honduras, pick up the guns and ammo there, and then air drop them to their contras in Nicaragua.

A Real Challenge

Talk about worried: I was being assigned to fly the Caribou! John had thought I flew it with Air America, whereas I had never even been inside one, let alone *pilot* one! Holy Shit! That's why I'm here! They needed another Caribou pilot. I was smart enough not to admit I'd never flown the Caribou. I hitched a ride to the nearby military airport where our aircraft were. There I saw dozens of disabled old military airplanes with flat tires, surrounded by large piles of junk: rusted hunks of metal, discarded engines, and rows of tarp-covered pallets. I spied our caribou; went to it and dug out the Aircraft Flight Manual. Back in the safe house I locked myself in my room for the next three days, and memorized the manual—cover to cover: the layout of the cockpit, operating techniques, every flight condition, all the "normal" and "emergency" procedures, and most importantly: the critical airspeeds, such as what speed I needed to attain on takeoff before attempting to raise the nose wheel, and very important—what was the airspeed to hold on final approach to landing, and a matter of life and death speed—how slow you could fly before a plane would stall. That's when the airflow over the wing separates, causing a sudden loss of all lift, and the plane *does* "fall out of the sky." (In the Caribou—59 knots.) Normally these things are learned in a week-long ground school and a week of actual flight training, *not by reading about them in a book and trying to memorize them.*

My First Flight to Aguacate

I was a nervous wreck as the van made its way to the Ilopango airport, hoping and praying I'd find the Caribou cockpit to be reasonably similar to what I had studied; that I'd be able to locate all the switches, and get through the checklists and procedures without my copilot noticing my hesitancy. My first flight—that everyone thought was my first flight in the aircraft down here, was actually my first flight in the aircraft *ever!* Acting as if I was not in a hurry (to disguise my lack of familiarity) I was able to get through the pre-start and start. My copilot called for "taxi clearance" and we were on our way. We got to the runway, were cleared for takeoff, and did so, me remembering the speed when I could lift the nose wheel and become airborne. You might imagine the thrill and satisfaction I had when seeing the ground fall away beneath me and calling out "Wheels Up"!

Halfway to Aguacate I passed over a larger Honduran airport: Tegucigalpa. I had been told that under no conditions was I ever to land there. *Crash before landing there!* It was the Top Secret headquarters for the CIA, from where they ran every operation in Latin and South America. A couple months before I arrived, an unannounced pilot from I think

Venezuela, landed his plane at Tegucigalpa, and right there on the ramp, after getting out of his airplane, in front of God and country, a senior CIA officer (whose name you might recognize) shot him!

Still several miles from our destination I spied the tiny village of Aguacate, in the middle of a mile-wide, flat green valley. Under me the valley was only a couple hundred feet across, and in the bottom of it I observed what must be the runway—a narrow, badly rutted, red dirt path. I had made an okay takeoff an hour ago, and was now about to try a landing. Luck was with me—having flown landings at 125 knots in the Learjet, now at only 70 knots in the Caribou, I had plenty of time to make the necessary corrections during my approach. The landing went fine (and I don't think Jerry was any the wiser regarding it being my first flight). I *might* be able to pull this thing off!

The Operation at Aguacate

The runway was nestled in the narrow trough of the valley. The ground sloped up steeply on the south side, on which there was a one-room building that served as our operations office, a dilapidated (mostly canvas) pilots' hostel, and a small cottage—manned by two CIA guys. Since Congress still had not approved the CIA funding for this operation, the two CIA guys assigned here were not supposed to talk to us, *or even to notice we were here!* However when they went to lunch they left their cottage unlocked, and conveyed to us that no one would know it if we snuck in. And we did, since it served as our only intelligence briefing. One wall was a battle map of Nicaragua, showing where the "Sandinistas" (communist government soldiers) were last spotted, and where their anti-aircraft guns were located. The first night I was not assigned a mission, but the other Caribou pilot (Buzz Sanders) was assigned a midnight takeoff. Buzz had the reputation of being an out and out global mercenary and had "balls of steel" like no one I ever met (except maybe Colt). Two hours before his midnight launch, he just laid down on one of the cots and took a nap (while wearing a black tee shirt that read *"Kill em all and let God sort it out"*). Oh, another thing about Buzz: he had a wife in Miami, a wife in Puerto Rico, and one in Colombia.

My First Mission

The next afternoon, in the middle of my "Franks and Beans" military K rations, I was told I'd go that night. I was surprised, since dark storm clouds had begun forming around one p.m. and were getting worse. If this same weather were over our drop zone, we would not be able to find it. Our drop time was 3:00 a.m., meaning about a 1:45 a.m. takeoff. While I had the coordinates for the drop zone (the guerilla's location), this was decades before GPS. Finding them was next to impossible, and only accomplished by the skilled use of a years-out-of-date navigation system called LORAN-C. The pilot flying the aircraft could not keep his head down looking at the LORAN scope on a lower center console. It was the copilot who monitored this ancient navigation device and hollered headings to fly, and some were much better than others in interpreting it. The distorted unclear screen was a labyrinth of hundreds of numbered intersecting grid lines. After receiving my flight particulars, I went back up to the hostel to waste the next five hours and take a couple of nervous pees. (I certainly was not able to take a nap like Buzz.)

About midnight the thunder started. An hour later the rain started, and *did it!* A torrential downpour. By the time Jerry and I started down the steep path that led down to the runway, it was a gushing stream of muddy water about a half foot deep. The mechanic for our aircraft (an extremely good-natured Filipino named Alex Custodio) met us at the aircraft and assured me (but not as enthusiastically as I would have liked) that the plane was "ready to go." It took me four attempts to get the right engine started and running.

The Flight Down

My second flight in the aircraft: a night takeoff in pouring rain, with no runway lights, just .45 caliber ammo cans stuffed with burning rags to line the runway edges. Made it off okay. It took about an hour and and a half to twist and turn our way through towering cumulus clouds to get in the area of the drop zone. Jerry had his head down the whole way, trying to interpret the LORAN. I was looking outside, but it being pitch black and with a solid cloud coverage, there was no way I could navigate by any terrain features below. Oh, the drop zone coordinates radioed in from the Contras (the guerillas), were only where they *thought* they were. (After running backwards for two hours, in the dark, and being shot at, it's real easy to lose track of your actual position.) We could forgive them if they weren't where they said they were, which they seldom were. On these trips, in the cargo bay were two guys: my kicker who would shove the stuff out (Dan Gamlan) and the number two Cuban guy talking to the Contras with a hand-held radio, trying to get their exact location. The number one Cuban guy—running the operation, was Felix. He never went on the flights. (In his wallet he carried a photo of him shaking hands with George Bush senior.)

Who Was the Cuban Guy in the Back of the Aircraft?

Raphael. A guy rumored to be a storied "hit-man" for the Agency. And I believed the rumor. Observing him I came to the conclusion that guys who did what he did, definitely marched to their own drummer! No smiles, no jokes, not even an occasional remark. Never said a word at mealtime. One night about a week ago he ended up sharing a room with me. When I went to sleep he was sitting on the edge of his bed, his head in his hands. When I woke up in the morning, *he was still sitting exactly like that.* Tonight it was Raphael who was with us, using his radio to try to determine his Contras' exact location. He did, and as I crossed over the position Dan released the load out the open rear hatch. As soon as it was clear I turned towards home and poured the coal to it.

The Way Back and Landing

On the way back the weather did not improve; rumbling thunder, lightning on all sides, and the steady loud drum of rain on the top of the aircraft (and the cockpit leaked). I was (thank you God) successful in finding Aguacate. Unfortunately, the rain had extinguished half the burning ammo cans lining the sides of the runway. While circling overhead deciding what kind of pattern I could use to land (without flying into the high hills on each side of the strip), my heart almost came out my throat! *The right engine quit cold!* Not only was it just my second flight in the airplane, it was night and in pouring rain, and now—*single-engine!* Not sure what Jerry was doing, but lots of frantic moves attempting to restart the engine.

I "feathered" the engine—manually pulling the lever that would streamline the propeller blades so they would be fared, greatly reducing the drag, helping our single-engine operation. Regarding the circling approach to landing there's an expression every pilot knows: "when making an engine-out landing, never turn into the dead engine." This can cause a fatal crash. So I had to make a tight left turn to the runway (away from the failed engine), almost brushing the trees on the high terrain to the south. I lined up on the few ammo cans whose burning rags had not been rained out, and landed with a splashing thud. After I parked it was ten minutes before my calves stopped shaking and I could get out. I was drenched, but not from rain. Jerry was slapping me on the back in a congratulatory and thankful manner.

The details of this operation were never to leave the circle of we participants, primarily because the funding for it had not yet been authorized, and it was not yet supposed to have started! I couldn't mail anything to Kathy and could only place a call when I was back in the safehouse in San Salvador. I did make contact as frequently as I could, but was not able to share anything of what you have just read. Still, hearing my voice once a week seemed to be filling the bill, as a testimony to my health and welfare. So no insurmountable problems on the home front.

Assigned Another Mission

Three days later I was told to get ready for a one-thirty a.m. takeoff. It was a better day, with just scattered clouds. Just before straggling down to the runway, in our toilet taking my last nervous pee, I glanced down to the wood-slatted floorboards, and there glaring up at me, was the biggest and ugliest giant toad I ever saw. As big as a football. I backed out slowly. This time I had no trouble starting the engines. Airborne, as soon as I had enough altitude to clear the ridge to the south, I banked right and began my route into Nicaragua, turning the aircraft as necessary to stay clear of an occasional cloud. Jerry was my copilot again. My kicker was a different guy—Gene Hasenfeld, and the Contra liaison guy on board was again—Rafael. About halfway to the drop zone, our LORAN navigation device went out! With the full moon I might be able to *visually* navigate to the Contra position. I was paralleling a wide southerly flowing river. On the map, in about forty miles the river made a ninety degree turn to the west, and if I made that turn and flew another twenty miles down the river, the drop zone should be there—about a hundred yards south of the river. I maneuvered the plane until I was centered over the river.

A Heart-Stopper!

I was skimming the surface, the racing moon reflecting on the shining flat black water in front of me. Twenty miles more and I would follow its turn westward. The cockpit window was open; the cool air rushing past my cheek. Things were going pretty good. Well things *were* going pretty good. Suddenly Jerry and I were blinded, struck sightless by a million lumens filling the cockpit! Heart pounding, straining to see, I spotted the source: a huge spotlight in front of us on the left bank—fixed directly on us! The next second the sky in front of us turned *fluorescent bright pink! Hundreds if not thousands of tracers going by!* Sandanista machine-guns had opened up on us. Nothing I could do—went right through the deadly pink veil, shuddering at the pings as a hail of bullets pierced the aircraft. In two seconds we were through it. *We'd escaped!* I knew one thing—one *great* thing: I personally hadn't been hit. Jerry's exclamations indicated he had to be alive, and the engines didn't miss a beat. I grabbed the mic and called Gene in the back; good news—he and Raphael hadn't been hit! God knows how many rounds went through the aircraft, and none of us got hit!

I continued down the river till it turned west, then banked to the right to stay centered over it. Seven minutes later I was where a hard left turn would put me right over the supposed position of our Contras. I told Gene to tell Raphael we would be over the drop zone in thirty seconds. Gene said Raphael already knew that because he was using his hand-held radio talking to his Contras. But while the Contras could *hear* the airplane, they were unable to give directions to put us precisely over them. After a good ten minutes of Raphael screaming at his Contra leader, he shoved the radio into his pocket, grabbed Gene's parachute off the hook, put it on, *and ran out the back of the airplane!* In the middle of the night, somewhere in the middle of Nicaragua, maybe right over the Sandinistas, he just jumped out of the plane! We had no choice now but to bring the load back (rather than risk donating it to the enemy). The flight back was uneventful (this time with both engines). I have no idea how he accomplished it, but two weeks later Raphael comes walking into the safe house carrying Gene's parachute!

A Perhaps Should-Have-Been Avoided Tragedy

One morning about 07:30 Bill Copper roused me out of bed and told me that Jerry and I had to get out to the airport, fire up the Caribou, and get over to Aguacate as fast as we could. A "life or death" mission had come up. Funding group B (who financed and directed my Caribou operation) had their most loyal and well-trained Contras surrounded by the Sandinistas, and would be wiped out to the man, *unless I could get them ammo right now!* These supplies, as usual, were stock piled at Aguacate. Jerry and I rushed to the airport and made a quick flight to Aguacate. The head Contra general—General Bruno was already there and waiting to brief us.

The briefing was in "operations"—that small one-room cottage with one wall-mounted air conditioner. To keep the cool air inside, hanging in the open doorway was a drape of thick plastic you had to brush aside to enter. The general was on a platform at the front of the room, using a wall map to show the location of his guerillas. Uh Oh! Big problem—a very big problem: The Contras needing the supplies were too far south in Nicaragua. No matter how many ways I planned it, my *Caribou did not carry enough fuel to get down there, make the drop, and be able to make it back to Aguacate*. No way the Caribou could do it. I reluctantly made that fact known to the General. Speechless he dropped both arms to his side. An expression of pain and disbelief covered his face. This meant his troops were going to be wiped out!

In the following hushed silence a 16-year-old Honduran mechanic next to me, knowing I spoke Spanish whispered an idea to me that nobody in the room (including the General or I) had thought of. The kid said "I know the ammo and supplies here are from funding group "B," only supposed to be delivered by your Caribou, but it doesn't have the range to do it. What if you just load up your plane here, fly the supplies over to San Salvador, and let the C-123 do it. They got the fuel range to do it. Just fly the same route they always do. Had to admit, a hell of an idea. (Only problem: the C-123 belonged to funding group "A.")

I was amazed this kid knew so much about our operation and had come up with this solution. I raised my hand and told General Bruno I might have an idea. Understandably he was all ears. I relayed the kid's plan (not attributing it to him lest it be discounted immediately). It only needed General Bruno to get approval from funding group "A" *to borrow their C-123 for one flight*. He said that would not be a problem. Jerry and I loaded all the supplies into our plane, and flew them to San Salvador, and had them loaded on the C-123. Piloted by Bill Copper and Buzz Sanders, the C-123 could be airborne by noon, on the way to General Bruno's surrounded troops.

The Flight Down

Once his plane was loaded, Bill did the standard C-123 route; first flying south off the west coast of Nicaragua (a safe distance out to sea). When he was far enough south to be safely over Costa Rican waters, he turned east flying across friendly Costa Rica—towards the Caribbean Sea. The planned route was supposed to be that once over the Caribbean, he'd turn north, staying over the water, and fly up to where they would turn into Nicaragua and the drop zone.

But it was a beautiful day, deep blue skies, friendly puffy white clouds; everything copasetic. As a pilot, flying in hostile conditions you've got to be wary of these balmy sunlit conditions. They can give you a false feeling of safety and cause complacency, decreasing your regard for the ever-present danger. This in fact occurred. Before reaching the designated point to turn north (over the water off the east coast of Costa Rica) Bill opted to turn northeast; *take a diagonal shortcut across the southeast corner of Nicaragua.* Save ten or fifteen minutes.

This turned out to be a single, tragic example of a momentary lapse of discipline. Still over Costa Rica and a little south of the Nicaraguan town of El Castillo, Bill turned to a northeast heading, crossing the San Juan

River—entering Nicaragua on what would have been a shorter direct leg to the drop zone. Unfortunately, there was a Sandinista Special Forces camp on the north bank of the river. They spotted the C123 and radioed ahead, where the waiting anti-aircraft emplacements were ready, and blew it out of the sky! The kicker, Gene Hasenfeld bailed out, but Bill and Buzz were killed on impact. *I could not help but think, if I hadn't relayed the teenager's idea about this flight, it wouldn't have gone, and Bill and Buzz would be alive.* This event made the headlines and weekly magazine covers, alerting the population to another clandestine government shenanigan. Congress was enraged and voted not to approve CIA funding for the operation; the end of the project and another job.

Chapter Fifty-Eight
BETTER LATE THAN NEVER

Chet Falk Again

While recuperating from my questionable work for Colt and Rich, and scaring myself to death in Nicaragua, I got a call from a friend, with news about Chet Falk. You remember Chet, my pilot friend—first from the Marine Corps and then Air America. The guy I was flying with when I got shot down in the Delta. Just about the most dedicated Marine I ever met; except he didn't *look* like one. Oh he was tall and had that military crew cut, but it was on top of a round, chubby, juvenile-looking face. And he was "pear shaped" with narrow shoulders and wide hips. Perhaps because of this appearance, when he met with the board to be accepted as a Regular Officer (a "lifer") *they turned him down*. This absolutely crushed him, so he did what most passed-over Reserve officers do: he didn't renew his temporary commission and left the Corps.

He heard about Air America, applied and was hired. When he walked through my door in Saigon in 1967, though I hadn't seen him for years, I recognized him immediately. Chet was single—in fact never married, which he appeared not well-suited for. He definitely wasn't a womanizer; never was comfortable interacting with the ladies, although in Saigon he made one exception—conversing with the young Vietnamese secretaries, who felt safe with him, recognizing he was no threat and appreciating his dry humor.

A Terminal Medical Problem

After Air America disbanded, the pilots went to the four winds: Malaysia, Indonesia, Alaska, Iran, Africa, and parts unknown. The fella calling me said Chet had terminal cancer. He was living alone in Rialto. California, in the house he had grown up in, that his deceased parents left him. Now with no living relatives and only in touch with a couple Air America pilots, he had no one to count on; completely alone. Since he worked for me in Air America and served with me in the Marine Corps, I decided to give him a call; let him know I hadn't forgotten him (as well I shouldn't have). On the first call I got his answering machine, causing me to listen to the whole "Marine Corps Hymn" before I could leave a message.

When I did get through to him, I was able to sense a brave but understandably resigned attitude. He said he'd gone to the emergency room one night with unusual nausea and dizziness. Next thing he knows, it's the following morning and a nurse is at his bedside asking him to sign a permit for them to do a cranial operation—*that he had undergone during the night!* They had diagnosed an aggressive cancer of the brain stem. They did the best they could. Nothing more surgically could be done. The only question now was, would it be six months or a year? He was now under the care of the doctors at the nearby VA hospital in Loma Linda.

My First Visit to Chet

I booked a flight to Los Angeles, rented a car, and made the hour and a half drive to Rialto. It was as rewarding a reunion as could be had under the circumstances. I straightened up the house, did the laundry, cleaned out the refrigerator, and made the grocery runs. On his desk was a stack of medical bills and insurance forms to fill out. He told me that a couple times each week, when he woke up in the morning he would pledge to tackle it. But somehow—every time he'd start, he'd become discouraged and then just give up. He just didn't have the energy to stay with it. Before I left I at least made a dent in this correspondence, but I'll tell you, not being terminally ill and with all my faculties, even I got frustrated at the complex, almost unanswerable questions. Back in Florida I stayed in touch with him. On a call a month later, he told me that his condition had deteriorated to the point that the doctors told him that unless he could arrange full time care in his home, they were going to have to hospitalize him!

Miss Hanh

In the late sixties when Chet was in Saigon, one of those young Vietnamese girls working in our Admin Office had caught his eye. I doubt he and Miss Hanh ever went on a date together, and I'm sure they never slept together, but he was sweet on her and she appeared of similar feelings. I guess it could have been called "puppy love." She escaped Vietnam just days before Saigon fell and was flown to Los Angeles—where other Vietnamese had set up a refugee assistance program. They got her an interview with Travelers Insurance. She was hired and rose rapidly through the ranks, ending up eleven years later, still with Travelers, but in Tulsa, Oklahoma— as the Vice President of Claims for that state.

After arriving in the states, Miss Hanh and Chet evidently wrote and phoned each other from time to time. Miss Hanh (now a still unmarried 50-year-old) learned about Chet's dilemma: *if he didn't have full time in-home care he was going to be committed.* She quit her well-paying position with Travellers, put her things in storage, sold her house, and travelled to California to become Chet's required "24-hour care!" Once there she was an angel. She cooked for him, cleaned the house, did all the shopping, took care of all his needs, monitored his medications, and was a constant compassionate companion (and I'm sure—a companion only). Talking to Miss Hanh on the phone I learned that in recent weeks Chet's condition had worsened, especially his hallucinations. He thought people were looking in the windows, and asked her to pull the blinds. Although she resisted, the doctors at Loma Linda ordered her to bring him in. He would have to be hospitalized, and sadly but realistically assigned to the palliative care ward (the Hospice of a hospital). Hearing this, I again booked a flight to California to be with Chet, perhaps for his last days. There, daily—with Miss Hanh, I visited him in the hospital. At his bedside I would watch as she mopped his brow, spoon fed him, and when not doing that, would just stroke his forehead, or if he dozed for an hour or two, just sit there silently until he awoke.

Better Late Than Never

On one of the last visits before he passed, sitting alongside his bed with Miss Hanh I noticed him making an effort to reach out one thin arm towards her, and form some words. I took this as going to be something very much on the personal side, so quickly exited the room. After wandering the halls for ten minutes I peered in the doorway. Miss Hanh was no longer at his bedside but was standing at the foot of the bed—eyes fixed straight ahead at the open doorway, trembling. I approached her and saw tears streaming down her cheeks. She looked up at me with an expression of pained rapture and exclaimed, "He said he *loved* me!"

Chapter Fifty-Nine
TO THE MIDDLE EAST (AND HOW I SAW IT)

Flight Safety International

October 1987: Kathy and I were living alone in the house in Hobe Sound. (Mark and Samantha were professionals gainfully employed out of state.) During this time our income was still the proceeds of the DEA project, and what I was earning flying for those charter operations. *But a break!* Here on the West Palm Beach airport (where I flew for SSL Systems, and only 20 minutes from home) there was another aviation employer: FlightSafety International—an established company that administered annually-required FAA recurrent training to *already certified* jet captains. They were overloaded with South American Learjet captains and needed a Spanish-speaking Learjet instructor. They scheduled me for an interview that included me giving a classroom presentation in Spanish. (With my lack of fluency, the only way I was able to do this was to practice it a hundred times the night before.) It went okay and I was hired!

A Surprise Offer

One of my Learjet students was the Chief Pilot for McDonnell Douglas in the Middle East. One day he asks me if it's true I was a Marine attack pilot and also a Chief Pilot for Air America? I had no idea how he found that out, but I answered, "Yeah, Bob, that's right." He informed me his pilots were flying for the Saudi Air Force, and asked if I would be interested? Based on the salary he quoted I had to say yes. A week later I received tickets to the McDonnell Douglas head office in St. Louis. There I had two interviews, the second one being from a guy from Langley (the CIA headquarters). The result: I was offered a job with Middle East Logistics Support, in Riyadh, Saudi Arabia.

A Couple Setbacks Before Joining McDonnell Douglas

I had to take a "new hire" drug test, and it came back "positive." *I'd failed it.* I found out why: The day before my test—while earning another flight-rating, I had a long, hard day, taking three flight checks! Knowing I was scheduled to give an early FlightSafety class the next morning, I needed a

446

good night's sleep and *had taken a valium*—which caused the "positive" on my drug test. I took a second test and when McDonnell called for the results, the clerk got the first letter of my last name wrong, and told them they did not have a "negative" test result for that name. It *appeared* I had failed again! It only took a couple days to clear up the "name" thing, and I was hired. When Kathy heard the details I think she was actually excited. She knew there would just be a 90-day probation period before she could join me, and she was able to rent our house to her brother—effective on whatever date she would leave to join me. The following week I packed two suitcases and was on my way to the Middle East!

Arriving in a New and Strange Country

My flight touched down at the Riyadh, Saudi Arabia airport a little after two in the morning. The terminal was a spectacular architectural overkill; a huge, glistening, cavernous, stadium-sized interior space. All the walls and the ceiling were made of polished cream and taupe marble, with lots of apparently real gold trim. It was the most ostentatious, garish display of opulence that I had ever laid my eyes on. Five times the size that would be required (now or ever) and a décor that eclipsed the foyer of any palace. Coming out of Customs and Immigration, I spied the chief pilot I trained in Palm Beach. He gave me an enthusiastic greeting, hustled me to the car, and we were on our way. It was about ten miles to town; ten miles of five-lane wide, completely deserted highways, bathed in the amber light of sodium lamps atop towering 100-ft- tall stanchions. We arrived at the compound in which I would live. It was located well outside the city limits and surrounded by barren land as far as the eye could see. It was a half-mile square block completely enclosed by a ten-foot-high concrete wall, the top of which was embedded with shards of glass. The guard at the gate waved Bob through and he took me to my new Saudi domicile. It was a much larger and grandiose home than I would have anticipated, or that was necessary. He gave me the key and told me he'd pick me up at seven. *Seven? Geez.* It was already past three!

A Trip to Town and My New-Employee Briefing

And he was there at seven sharp. As we left the compound (now in daylight) he showed me the pool, the gym, the tennis courts, the bowling alley, the movie theater, and the dining hall. *This place was nothing short of a resort!* I was excited and anxious to share this with Kathy. At the McDonnell Douglas Offices in downtown Riyadh, I got the standard "new employee" briefing. The head of Human Resources covered all the "do's

447

and "don'ts" of being in Saudi Arabia. At the end of the briefing he took me to the Disbursing Office to change my US dollars into Saudi Riyals. I arranged the new bills in ascending order according to their value. "No, don't do that. We're in a Muslim country, and that's how Jewish people arrange their money. You don't want the Saudis to think you're Jewish!"

A Hint of What We Had to Deal With

The HR guy told me that to appease the Saudi government, McDonnell Douglas had to employ one Saudi for every American employee in-country. And furthermore, employ them as managers—*each and every one with their own desk*. The company understood that they absolutely could not hire Saudis as errand-runners, or cooks, or janitors, or to do handy-man jobs around the buildings. It was beneath the dignity of a Saudi man to be asked to carry something or do any manual labor. He said in his office he had 19 Saudis, 16 of whom claimed to have royal blood or were best friends with some prince. They never came in before ten, read the paper till eleven, had tea till twelve, took a two-hour lunch, came back at two, and left at about 3 (knowing that no performance issue would ever result in their being fired).

A Briefing on Our Flying Routine

After my session at headquarters Bob was anxious to show me our flight operation, which was not located at the International Airport. We operated out of a smaller military airport. Bob gave me a walk-through of the hangar and offices and introduced me to our maintenance staff. He gave me the lowdown: our Lears were owned and scheduled by the Saudi Air Force, and I would be a Saudi Air Force pilot, *responding without question to the whims of any Saudi Air Force officer.* Our mission was flying a daily route that spanned the Kingdom—landing at five military airports. Each of these airports was operating the F-15 Eagle; a state-of-the-art fighter/bomber manufactured by McDonnell Douglas. At these airports we'd drop off the parts needed to get one or more of them back in a flying status (there was always at least one not in an airworthy state). We'd also drop off the Saudi pilot who hopefully (if he got around to it) would fly it back to Riyadh.

A Surprisingly Awkward Invitation

About 3 p.m. Bob left me off at the compound. I was again impressed by the size and extravagance of what was going to be my home. Kathy would be surprised and pleased. Tired as I was, I didn't give in to taking a nap. Being a "sun-freak" decided to go to the Olympic pool about 50 yards from my house. I put on my bathing suit and was out the door. The guy who had given me the new-employee briefing was just being dropped off at his house next door to mine. Seeing I was bound for the pool, he cautioned me: "Roger, you must be careful over here, even at this late hour of the day one can get burned real easy. After supper if you'd like, *come on over and I'll give you a nice back rub with aloe lotion.*"

Which Brings Up One Appeal of This Country

I learned there was a prevalence of gay men working in Saudi Arabia. Just like many homosexual men sought out the priesthood because it was a celibate lifestyle—*their perfect cover.* Similarly, here in Saudi Arabia it was absolutely prohibited for a man to be seen with a woman who was not his wife, mother, or sister. If he was, strict punishment evolved, including prison sentences. Here it was commonly accepted behavior for two men to be seen walking together (holding hands), eating together—even in candle-lit darkened corners. And while I could not check into a hotel with my wife without showing the notarized copy of our marriage certificate, *two Saudi men could check-in to a single room!*

In our flight department there were two individuals that in the five years I would spend here, not once did I ever see them with a woman, or did they ever mention one with any indication of approval. It was as if both these gentlemen chose to subjugate their sexual orientation. In the workplace, without a single lapse they refrained from ever displaying their inclinations. That back rub offer was the only indicative advance I had. (I did notice that when vacations were taken, the two above individuals often chose the same time and destinations.)

Flying the Line

I completed my training and was soon flying that daily schedule to the five military bases. The weather was always clear, no snow, sleet, rain, or fog. No real challenges. Talking with my Saudi Air Force pilot passengers I learned they had undergone training in the F-15 at Eglin AFB in Florida, and were especially proud to say they were a jet captain. In fact it may have been the most prestigious position any young Saudi could hold! However, Bob told me they recognized their lack of aptitude and the inflight danger involved, so only rarely took to the air. (One of our pilots remarked they were like chickens; *you had to throw a rock at them to get them off the ground!*) A year ago a rumor emerged that the Yemeni Air Force was going to launch an attack on Saudi Arabia on such-and-such a day; and on that day 70% of the Saudi Air Force pilots called in sick! Thankfully there was no attack. I later heard a joke about their lack of fighting spirit: *the Saudi government said they would spare no cost in defending their country! And so they were going to hire the North Korean Army.*

Third Country Nationals

Since no Saudi man would engage in an activity that required the slightest bit of manual labor, every such position was filled by a "third-country national"—mostly Filipinos, Koreans, Bangladeshis, and Sri Lankans. The 1985 census of Saudi Arabia showed that one out of five persons living in the country was a third-country national. Recently Saudi Arabia had won the Middle East Little League Baseball Championship *without a single Saudi kid on the team*; every last one was the son of a Filipino worker. While the third-country men had it tough, the third-country women were even worse off. They ended up as poorly treated maids, cooks, or nannies (and to provide other services you might imagine). Upon arriving every third-country national had to give their passport to their employer. No matter what abuse they suffered, they could not leave the country until released by their employer (who could destroy their passport at will).

But Not Much Respect For Saudi Woman

Even now in 1988, in public Saudi women had to wear a face veil (the hijab) and the full length black gown (the abaya), could not drive a car, or be seen next to a man who was not a blood relative. The religious police—an official vice-squad called the "Muhtawah" patrolled the streets carrying switches, searching for some female not properly covered. And Saudi women—not being able to work, just stayed in school—going on to earn useless Masters or PhD's. In the Saudi women's colleges, if a course was taught by a male professor, he could not be in their classroom. He had to teach it via closed circuit TV.

Receiving Mail

We qualified for the US Military mail service and that was good, because here in Saudi Arabia there was no postal delivery; everyone had to go to the main Post Office. And why? Because even in the big cities the streets did not have names, nor did the houses have numbers. The streets here in Riyadh (the capital) were referred to by the activity located on that street: The street holding the Pepsi Cola plant was called "Pepsi" street. The street on which the chicken vendors set up their stalls, was called "Chicken Street." The street leading up to the high platform and guillotine—where each Friday the criminals were beheaded, was called "Chop Chop Street."

Being a Serious Muslim
I noticed most of the Saudi men driving past me were not wearing their seat belts. An old hand told me that if a Muslim driver wore his shoulder harness, it would be viewed as him taking personal measures to assure his safety, *demonstrating that he did not have confidence in Allah to protect him!* Many westerners have seen Muslims drinking alcohol or womanizing in foreign cities and thus concluded they are all hypocrites. But most are seriously devout. One day at 41,000 feet I gave the standard inflight radio report stating the estimated time of my arrival at my destination. One of my Saudi passengers heard me. He came up to the cockpit and instructed me to make the call again, only this time, preface it with *"Inshallah,"* meaning "God willing." (In other words, I would not be arriving when I said—or at all, unless Allah willed it.)

Kathy
The company was good to their word. A week after my 90-day probation was over, she arrived at that magnificent King Khalid International Airport. Like me she was very impressed by it as well as the extravagant house and the fantastic compound we lived on. She would go on to take full advantage of all the facilities and scheduled activities on the compound. Our time together in Saudi was wonderful. Each year we took a 30-day vacation visiting several countries each time. Kathy became a world traveler. And something new: while in Saudi our closeness grew, and in spite of the discomfort it caused her, from time to time she chose to have me inside her (which even with my still-present deficiencies, I was gratefully, usually able to do).

A New Assignment
I was assigned to head up a new high-profile program. (Perhaps because I had been a jet flight instructor in the military, at Learjet, and FlightSafety Int'l.) But for whatever reasons I was selected to single-handedly administer initial jet aircraft training to young (well-placed) Saudis *who in spite of no experience*, were being given the opportunity to start their career as a Saudi Air Force pilot!

My first student was a not so young, aspiring Saudi named Mohammed. I administered a week of classroom ground school—with slides, videos, and numerous training aids, and then after he passed (barely) a written test on the subjects covered, I scheduled him for his first training flight. On it I took the left (captain's) seat to handle the controls, so he would not have to control the aircraft. He could just observe how I managed the five basic phases of any flight (takeoff, climb, cruise, descent, and landing). I did these in as uncomplicated a fashion as possible. On our second flight I put him in the left seat, where he would handle the controls, and start the perhaps lengthy process of gaining the skill necessary to someday be qualified to fly the famous F-15 Eagle. (Which was the objective of this training program.) Putting him in the left seat provided me with a shocking awareness that was *not* encouraging!

Forget about what the higher-ups thought should be taught—high-bank, unusual aircraft attitudes, and stick-yanking dogfight maneuvers. Although they envisioned my program to be imparting these skills, I found that I had to start with the most elementary basics. Even trying to teach them to safely taxi the aircraft took days. For Mohammed, a takeoff would have been *Advanced* Training. He was having major difficulties before we even moved! Still parked—just doing the checklists, he stumbled over the nomenclature of the systems and their switches. By the time we got the engine started, half the total flight period had already expired.

Ah Ha, an Explanation!

I soon discovered that aviation aptitude played no part in a young Saudi gaining access to this program. Every new pilot I got was either a prince, related to a prince, or a dear friend of a prince. In addition to that the applicant had to have made a trip to the states, taken the required flight training courses *and been awarded a USA Commercial Pilot's license*. I was floored to find out a common practice among the applicants: They would give their passport and $10,000 to an older and experienced Emirate Airlines captain, who then—carrying the applicant's passport, traveled to the United States as him, underwent the training and received the necessary US Commercial Pilot's license *in the name of the applicant who had given him his passport.* So frequently when I got a supposedly properly licensed young pilot, he actually had not gone to the states or earned that license, having just resorted to the shenanigan described above.

And What if I Couldn't Produce a Single Captain?

It was obvious to me that—if ever, it would be years before my trainees could operate jet aircraft in an even reasonably safe manner; and in no way would they ever be F-15 fighter pilots! And the Saudis historically dealt harshly with any American mentor who failed to bring his Saudi students up to speed. They usually found something wrong with his visa and deported him. I couldn't imagine being able to ever show the brass even one young man, and say, "Here he is—a red hot, qualified captain, a future "top gun"! Consequently, *I was concerned about whether or not I'd be able to last here.* Although one thing may have saved me: The trainees could rightfully claim they were jet pilots (even though they would be in training the rest of their adult life). Evidently just being able to flaunt their "flyboy" status and wear a set of wings, was more than enough for these individuals to be perfectly content making no progress whatsoever. If they had to be in training the rest of their lives, that was perfectly okay. It was a prestigious and highly paid pastime.

Wow, a War!

On August 2nd Iraq invaded Kuwait to reclaim an area that used to belong to Iraq, that they wanted back. US ground troops and Air Force squadrons began pouring into Saudi, and McDonnell Douglas—in fear of an Iraqi incursion into Saudi, ordered all the wives and kids to immediately leave the country! Kathy was back in the states by mid-August. When after three months it looked like Iraq would make no attempt to invade Saudi Arabia, McDonnell Douglas authorized the dependents to return to Saudi. *Kathy was back in the house on January 12th.*

On the evening of January 17th I was sent to a small, hard-packed dirt strip in the An Najaf province *of Iraq* to make a pick up. Living there in tents was a small contingent of personnel doing I don't know what, but I'm sure it was for the Agency—in advance of some coming activity. Shortly after dark four highly energized individuals (everyone that was there) carrying aluminum cases scrambled on board the aircraft. One young one who couldn't contain himself, blurted out, "We can't tell you why, but you got to get out of here quick, something's gonna happen!" Without needing that ominous warning I spun her around and was airborne.

When I got back to Riyadh it was late, no moon and pitch black; could barely make out the lights of Riyadh some miles ahead. *Whoa!* The aircraft rocked violently right wing up, and I felt the "whop" of impacting air. I had almost hit something, or something had almost hit me! *Shit!* It happened again, this time on my left side. Unknown to me, two squadrons of US Air Force fighter/bombers had just launched from Riyadh "dark" (no exterior lights on). I was arriving as they were departing. I had just missed being rammed by two of these departing unlit bombers! These aircraft who almost rammed me were part of our first launch of the Iraqi war! *So Kathy had gotten back just in time to see the war start.*

Saddam's Scud Missile Versus Our Patriot Missile

Shortly after this attack on Bagdad, Saddam began flinging his Scud missiles into Saudi Arabia. We countered with the anti-scud "Patriot" missile. Its supposed success brought fame and fortune to the manufacturer; albeit truth be known *the missile was a failure.* Sometimes it did hit the incoming Scud, but it was drawn to the heat of the rocket motor in the tail, leaving the forward-located *warhead* to continue its ballistic trajectory to wherever. And I say "wherever" because the Scud had no target guidance. It was like a thrown stone. Several—by sheer accident hit random buildings in Riyadh, but most landed harmlessly in the desert. They looked like they were built in a 9th grade shop, with wooden 1x2 stringers and chicken wire. The rivet lines were not evenly spaced and about two out of ten rivets had not been installed. Living in the compound, the most frightening thing for Kathy and I was when a nearby battery of Patriot missiles launched a salvo of rockets. The missile goes supersonic within one second of being fired, which meant that while Kathy and I were crouched in our bedroom hallway, every few seconds for five minutes *we were deafened by a sonic boom!* (At first we frightfully thought these were the retorts of incoming Scud rockets.)

A Testimony to Inhumanity

In February, Desert Storm—the ground assault of US troops into Kuwait and eastern Iraq began. It was an immediate and decisive victory. The Iraqi troops that had been in Kuwait fled in terror towards their homeland, using the only paved road leading north. They used Kuwaiti vehicles loaded with Kuwaiti women and children to discourage being attacked. It didn't work; aware of this several-mile-long caravan of vehicles, we chose to launch airstrikes. (I'm hoping without knowing half of those vehicles contained Kuwaiti women and children.) Since the terrain on each side of the road was sand, no car could leave the pavement. Our F-15 Eagles (flown by Americans) rocketed the lead vehicles in the caravan, converting them into an impassable obstacle, thus bringing the caravan to a stand-still! Hard to believe (with a clear conscience), but what then ensued was a free-for-all; our aircraft emptying their complement of rockets into the line of stalled vehicles. An hour later what remained was a long queue of flaming, twisted black metal, containing the charred bodies of those that had burned to death clawing their way out the windows and doors. (Local GI's took photos of the trapped cremations, which they put into booklets, and then had the gall to sell to anyone willing to pay five bucks apiece for them)!

An Incredulous Face-to-Face Experience

Alas, in my third year I finally got a very westernized Saudi trainee (who had often traveled to the States and other European countries) and who I felt would be the first one to have a chance. I worked hard with Amir and he recognized and appreciated it. I began to feel like—for the *first* time, I had met a Saudi I could consider a friend. However something happened between Amir and I that vividly demonstrates one of the tenets of the Islamic faith. You and I will admit that from time to time we may have told a "white lie" or maybe even a real lie. But in each case we knew the listener did not *know* it was a lie. If they already knew it was a lie, we would not have been able to speak it. One day when I asked Amir a question, about whether or not he had done a certain thing—which both of us knew he had, and the answer was "Yes," *he looked me straight in the eye, never wavering, and calmly said "No."* He was able to do this, fully aware that right then, at that moment, I knew it was a bald-faced outright lie he was mouthing.

Time to Leave, and Our Plan For a New Home

About three months later we came to a decision: as much fun and diversion as our Middle East sojourn had provided, including the more than comfortable compound life, the good pay, and exotic annual vacations, we decided it was time to return to the States. We might even have enough savings to compensate for me having no retirement. During our years in Saudi Kathy and I had spent many nights designing a small Spanish-style home—our dream house if you will. One of our neighbors had been an architect and made a set of building plans—for free. We knew that at some time after arriving in the States, we could use our Saudi savings to build our new home, and then use the proceeds from the sale of the original Hobe Sound home for the financial security we would need in our old age. In any case that was our plan. We gave Kathy's brother (renting our Hobe Sound house) a month's warning so they could find another home. We held a garage sale for much of the Middle East memorabilia we had accumulated and began making preparation for our Saudi exit and return to Hobe Sound.

Chapter Sixty
SOMETHING IT WASN'T TOO SMART TO TRY

1992: Hobe Sound Again

The move back into our home in Hobe Sound went smoothly. It was just like it was when we left. Kathy's brother and his family had taken good care of it. Even with my Saudi savings I was still worried about financial security in my old age, so I flew a couple flights a week for that charter company in Ft. Lauderdale, leaving me time to enjoy the rest of the week at home. A few months later someone told me how much our house was now worth, and I was happily surprised; gave up my flying job and thought it might be time to plan on building our dream home, and when we're in it—sell this one.

Our Final Home and Where It Might Be

It would be a Spanish style home—white stucco walls and a roof of red barrel tiles. Unusual and special about it would be that behind the garage would be a walled-in but unroofed large terra cotta paved enclosure with a fountain in the center and benches around it. The two side walls would have large see-through arches with hanging plants. It would be our private (hopefully sun-drenched) Mediterranean getaway. Stretching completely across the far end of this patio, would be three steps that led up onto an also terra-cotta paved terrace. From it one entered the house through a pair of multi-paned, glass double doors.

Having had a home only a few hundred yards from the ocean we decided to build our new home inland. Perfectly content with each other's loving company, an outlying wooded area would be fine. No need for neighbors. West of I-95 there were miles of wooded areas; the most promising locale was near Indiantown—about 20 miles southwest of Hobe Sound; lots of tall pines and not swampy. We found ourselves there the most often, hoping to find a couple acres. One afternoon Kathy came bursting in the door. "Roger, you're not going to believe it; exactly what we've been looking for! I found it! Wait till you see it!"

"You sound pretty excited. We can take a ride there tomorrow and you can show me."

"No sweetheart, I want you to see it now! It's not that far; right near where we were looking. You're going to love it!" She pulled me up out of my chair, to the car, and using the realtor's hand-drawn map, in thirty minutes we were there. It wasn't on a main road; two turns off Route 76 and then about a half-mile down a hard-packed dirt road. Viewing the property from the street I could see why Kathy was excited. We wandered the property from corner to corner. There was a large flat grassy area in the center (perfect for the home) with groves of tall pines on both sides and extending behind it, and most of these pines were the revered Long Leaf pines. It was beautiful and respectfully silent, except the whisper of the breeze through the pine boughs. It *was* exactly what I was envisioning.

Overcome by the perfection of the site we put off the practical questions about how far to a Walgreens or Home Depot. The closing on the lot went smoothly except something was amiss with the old survey and I had to pay for a new one. It cost more than I expected, especially since two guys did it in about an hour. The head guy told me "You'll be glad you have it—you'll have occasion to use it many times." He would turn out to be right. A few days later we were the proud owners!

Building Your Own Home at 61 Years of Age

I had been considering it since day one, to act as the General Contractor, supervising each step of the construction and even doing the ones I could. I knew it would be demanding and physically exhausting, but I was able to convince Kathy I'd be up to the task. I suggested it might be neat if rather than continuing to live in the Hobe Sound house, we leased a camper, parked it on the property and lived in it while I was building the house. That way there'd be no driving back and forth; more time to spend on the house and keep an eye on the sub-contractors. And I didn't even have to coax her. As the wonderful wife she was, she jumped up and ran around the table to me. "Oh Roger, what a great idea. It'll be so much fun."

I told her I was glad she thought so, but it wouldn't be a big one so she may be ready to divorce me by the time the house is done. Hearing this she acted like she was going to punch me. Maybe just because I'm a shiny-metal kind of guy, but after I saw one of those polished aluminum Airstreams, that's what I wanted. We leased a 24 ft. long, 1974 Argosy Airstream. A truck-owning friend of mine (for just a steak dinner) towed it to the property. After unhooking the Airstream he noticed the electric poles stopped about 300 feet short of our property. I'd actually seen that, and knew it was going to cost us.

The First Night in Our New Digs

Kathy got Florida Power and Light to extend the electric line (install two more poles). Something they did in one day and cost $1200. They did us a favor connecting the power to the Airstream because it was further than the maximum of 50 feet from the road. The same day we installed a TV dish and moved two carloads of clothes and other items into the Airstream. For our first dinner there, Kathy did up a steak and baked potatoes with sour cream (and opened a bottle of Cabernet). After dinner while watching TV, Kathy sat close beside me holding my hand in both of hers. It seemed we had done the right thing, and it was going to be a pleasant 3 or 4 months.

Beginning Construction

Hopefully, getting all the proper permits was not an indication of how long this project was going to take. And that surveyor guy was right; only one week into the project and I had needed his survey twice. Finally—we had all the permits we needed. We spent the next afternoon coming up with a location and orientation for the house. Using a 50-ft metal tape and a laser penlight, we were bold enough to drive in the corner stakes. Since there would be a lot of scrap accumulating, I got a three-month rental on a large dumpster.

The first step was digging the trench for the footer. I leased a backhoe and went to it. At the end of the day I had two sides done, but was beat and not thrilled with the job. I gave in and hired a professional to do it. He completed it—all six trenches straight as an arrow. After a week of settling and drying, the foundation guys arrived and built the concrete block foundation upon the footer. That evening at sunset Kathy and I viewed the now raised outline of our new home.

Before the slab could be poured the plumbing and electrical contractors dug their trenches and laid their conduits. These contractors informed us the free plans we got from our friend in Riyadh were not sufficiently precise. This resulted in a week delay and $850 for a more precise plan. I worked with the electric and plumbing guys, mainly digging the trenches and running back and forth to get things out of their trucks (although that night my lower back and the rest of my body seriously complained). The following week the slab was poured. That evening—the setting sun reflecting off the still wet slab, Kathy and I again stood in front it, holding hands and looking at the actual floor of what would be our final home.

Body and Mind. The Good and the Bad
The first six weeks in our Airstream we found ourselves genuinely enjoying the new existence; kidding and roughhousing in our own little comfy cave. We got hooked on the *Seinfeld* re-runs, spending many a fun night laughing at Elaine and Kramer. It was early on, but it looked like three months were going to be easy. One night after supper I sensed that Kathy was in an unusually happy, grateful mood, even one of her rare *physically* loving moods. In spite of the discomfort it would cause her she wanted us to be intimate, and thankfully I was able to do so. Unfortunately, as well as every other attempt for the past fifteen years, it caused me to compare my performance to what Mireille had gifted me with. But it also painfully brought to mind my infidelity with her on that charter flight I took to Lyon.

The Second Month
We were advised to go with a concrete block ground floor and frame the second floor over the rear part of the house. I got some bids and we had the first floor done concrete block. I saved them hiring a third guy by using a wheelbarrow to deliver them the blocks and buckets of mortar, and a handful of other tasks that saved them time. It was completed in less than a week. Once again, at sunset the day it was completed, Kathy and I stood arm in arm, full of anticipation, viewing the ground floor walls, an undeniable sign of progress.

After the ceiling joists were installed over the garage and the living area, I ordered the plywood sheathing (rough flooring) to go on top of them, and am proud to say *I did it all myself* (which stepping across the gap between the separated joists was risky)! Next—framing the second floor would be the biggest step I'd yet personally undertaken. I was pretty sure I could do it (after reading a book on it I got from Home Depot). I did do it—eight hours a day for a week, but it wore me out completely—surprisingly more than I thought it should; to the extent I felt sufficiently beat that I gave myself two days off. I then had the roof trusses installed on the garage and the second floor. The view from the street now boldly stated that it was definitely going to be a house!

Making Great Progress But Wearing Me Out
I did the outside wall sheathing of the second floor and the two roofs myself! It was tough hefting 4x8 sheets of plywood up to the second floor and worse—to the roof. I started with a ladder but soon rented a scaffold. Too hot to work between noon and 3 p.m., but still got it done in three weeks. I

was real tired the end of each day, dozed before supper, and usually hit the rack about nine. Kathy was supportive, but insisted it was taking its toll on me. And she may have been right. After all my years of exercising, these daily activities were causing more fatigue and joint aches than I would have expected. One day returning to the air-conditioned Airstream, sweaty and overheated, I got the chills. *But then again Rog, you're over sixty! What d'ya expect?* Kathy joked that it was good my annual physical was coming up soon. Me? I told her she should get one too, since I'd noticed that often at the end of the day she was as beat as I was. (Although that could be understandable, since almost every day she was out there with me lugging stuff and running errands.) During the next couple weeks I installed all the doors and the windows.

Finishing Up, Thank God!

I confirmed a "go ahead" with the roofers. They were there in two days, put down a neat kind of stretchy rubber sheeting, and then laid the red barrel tile that Kathy had picked out. I was able to save a few bucks helping the roofers. First—they complained that two pallets of tiles had not been craned up onto the roof, so before they arrived I moved about 50 wheelbarrows full over to the base of the ladder. Second, having mastered the masonry saw, they'd mark a tile, throw it down to me, and I'd cut it and throw it back up. While it wasn't a back-breaking job, I was out there all day every day, and felt it.

Late in the fifth day, when the job was completed and the guys had left the property, Kathy and I did our ritual walk out to the street and viewed our new home, barely holding back the tears. Looking at me standing there—exhausted, shoulders slumped, Kathy remarked that we probably should have contracted to have the house built by someone else and just stayed in the old home until it was done. I had to admit she was probably right. I shouldn't have tackled this home-building thing alone—especially at my now 62 years of age.

The Last Couple Projects

The plumbing and electrical contractors did their interior roughing in. I did not offer myself as a "helper" this time. Kathy wanted lapstrake wood siding on the second floor, and I passed that job on to a professional siding company. Although afterwards I did do all the priming and painting, which saved a thousand dollars. (Doing the west side in the morning and the east side in the afternoon, I could stay in the shade).

460

Working side by side with the drywall guy, I found this to be a much harder job than you might imagine. First it would help to be seven feet tall, and carrying the 4x8 sheets—have forty-inch-long arms. And that "mudding" and "taping" of the joints is an art. We spent a week and a half on this part of the job (talk about aching shoulders). When it was done Kathy walked through all the rooms holding up color chips. We spent the next two weeks doing the interior painting. I didn't complain to Kathy, but I was glad the job was almost done, because I knew I was running out of steam.

One day, getting ready to go to Lowes to tell them we were ready to have the kitchen and bathroom cabinetry delivered, Kathy said she didn't feel so good, had woken up with a slight fever. I gave her the day off and took it off myself. She was only down for two days, and then ready to get with it and do what she could to help me finish the home. Man! Did we agree we were glad this frigging project was almost over! Once the cabinetry was in I tackled all the trim work, the inside door and window casings. I did this while the plumber and the electrician did the final installations of their hardware and fixtures.

Since it was a Spanish-style house Kathy wanted wood-flooring, and ended up buying a good-looking laminate from Lumber Liquidator. I decided to lay the flooring myself. I was on my hands and knees the whole day for two weeks, and being the cheap screw I was I didn't buy those $19 padded plastic knee guards. (Both my knee caps paid the price!) And geez—just my luck, in the middle of doing this flooring job I caught a real ugly summer cold. *What a project! Thank God It's almost finished.*

A couple days after finishing the flooring—only the base boards to go, we had all our stuff in storage delivered. The next day, while we tried to arrange the furniture, the dumpster people picked up the dumpster. Once it was off the property Kathy and I looked at each other and smiled; for some reason, the dumpster gone seemed to mark the official end to a long and tiring project. It was at last over. We were ready to move in! No more waking up at six, putting on steel-toed boots, strapping on a tool belt and walking around half the day carrying a skill saw, a half dozen 2x6's, or a heavy bag of mortar! And I was glad the project was done, since I still had some of that summer cold hanging on. The night I finally threw it, I woke up drenched at 2 in the morning. No two ways about it, Kathy was right, I should never have tackled this job. But at last! We're done!

Selling the Old Home

Fortunately for us it was a "seller's market." I had seen cars slowly driving up and down our street looking at the houses, so I just put a For Sale sign in front of ours. I probably did more sprucing-up work than necessary— at least everybody said I did. I replaced all the sinks and faucets in the house with new ones. And since a dirty or packed garage can make a home look old, I took every single thing out of the garage and off its walls (no benches, no shelves, no hooks—nothing). I then spackled every single hole and painted the walls a satin aqua green and the floor a glossy tan epoxy (that you could see your face in)! It sold quick.

Chapter Sixty-One
AT LAST, A PERFECT LIFE (ALMOST)

Nirvana

Life in our new home could not have been better; it was everything we'd imagined and more. The newest and strangest thing to me, was—for the first time in my life "doing nothing" was just fine. We had built the home with the kitchen facing east, so each breakfast the room was filled with the beautiful morning sun filtering through the backyard pine boughs. It was a time in the day that excluded any thoughts other than the most optimistic. I went from a one-cup coffee guy to a two-cupper; and could sit there with Kathy till ten. We'd take turns making breakfast. I had a healthy (and delicious) pancake recipe; one that included whole wheat flour, wheat germ, and oatmeal—always topped with "Pure Vermont" maple syrup.

Gonna Live to Be a Hundred

I was proud of myself, was thinking I'd almost completely bounced back. Feeling better every day. Even started back at the gym! But was embarrassed at my lack of endurance and the light weights I was using (as compared to five or ten years ago); but was smart enough to realize that at my age that was to be expected (and I was still using more weight than the few other guys there my age). The day of my annual doctor's appointment came up and to keep her happy, I promised Kathy I'd tell him about my complaints during the house building. Dr. Jay had been my primary care physician for years before we went to Saudi, so he knew I was a health nut; jogging, lifting weights, and playing tennis. Once in his office we began talking about old times, and he did admit I didn't look as sturdy as when he had seen me before I left for Saudi, but then again that was five years ago. He asked me a series of what I thought were good questions; about my recent activities, diet, sleep pattern, how I was feeling at differing times during the day, and even if I had any personal problems that might be weighing me down. (Fact was, in my whole life I'd never had less problems!)

He gave me a thorough physical, and at the end of the visit he said I was in "ship shape," just go home and enjoy my retirement, and that he'd call me if there was anything of note from the blood tests. I said maybe so, but I did really feel rundown and had even lost a few pounds. He responded "Well no shit Rog, look what you're doing at your age and in the middle of the summer. Your lungs are clear and your heart sounds like you're going to live to be a hundred. Let's see—you did lose six pounds, but what do you expect, sweating all day. Just take it easier from here on out, and drink more water." When I admitted how much water I *wasn't* drinking, he said (after an expletive): "The complaints you've been voicing are textbook symptoms of dehydration! I'd be willing to bet you've been dehydrated for two straight months." Kathy met me pulling onto the property, with a look that said *well what did he say?* I was pleased to relate his evaluation and suggestion about the water, which for sure I wasn't drinking *near* enough of.

Kathy and I even started a brisk mile walk a couple times a week, and she joined a Zumba class, and on the days she felt up to going, loved it. Man, I didn't think such an existence was even possible. And we had not yet exhausted the *Seinfeld* re-runs. For the first time in my life, no worries about money, and in love with my wife (who was still worried about what this project had taken out of me). She thought I should take supplements (like her friend had sold her). Or if not, at least get some recommended by Doctor Jay. Before calling him, he called me, said my blood tests had come back and he wanted to see me. *Holy Shit. That's never good when your doctor calls you.*

Shortly after sitting down with him he commented that he actually had been a little worried after seeing me on the previous visit; that even though my vitals were okay, he wasn't completely satisfied, and had sent my blood to a lab in Miami that was doing something called a nucleic acid blood test, first done in Germany just a few months ago. Right then—in front of my eyes Dr. Jay's face took on a serious, not-good look.

"Rog, not sure how to tell you this, but the fact is, you've got HIV, and worse—Stage 3. That's full-blown AIDS. You've contracted it somehow, and worse—by now, I'm sure, given it to Kathy. I couldn't stand; collapsed into the chair behind me. Seated, slumped, and stunned, his answer to my next question was: "Well if you'd come in a few months ago, who knows. A company called Gilead Science recently announced they were developing a cocktail that might be effective against Stage 1

HIV. But now, with the pathogen density you have, you're Stage 3, and to answer your question: You've got a year, maybe two. Women just sometimes remain carriers."

Mireille. Had to be! That overnight visit with her in 1986 when I flew those scientists to France.

Lightning Source UK Ltd.
Milton Keynes UK
UKHW020631141222
413904UK00010B/1181